Mechanics

William Shockley

Stanford University
Bell Telephone Laboratories

Walter A. Gong

San Jose State College

CHARLES E. MERRILL BOOKS, INC., COLUMBUS, OHIO

Merrill Physical Science Series

Robert J. Foster and Walter A. Gong, *Editors*

San Jose State College

Library of Congress Catalog Card Number: 66-28253

PRINTED IN THE UNITED STATES OF AMERICA

Editors' Foreword

As curricula become more crowded in this age of rapidly expanding knowledge and specialization, more and more colleges and universities are turning to integrated interdisciplinary courses to transmit the basic essentials of science to non-science majors. We believe that the rigid structure of most physical science textbooks has imposed severe limitations on instruction in these courses. Far too often, instructors trained in various specialities have had to attempt to fit the wide range of goals, abilities, and backgrounds of their students to a textbook, when the converse, of course, would be much more satisfactory.

In January, 1965, the editors, five authors, and representatives of Charles E. Merrill Books, Inc., met in San Francisco to implement a new conception of physical science textbooks. The result is the *Physical Science Series,* a collection of specially written, integrated materials in short, paperback form for the college physical science program. Our coordinated efforts were directed by three vital principles.

1. The Series permits maximum flexibility of use by instructors and students. Each paperback textbook represents a five-to-seven-week section of instruction, and may be used in any sequence or combination desired by the instructor. In addition, freedom of sequence within a single book is possible. This flexibility is especially helpful in courses that include laboratory experience. In this way it is hoped that each instructor will be free to choose the most appropriate materials for his students.

2. The subject areas are portrayed in a valid manner. Each book is written by a specialist in a different discipline—physicist, chemist, astronomer, meteorologist, geologist, and science educator. Thus, in place of a homogeneous blend of textbook statements, the individual paperback textbooks have distinctive scientific flavors. The student can discover both the contrasts and underlying unities in the viewpoints of scientists in different disciplines; he can, for example, compare the approach of the physicist, who performs lab-

oratory experiments, with that of the geologist, who depends largely on observations of natural occurrences.

3. Scientific communication is clear, concise, and correct. Each author is both academician and experienced teacher. He has designed instruction around carefully selected scientific principles logically related to laws, definitions, and associated phenomena. Technology is used to provide illustrative examples rather than a myriad of facts to be remembered. Mathematical reasoning is used only when the sciences are made more (not less) understandable for the non-science major. Scientific jargon and excessive nomenclature are avoided.

San Jose, California   *Robert J. Foster*

                                                                    Walter A. Gong

Table of Contents

Chapter 9
NEWTON'S LAWS, MASS AND ENERGY CONCEPTS, AND HISTORY

Chapter 10
PROBLEMS

INTRODUCTION

Since this book does not follow the standard format of texts in Mechanics, a rationale is due the reader.

The presentation is based on the true and tried principle of divide and conquer. In most books the new concepts of science and their logical relationships are taught simultaneously. The student is expected to acquire an understanding of the meaning of conservation of energy at the same time that he is learning the concept of energy.

By dividing the teaching problem into two parts, we have attempted to simplify the educational process for both the teacher and the student and to contribute to a deeper understanding of what mechanics is and how it was created. This book introduces conservation or, more generally, invariance principles, not by using science concepts that are new and difficult to the student, but instead through very simple subject matter with which he is already familiar such as counting pennies, turning coins from heads to tails, looking in a mirror, and playing competitive games. The logical processes used in mastering the selected puzzles and games of Chapters 1 and 2 involve the basic science-thinking tools that are required in the physical sciences themselves.

The important mechanics concepts of weight, force, action and reaction, and vector forces are presented in Chapters 3, 4, and 5. These concepts and the laws about them are developed as logical parallels to the invariance principles in the first two chapters. It is thus possible to fit the new mechanics concepts into the already developed logical structures of the games and puzzles of Chapters 1 and 2.

Chapter 6 contains a delineation of four basic science-thinking tools and can, if desired, be read immediately after Chapter 1. The methods of scientific inquiry presented in Chapter 6 are summarized in Fig. 6-1 (inside front cover). (These ideas are discussed from the viewpoint of science education in *Science*, Vol. 140, p. 384 (1963); IEEE *Spectrum*, p. 59 (June, 1966); and Office of Education Report OE4-10-216, Project S-090.) Although Chapter 6 bases its discussion on the examples of the discovery methods used in Chapters 2 through 6, it may add some additional insight when used as a reference while reading them. Chapters 7 and 8 are written to give the student opportunities to use the creative search-thinking tools of Chapter 6 to make his own discoveries about center of gravity, moments, and potential energy.

You will notice that the topics of weight, force, moment, center of gravity, and potential energy are treated with great thoroughness. The intent is to put the student in a position in which he could, if he had to, prove the scientific principles to another student or even to a skeptical jury in a court of law. Furthermore, he could obtain for a few dollars in a typical drug store all the equipment he would need to demonstrate the "desk-sized" experiments used in this book to establish the principles of mechanics selected for special emphasis in the first eight chapters.

In Chapter 9 several other equally important, but conceptually more advanced, topics such as the enormously significant concept of kinetic energy and the vector concepts of velocity, acceleration, momentum, and Newton's famous vector equation $\vec{F} = m\vec{a}$ are presented on a survey basis. This particular balance of emphasis between the first eight chapters and Chapter 9 is intended to serve the purpose of letting the student know what it means really to master a topic and, at the same time, to help him acquire an idea of the entire extent of the scientific field involved. It is our hope that this balanced emphasis will give the student perspective that permits him to differentiate sharply between those things he understands thoroughly and those he has merely surveyed.

Special attention has been devoted to introducing symbolic language—the special idiom of mathematics. The treatment is intended to make both newcomers and older hands more comfortable in the presence of mathematical reasoning. In keeping with the spirit of the Series, we have attempted to clarify some common ambiguities in the use of symbols and to show that the logic and philosophy of using the symbolic methods of mathematics can be appreciated by the use of very simple cases. The classification of the types of symbols commonly used in exact physical science, presented inside the back cover, should clarify confusions that often arise.

The problems include exercises directly related to the text material and to logical extensions of it. Some problems supplement the book so that it can be used as a laboratory manual. This last feature is especially emphasized in Chapter 5 in which the development of the vector force concept is based on desk-sized experiments that can be carried out at home with apparatus usually already available. The problems are classified by giving them code letters that indicate whether they are pencil-and-paper exercises (P), experiments (E), experiments probably requiring laboratory equipment (L) , those suitable for class discussion or written essays (D), and those which are logical extensions of the text material to new concepts not developed fully in the text (N).

The authors would like to express their appreciation to Professor Paul D. Hurd, who first brought them together, to the many students who participated in experiments with this material, and especially to Emmy Lanning Shockley, whose patience permitted the development of the material of Chapter 5.

Chapter 1

Mechanics and the Conservation Laws of Nature

1-1　What Is Mechanics?

Mechanics is an exact science. It is the oldest of the sciences. The law of levers and the buoyancy principle are named after Archimedes (287-212 B.C.), who lived in Syracuse in Greece. He was the first of the theoretical scientists.

A famous problem that he solved was to find out whether the jewelers had cheated his king. The king wanted to know whether his crown was pure gold or whether it was diluted with silver; but he did not want the crown damaged. In order to answer this question, Archimedes discovered his buoyancy principle. He was able to answer the king's question without harming the crown, except to get it wet when he weighed it while it was immersed in water.

Archimedes used concepts of weight, volume, and density in his studies. Mechanics involves all of these concepts and their relationships. It also involves many other concepts: forces, energies, masses, speeds, accelerations, motions of pendulums, bullets, planets, and satellites.

The gear box or transmission of a car applies the laws of mechanics to machinery. The science of mechanics is concerned with interrelationships that apply to very widely different things—for example, to both automobile transmissions and vibrations of violin strings.

The laws that Newton stated three centuries ago apply not only to the fictitious apple that fell on his head but also to the motion of an atom or an electron in a vacuum tube, to a space probe, to the earth moving around the sun, and to our galaxy moving in space.

In this book, we shall deal chiefly with "desk-sized" mechanics. We shall show how you use simple tools like rulers, cardboard, soda fountain straws, string, and weights like pennies to prove to yourself important laws of mechanics. With these tools you can, on your own, verify these laws and also experience some of the discovery adventures that Archimedes, Galileo, and Newton must have had.

1-2　What a Law in Science Is Like

The science of mechanics is based on laws of nature. These laws require that certain things be true, no matter what changes are made. As science has

1

advanced over the last two or three thousand years, deeper and deeper under-standing has been achieved. Some exceptions to old laws have been found. These exceptions have required that the laws have to be broadened to cover the new cases. However, the important laws are still just as good as ever when applied to the cases they were designed to explain.

An example will make this clear: "What goes up, must come down." This law was intended to apply to things like kites, balloons, arrows, rockets, and other solid objects that are projected upwards. Does it apply today or not? The Venus space probe *will never* come down. So the law *is wrong.* But all the same, you had better not throw a brick up into the air if you are in a crowd. It *will come down,* and you may have serious trouble.

To think properly about this law, you should consider not only WHAT it says but also WHEN (i.e. under what circumstances) what it says applies, and WHEN what it says does NOT apply. To make it useful, you can state the law in what we introduce in this book as the qualified law form, or QLF, thus:

	QLF 1-1 "What goes up, must come down"
WHAT	It is **always true** that any solid object projected up-wards on earth must come down,
WHEN	**no matter** whether it is a baseball, an airplane, or a rocket,
WHEN NOT	**but not if** it is a space probe or a piece of dry ice that evaporates before it falls back to earth.

The qualified law form emphasizes that important and useful laws may have WHEN NOT situations that may occur rarely or may make the laws a little untrue. The important laws of mechanics are in this class.

The meticulous thinker may object to combining "always" true with the exceptions covered by the WHEN NOT situations. The authors feel that the dramatic, familiar impact of "always true" outweighs the logical inconsis-tency. However, if the reader wishes, he may consider the "always" as a typographical error or, if he prefers, a misprint for "indeed" or "very".*

In this book we shall frequently emphasize the WHAT, WHEN, and WHEN NOT aspects of laws of nature and other important principles by using the key phrases **always true, no matter,** and **but not if.** To make them stand out when they apply to WHAT, WHEN, and WHEN NOT, they are printed in blacker letters (boldface type). We, the authors, intend in this way to help you, the reader, to understand that you have useful command over a law only if you know all three things: WHAT the law says is true; WHEN you can use it in terms of specific examples that mean something to you; and WHEN NOT to apply the law again in terms of examples (that you fully understand) of particular situations when the law fails. The com-

---

* Note that we print "very". instead of "very." as is conventional. Our method sets up correctly a one-to-one correspondence between symbols and ideas. The period ends the thought that contains "very"; the period is not part of the quoted thought. Care in correctly setting up one-to-one correspondences between symbols and what they rep-resent is given special emphasis in this book as an important tool for scientific thinking.

mon statements that "a law is an established fact" or "a law is something proved to be true" do not give this perspective. When a student first hears that Newton's three laws of motion have been replaced by Einstein's principles of relativity, he should understand that the WHEN NOT conditions for Newton's laws do not arise for the situations that Newton studied. Newton's laws are just as good as ever for a very big WHEN area of phenomena.

1-3   You Can't Beat an Invariance Principle—No Matter What

"You can't do it, **no matter** what" sounds terrible.* Our modern philosophy is: "Where there's a will, there's a way." But the experience of **"you can't** do it, **no matter** what" is often a very valuable clue both in real life and in science. **"You can't** afford it, **no matter** how small the down payment" can save you lots of grief if you use the laws of arithmetic and a budget to help make purchasing decisions.

We shall illustrate how two great laws of science are related to things people wanted to do but **couldn't do, no matter** what.

The first example is the perpetual-motion machine: Perpetual-motion machines, which could give you electric power in your house with no power bills or run your automobile without gasoline, are impossible because of conservation of energy. But attempts to make perpetual-motion machines have contributed to better understanding about energy.

The second example concerns alchemy: **no matter** what base metals, like lead and tin, you alloy together and treat chemically, **you can't** make gold. This fact stopped the alchemists who used all means they could imagine, including magical spells, to try to make gold. The chaotic, frustrating failures of alchemy finally became useful to mankind when the facts made familiar by alchemy's bad hunches were brought into an orderly relationship, creating the science of chemistry. Chemical experiments prove that atoms preserve their identity in chemical reactions: the number of gold atoms at the end of a reaction is always equal to the number at the beginning. The atoms of each chemical element are conserved in the reaction. This simple idea explained alchemy's failure. This law of conservation of atoms in a reaction is the reason why the equations for chemical reactions must balance. (Atomic energy introduces **but not if** conditions in the law of conservation of atoms; this is a subject not for mechanics but for modern physics and chemistry.†)

Whenever you run up against a situation **you can't** change, **no matter** what you do, there is likely to be a hidden law that stops you. Usually something at first unseen doesn't change although its surroundings do. For example, the invisible atoms in chemistry maintain their identities **no matter** how they unite with other atoms or separate from them in a chemical reaction.

Two examples will further clarify the significance of invariance and conservation. Although these examples use simple, everyday concepts, their

---

* The **you can't** is the WHAT that is **always true** in a statement like this; hence, we **treat it** like **always true.**

† See, for example, Isaac Maleh, *Modern Physics*, and John McAnally, *Chemistry*, in the Merrill Physical Science Series (Columbus, Ohio: Charles E. Merrill Books, Inc., 1966).

logical aspects are very like science. The first example is so obvious that you may wonder if it is worth taking time to discuss. However, it does give a strong hint of the strength of the invariance that is hidden in the less obvious, two-king problem that follows it:

Suppose that a group of holdup men want to find a safer way to make a living. They have some money. They decide to make more money by gambling. So that no one will recognize them, they gamble in private, among themselves. They form a corporation to share their profits. They gather by themselves in a room, with their money, and play poker against each other eight hours per day. They find that no matter how hard they play, the corporation always breaks exactly even.

Why can't they make money this way? There is a law of conservation of money in their room. The total amount of money in the room is invariant during any day's game—**but not if** they send out some money for meals.

This is an obvious example of how a *conservation* law sets up a situation **you can't** change, **no matter** what you do.

Sometimes the invariance principle is much more subtle than conservation of money in a room. Before you find the principle that makes it impossible for you to solve the problem, you may continue to believe that there is a solution. Then you will continue to try until you become convinced that it **cannot** be done, **no matter** what. The following two-king problem has been selected to illustrate such a situation.

Suppose that for some reason (it might be, for example, to win a bet) you want to lose a checker game that you have almost already won. Only two pieces are left. You have king *A* and your opponent has king *B*. As shown in Fig. 1-1(a) you have moved king *A* so as to drive king *B* to the lower right-hand corner of the checkerboard. It is now *B*'s move.*

B moves to threaten your king *A* as shown in Fig. 1-1(b). Then you must move *A* because you can't wait for *B* to take *A* on *B*'s next move. You move to the position shown in (c). Then *B* will want to attack *A* again. In (d), *B* does attack *A*, but you must move *A* away again so that once more you can't allow *B* to take you.

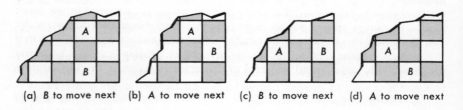

(a) B to move next (b) A to move next (c) B to move next (d) A to move next

Fig. 1-1. Sequence of three moves in a checker game with two kings.

Figure 1-1 shows only a corner of the board. Perhaps this restriction keeps you from seeing how to let *A* be taken by *B*. Suppose that *A* moves off

---

* In checkers, a king is allowed to move in any diagonal direction for one square. Figure 1-1 shows several such moves. In order for *B* to take *A*, *B* must be next to *A* and be able to jump over *A* diagonally to a vacant square just beyond *A*. That is why *B* is safe from *A* in Fig. 1-1(b); there is no vacant square behind *B* for *A* to jump into.

to a faraway corner and *B* follows; then it may become possible for *A* to move so that *B* can take him. If you try this, however, you will find that it is **always true** that *A* **can't move** so that *B* can take him **no matter** how far apart they get or what corner *A* moves into or anything else that stays in the rules for checkers.

Is it that you are unlucky? Or not clever enough? Or is there an invariance principle involved? Think this over, as a problem, before you read ahead or look at Fig. 1-2.

The hidden invariance principle is found by discovering a key attribute of the checkerboard that leads to an orderly relationship in this confusing situation. Figure 1-2 shows the rows numbered from 1 to 8 and classified into two kinds: *E* for even and *O* for odd. The permitted moves of checkers are always one square on a diagonal. One square along a diagonal always moves the checker up or down by one row so that it always moves to an adjacent row. Consequently it always changes its kind of row. This change is a consequence of the fact that the whole numbers always alternate: *O E O E O E*, etc. In other words, if a checker starts in an *E* row, after a move it will be in an *O* row and vice versa. This fact leads to a principle or law that can be stated in the qualified law form as follows:

QLF 1-2 The Odd-Even Law of Checkers*	
WHAT	It is **always true** that a checker changes its kind of row on every move (i.e., from *E* to *O* or else from *O* to *E*),
WHEN	**no matter** where it is on the board or which move it makes,
WHEN NOT	**but not if** you cheat by moving two squares when your opponent isn't looking.

As the table in Fig. 1-2 shows, for both *A* and *B* the rows go *O E O E;* but before B's first move, the situation is *A* on *O* and *B* on *O*. Consequently, the odd-even law of checkers leads to an invariant sequence in which *B*'s move always puts the two checkers on different kinds of rows. On the other hand, *A*'s moves always put them on the same kind. **No matter** what you do, **you can't** vary this sequence. It is called an **invariant** sequence. The fact that the sequence cannot be varied is the **invariance principle** of this two-king problem. This same *S* and different *D* sequence is given as the last column of Fig. 1-2.

This reasoning answers the question, "Can *B* ever take *A*?" The answer is called a **theorem** because, as for a theorem in geometry, the reasoning is a **proof** based on **postulates.** In this case, the odd-even law of checkers is the most important postulate. The theorem is: "*B* can never take *A*." The proof is as follows:

Consider what would have to happen so that *B* could take *A*. This requires that when it is *B*'s move, *A* must be next to *B* so that *B* can jump over *A*. This in turn requires that on *A*'s move just before *A* is taken, *A* must move to a

---

* This law is closely related to the rule for telling whether you have the so-called "move" or not as described in books on how to play checkers.

square next to *B*. A pair of squares next to each other is always on rows of different oddness or evenness. Therefore, for *A* to move where *B* can take *A*, the move *A* makes must put *A* on a different kind of row from *B*. But the table of Fig. 1-2 shows that it is **always true** that *A*'s move puts *A* in the same kind of row as *B*. Therefore, it is absurd to suppose that the situation of Fig. 1-1 can ever become one in which *A* moves where *B* can take *A*. Q.E.D. (In Latin Q.E.D. means "what was to be proved": *Quod* = what; *Erat* = to be; *Demonstrandum* = proved.)

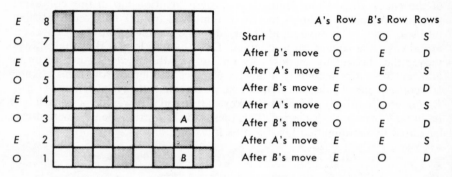

		A's Row	B's Row	Rows
	Start	O	O	S
	After B's move	O	E	D
	After A's move	E	E	S
	After B's move	E	O	D
	After A's move	O	O	S
	After B's move	O	E	D
	After A's move	E	E	S
	After B's move	E	O	D

Fig. 1-2. **Invariant row sequence for two kings on checkerboard.**

This proof was based on showing that what was needed for *A* to lose was absurd; i.e., the required move of *A* into a different kind of row than *B* was impossible. A proof like this has a special name: *reductio ad absurdum*. It gets its name as follows: What we wanted to prove was that *A* couldn't lose. But what we did was to consider the opposite: We assumed that *B* could take *A*, which is the same as assuming that *A* can lose. Then we showed that it was absurd to suppose that *B* could take *A*. In other words, we reduced the problem of proving the statement to that of proving that the opposite was absurd. Hence, the principle of *reductio ad absurdum* consists of reducing the problem of proving a statement to be true, to showing, instead, that the truth of the opposite statement is absurd.

Stated another way, *reductio ad absurdum* proves a statement to be correct by proving that it cannot be wrong.

Sometimes patterns of reasoning like that given above can be more easily grasped if they are displayed in a **logical structure diagram.** The exact form of the diagram may sometimes be a matter of choice depending on the length of the logical step the user may naturally take. Also, one user might feel that what another user takes as a postulate, such as the fact that whole numbers form an invariant odd-even sequence, should be proved from something more basic.* One example of such a logical structure is shown in Fig. 1-3. It starts

---

* We may remark in passing that you will encounter an example of reasoning very close to proving the odd-even sequence when you consider the remainder after dividing by three in the next chapter; this remainder generates an invariant three-term sequence of the form 0, 1, 2, 0, 1, 2 or zero-one-two-zero-one-two instead of the odd-even sequence which may be expressed in the form zero-one-zero-one, or 0, 1, 0, 1, or odd-even-odd-even, or *O E O E.*

with two postulates that lead to the odd-even law of checkers as a theorem via a proof that consists of comparing the effect of one move on the kind of row. The odd-even law then becomes, in effect, a postulate in the next proof that leads to the invariant sequence of Fig. 1-2. The logical structure finally ends with the theorem that *B* cannot take *A*.

In this section, we illustrated the importance of conservation laws and invariance principles for four cases:

1. Conservation of energy prevents the making of perpetual-motion machines.
2. Conservation of atoms of chemical elements prevented alchemists from making gold.
3. Conservation of money prevented the ex-holdupmen's gambling corporation from showing a profit.
4. The invariant odd-even sequence prevented king *A* from being taken by king *B*.

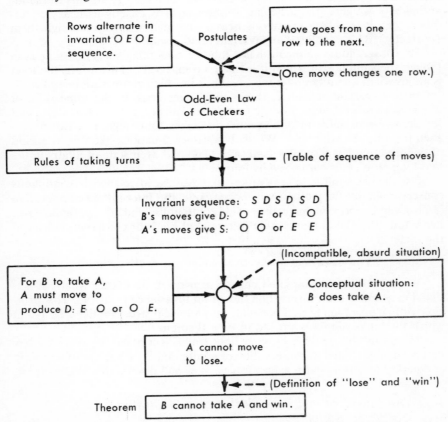

Fig. 1-3. Logical structure of two-king problem with postulate-proof-theorem structure occurring three times, once in *reductio ad absurdum* form. (Some details of the reasoning are connected by dashed lines to the main features of the logical development.)

All four of these examples showed that the observation **"you can't** do it, **no matter** what" was an important clue. In each case the observation led to the discovery of a basic **invariance principle** or **conservation law.** In the next section we shall define these terms more generally.

1-4   Invariance and Conservation Defined

We shall encounter many invariance principles and conservation laws. The distinction between **principle** and **law** is not important, but has arisen in practice. We shall take invariance principle as the broader class or genus, which includes conservation laws as special cases or species.

By **invariance** we mean something that does not vary at all; you get the same identical thing every time. In Fig. 1-2 we see that the odd-even sequence has an invariant pattern of alternation. This pattern applies to the rows and the whole numbers. In Chapter 3 we shall discuss the simplest of all invariants, the number of objects in a set of objects. We shall then relate this to the invariance of weights. In particular, if one weight is exactly as heavy as another, then it is always exactly as heavy—no matter how you weigh them (correctly). This equality is an **invariant relationship.**

By **conservation** we mean that a total of something stays constant even though the subtotals of which it is made up may vary. This means the total is an invariant quantity under the situations in which conservation applies.

In an invariant sequence, things may come back to the same state of affairs after several steps. For the odd-even sequence, it takes two steps; and for the two-king table of odd-evenness, it takes four steps, i.e., two moves each for king A and king B. We shall consider situations like this as a kind of conservation law also. We shall say: "The odd-even state of affairs in the two-king problem is *conserved* by four plays."

Usually the kind of conservation that we use in science is **continuous conservation,** like the money in the poker game. But **intermittent conservation** is also very important in science. The continuous kind, the periodic (i.e., every four plays) kind, and other intermittent kinds of conservation lead to the same effect:

"You can't beat a conservation law, **no matter** what."

When you find a **"you can't** change it or do it, **no matter** what", it is a signal to search for a conservation law or an invariance principle. This principle or law may then fit as a postulate into a logical structure like Fig. 1-3 in which the impossibility is proved to be a theorem.

"You can't lift yourself by your bootstraps" is a practical, everyday law that is directly related to conservation of matter and the invariant relationship of equality of action and reaction forces. We shall discuss this in Chapter 4.

1-5   The Power of Invariance Principles Illustrated by the Odd-Even Sequence

Once you have mastered an invariance principle or conservation law, you will find that you can save yourself lots of work with it. The odd-even sequence of whole numbers is one of the very powerful laws. We shall show the power of the odd-even invariant sequence for several simple examples. But first you should know that some applications of the odd-even sequence are very advanced.

Atoms and their innermost parts have a special kind of odd-evenness called **parity.** They have conditions that can be described as even or odd. When a nucleus in an odd state emits a particle, as it does for the radium atoms that make your luminous watch dial glow, parity of the whole situation is conserved—at least that is what all scientists thought before 1956.

In 1956 Drs. Yang, Lee, and Wu, working at Columbia University in New York City and the National Bureau of Standards at Washington, D.C., found out that parity was not quite conserved. There were special WHEN NOT situations when it failed. This demonstration was so fundamental that the Nobel Prize committee gave Yang and Lee the Nobel Prize in Physics less than two years later—this is probably an all-time speed record. Usually five or ten or even more years elapse between completing the research and the receiving of the Nobel Prize.

The Yang and Lee work has to do with odd and even properties of space. One aspect of this can be illustrated in very simple terms. Consider the letters S and Z drawn on square cards as shown in Fig. 1-4. The S card has the letter S drawn with straight lines so as to be exactly like Z backwards. When you look in the mirror at the cards as they lie on the table they seem to be interchanged. The reflection of the S card looks like the Z card, and vice versa. If we call the S card "right-handed", then we should call the Z card "left-handed".

Fig. 1-4. There are only two kinds of Z cards, right-handed and left-handed.

"Z" card

"S" card

There are only these two kinds of square cards that you can have with marks like Z or the angular S on them. For example, an N card is identical with a Z card; all you have to do is to rotate the N card through 90° and it becomes a Z card. But you can't change an S card to a Z card except by erasing the middle line and replacing it by a new line. But if you look at an S card through a mirror, then it appears to be a Z card.

Have you ever stood between two nearly parallel mirrors so that you see a long row of reflections of yourself extending off to the dim distance? This often happens in barber shops or in clothing stores with three panel mirrors.

The images of yourself that you see are alternately left-handed and right-handed in the following sense: If you are a man and look into one mirror, the image you see has the buttons of his coat on the left-hand side. He will try to shake hands with you left-handed if you extend your right hand to him.

What happens to your many images in the pair of parallel mirrors if you hold out your right hand? Your nearest image holds out a left hand; the next nearest image holds out a right, etc. The sequence starting with you goes *R L R L R L*, etc. Is this related to *E O E O E O*, etc.? If so, how is it related?

There is a one-to-one correspondence between *E O E O E O* and *R L R L R L*. If a ray of light that goes from your right hand to your eye bounces off an even number of mirrors, you see a right hand. If it bounces off an odd number, you see a left hand. In this correspondence, zero acts like an even number. If you look at your hand through zero mirrors, i.e., you look directly at it, it looks like a right hand.

This example shows the great power that the odd-even sequence has in penetrating into situations that do not at first seem to be at all related to the fact that the series of whole numbers 0, 1, 2, 3, 4, . . . is alternately even-odd-even-odd. . . . Why should this invariant sequence found in the whole numbers have anything to do with the set of right-handed and left-handed images? The answer is our discovery that the images we see in the mirrors can be put in a one-to-one correspondence with the whole numbers that brings *R L R L* into accord with *E O E O*. You can assign an integer number to each image you see depending on how many mirrors you count between your eye and the image. There is a common thread of invariance principles connecting this example with those of Sec. 1-3: perpetual-motion machines, gold in alchemy, the ex-holdupmen's gambling corporation, and the two-king problem.

The influence of the odd-even sequence discussed in respect to the multiple images of a pair of parallel mirrors extends much more deeply into concepts of right- and left-handedness. Consider the fact that one key attribute for both two-dimensional space (represented by the table top on which the cards lie) and three-dimensional space (where you stand between the mirrors) is that if you change things by reflection, they look either right-handed or left-handed but never any other way. Figure 1-5 illustrates this for a squared-up version of a glove.

How about one-dimensional space? Consider a short line, like a Morse code dash-dot symbol -• and also •- which is the mirror image of -•. Again there are only two ways to make the line; they can again be called right-handed and left-handed, or even and odd.

Considerations about space were used by Yang and Lee in their Nobel Prize work. Their research was based on thinking closely related to the right- and left-handed glove situation shown in Fig. 1-5. Instead of gloves, they thought about atoms and their nuclei. This requires a more subtle definition of right- and left-handedness. The nuclear definition is really closer to oddness and evenness. As mentioned above, it is called parity.

The same reasoning applies to mathematical four-dimensional space. However, in this book it would take too many pages to explain how you think

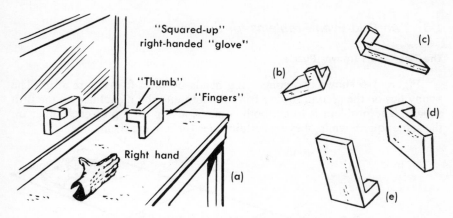

Fig. 1-5. A right-handed glove looks left-handed in a mirror, and you can get only right-handed or left-handed gloves by reflections. There are no other kinds. (Which of (b) to (e) are right-handed and which are left-handed?)

about mathematical four-dimensional space. But in space with four dimensions, just as for one, two, and three dimensions, there are only left- and right-handed things. There is no new class. In fact, the same is true for any number of dimensions: for example, five- and six-dimensional space. For all of these spaces, the odd-even sequence applies.

The purpose of this discussion of the even-odd invariant sequence and its relationship to problems in nuclear physics and right- and left-handedness in space has been to give the reader a dramatized, vivid example of how widely an important invariance principle may apply. It may relate to relatively simple cases like the two-king problem on the one hand and, on the other, to Nobel Prize work in nuclear physics. The important invariance conservation laws of mechanics have similar breadth of application.

We have chosen to illustrate the importance of invariance principles not first for mechanics but instead for the simpler cases of checkerboards and mirrors. This sequence permits you to acquire an appreciation for the logical patterns of exact science without first having to become familiar with new, exact scientific concepts. The concept of weight, which we discuss in Chapter 3, will be the first of these we develop. The logical structure of the development of the weight concept bears a close resemblance to the simpler examples of this chapter and the next.

This sequence of teaching an exact science is the new experiment in pedagogy discussed in the Introduction.* The intention is to enable you to accomplish or, at a minimum, to sense the feeling of accomplishment that went with discoveries of science.

In the next section, we offer an opportunity for you to try to apply your knowledge of the odd-even sequence to some new problems.

---

* One description of this pedagogical approach has been described as "Articulated Science Teaching and Balanced Emphasis" by W. Shockley, IEEE *Spectrum*, June 1966, pp. 49-58.

1-6   Two Odd-Even Problems for the Reader

The Two-Coin Turnover Puzzle

Figure 1-6 shows two coins lying heads up on a five-square strip. The penny lies on the second square from the left, and the nickel lies on the fifth square. The problem is to get both coins heads up on top of each other on the same square while obeying certain rules for moving them.

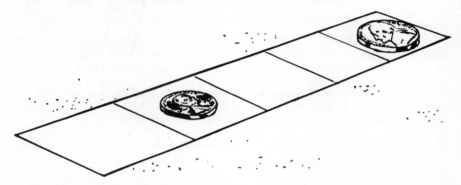

Fig. 1-6.   **A penny and a nickel both face up on a five-square strip for the two-coin turnover puzzle.**

The rules are these: You must move the coins one at a time and only to the next square. You *must* turn the coin over each time you move it. You can move penny and nickel alternately, or move either coin two or three times before you move the other.

For example, suppose that you try to get them both heads up on the far right square: First move the penny to the middle square tails up, then to the next-to-the-end square heads up, then to the end square tails up. Both coins are on the same square, but only one is heads up; hence, the problem has not been solved.

But what happens if you move the nickel back to meet the penny? Does it work then? How about it? Can it be done? Is there an invariance principle that stops you? If so, what is it?

Take 1 or 3 Game

Twenty matches (or paperclips) lie on a table between you and your opponent. It is your play. You are allowed two possible plays. Either you may take away one match leaving nineteen, or you may take three, leaving seventeen. Then your opponent has the same two choices of taking one or three. And so on. If two matches are left, the next player must take one. Finally the pile gets used up. The winner is the player who gets the last match, leaving none for his opponent.

If it is your play when there are just two matches left, you will lose for sure because the rules do not permit you to take two. Therefore, you must take one and he then takes one and wins. Q.E.D.

Does this game have an invariance principle?

These two examples and some others given as problems at the end of the chapter should show how the odd-even invariant sequence can be a very powerful tool to solve appropriate problems.

There are many problems in mechanics that can be solved simply by applying general conservation laws.

1-7 Some Puzzles Involving Conservation Laws in Mechanics

This section gives you some examples of applications of conservation laws to mechanical problems. Three involve conservation of energy, and one involves conservation of matter and Archimedes' principle, which we derive in Chapter 8 as a theorem from the law of conservation of potential energy.

These problems (except for the magnetic shield) may seem very puzzling to you now; but after you have completed Chapter 9, which discusses applications of conservation of energy, they should be as easy for you to solve as the problems and puzzles of Chapters 1 and 2.

The Soda-Straw Parallelogram Machine

Figure 1-7 shows the parallelogram lever machine made of soda straws and pins. Although it is presented here as a puzzle, it uses mechanical principles that come into your everyday life. It is simply understood by a conservation law you will learn in Chapter 8.

You can make the apparatus of Fig. 1-7 with a dozen pins and about eight soda straws. (However, a supply of 20 straws to start with is a good idea.) It is important, first of all, to mark carefully where the pins go on all the vertical and horizontal lengths. Otherwise, you will not get an accurate parallelogram, and it will jam instead of tipping easily by rotating on the two pins through the straws attached to the book as shown in parts (c) and (e).

Now, as shown in part (b) of Fig. 1-7, hang five paperclips on each end straw so that it balances. If you hang one extra clip on either side, that side will go down, as shown in (c), until it hits bottom.

Now try to unbalance the machine another way. Take off the unbalanced clip. Make the machine level again. Now move one set of five clips all the way out and the other set all the way in, as shown in part (d). Does it unbalance? A teeter-totter would. What do you find?

What you find is that **you can't** unbalance it **no matter** what you do about putting five clips in or out on one side **no matter** where you put five clips on the other side. Furthermore, with five clips on each side, it will balance in any position, as shown in (e).

Why is this so different from a teeter-totter? Why can't you unbalance it? What is the invariance principle, or is it a conservation law? What common everyday mechanism, which you have often used, involves the same principle?

We shall discuss answers in Sec. 9-7 of this book.

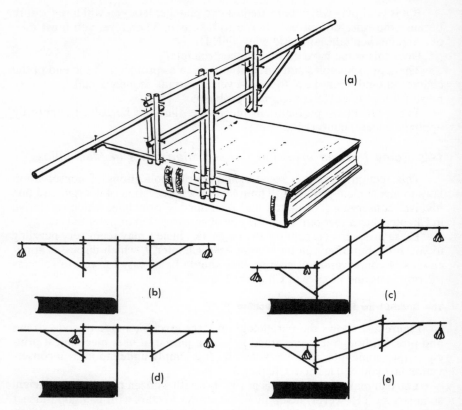

Fig. 1-7. The soda-straw parallelogram machine. (a) Structure of machines showing pins as bearings. (b) Machine balanced with five paper clips on each side.
(c) Machine unbalanced with five on one side and six on the other. (d) Machine
balanced with five on one side and five on the other at very different distances out
and in. (e) Another balanced variation of (d). (Learn the answer in Sec. 9-7.)

The Melting-Ice and Water-Level Problem

Figure 1-8 shows a cylindrical glass containing an ice cube floating on
top of six other cubes that hold it up. When the ice melts, does the water level
go down or up? Or does it stay practically at the same height?

What conservation law and invariance principle tells you that as the ice
melts, the water level neither rises nor falls but stays at practically the same
height.

Archimedes' Screw, Perpetual-Motion Machine (Conservation of Energy)

Figure 1-9 represents a form of perpetual-motion machine. As the screw
rotates, the bottom end of the open pipe fills with water. This water stops at
the lowest part of its turns of the screw. The screw is turned by the water

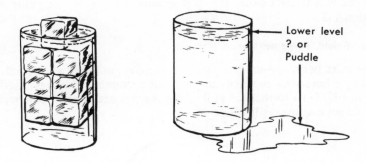

Fig. 1-8. **When the floating ice melts, does the water level go down or up? (This is Problem 1 of Chapter 8.)**

wheel. The water runs out of the open end of the pipe at the top and flows through a spout and turns the water wheel. Obviously (?) the screw is balanced because the water is in the lowest part of each turn of the pipe. This means it is easy for the water wheel to turn the screw through the gears.

Once it is started, the machine will run—forever. You can even make the shaft from the water wheel run another machine like a flour mill.

Will it work or not? Again a conservation law, the law of conservation of energy, says NO!

We shall discuss this more fully in Chapter 9, and then you should be

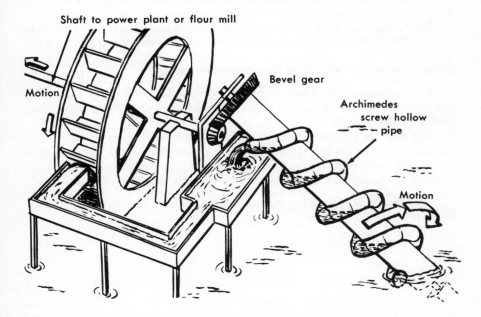

Fig. 1-9. **Archimedes' screw, perpetual-motion machine. (See Secs. 9-4 and 9-7.)**

able to see why it can't work. It is just as impossible as making king *A* lose in Section 1-3.

Magnetic-Shield, Perpetual-Motion Machine

The next perpetual-motion machine employs an iron wheel that is attracted by a horseshoe magnet. Imagine that a magnetic shield is inserted as shown in Fig. 1-10 so that the pull of the magnet exerts an unbalanced pull on the wheel and makes it rotate.

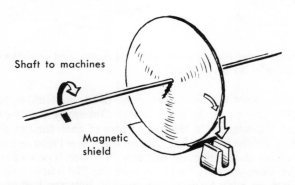

Shaft to machines

Magnetic shield

Fig. 1-10. **A magnetic-shield, perpetual-motion machine. (See Secs. 9-4 and 9-7.)**

Evidently this can go on forever, and the rotating wheel can be used for driving other machinery. Possible or not?

No! Conservation of energy says it can't work, and studies of electricity and electromagnetic fields show that conservation of energy applies to them.*

Creative Search Has Discovered Conservation of Energy

How conservation of energy was discovered for the field of mechanics will be discussed for the simplest cases of all in Chapter 8 and more completely in Chapter 9.

But first, in Chapter 2, we shall illustrate for still simpler cases than mechanics itself how the scientist engages in creative search for new principles. This will make it possible for you to appreciate better the processes of creative inquiry that man has used to discover the laws of nature.

---

* See Francis E. Dart, *Electricity and Magnetic Fields*, Merrill Physical Science Series, particularly p. 86.

Creative Search Patterns in Theoretical Science

2-1 An Educational Experiment

What would you say if you were challenged to invent a new teaching method that was capable of doing the following, seemingly impossible things?

1. It must portray in an authentic manner how the scientific thinker searches for, organizes, and uses laws in theoretical science.
2. It must express scientific laws in the forms that have the greatest capacity for prediction.
3. It must teach these powerful, scientific-thinking processes and laws to a person who has little mathematics or scientific background; and in a period of four hours, he must be able to learn and understand an example well enough to teach it to another person.
4. It must be useful during the entire lifetime of the person, so that whenever he recalls the example, he can apply its principles to new situations about the nature of theoretical science.

We invite you to be a partner with us now in an educational experiment that accepts the challenge to attempt such a feat. After you have studied this chapter, you will know to what extent the first three goals were achieved. The degree to which you will achieve the fourth goal, of course, will not be known to you until some future time, when you will have had opportunities to recall and apply what you have learned to new situations.

We have called the invented examples of this new teaching method *Creative Search Patterns in Theoretical Science*. In this chapter you will learn in detail one of the examples of this method. We have named it the *Tennis Tournament*. It and others described in this book already have been taught to hundreds of students in junior and senior high schools, in college physics and general education science courses, and even in seminars for Ph.D. candidates in electrical engineering.

This educational experiment, in which you will be involved, rests upon a bold assertion: *Research in theoretical science is like solving a tennis tournament puzzle.* By this provocative statement, we mean that the detailed example you will learn in this chapter is a valid example of the thinking processes and laws in theoretical science. Our strategy, therefore, is to teach you a simplified analogy, or model, of a very complex topic. The advantages are several. A 12-year-old child, science student, college president, housewife, or scientist can come to grips immediately with authentic scientific thinking processes and discover key attributes and laws. This is because the teaching method is stripped of complex technicalities; it deals with common phenomena whose laws can be expressed by simple counting operations, and it explains by example and simple cases the essential aspects of the scientific enterprise.

We make this prediction. Through your diligent cooperation, and after studying the details of this chapter for about four hours, you will take some giant steps toward achieving these understandings:

1. Scientific laws are discovered by **creative search patterns** of thinking that involve the basic elements of *Question-Familiarity-Hunch-Results*. The discovery of new knowledge is facilitated by the use of powerful *Search-Thinking Tools* to select, analyze, and predict significant attributes and law relationships.

2. The *results* of the search can be stated in **qualified law forms** and arranged in a *logical structure* of laws, all reported in compact forms useful for maximum prediction power.

We begin this educational experiment by introducing you to two new problems. The problems are called the *Checkerboard Puzzle* and the *Take 1 or 4 Game.** We hope that they will further whet your appetite for scientific thinking.

You will have an opportunity to try to solve the problems. If you cannot, then carefully study the detailed, scientific thinking processes taught in the *tennis tournament*. Then, after mastering this example, try again to solve the problems (of Chapter 1) that you could not understand before. Whether you can or cannot solve on your own these two new problems of Sec. 2-2 and 2-3, it will be interesting for you to compare your present thinking with the thinking style of a theoretical scientist, as displayed in the tennis tournament example.

2-2   The Checkerboard Puzzle

Here is the first problem to test the power of your scientific thinking. Collect 31 paperclips (toothpicks broken in half also will do). Then draw a large square figure (see Fig. 2-1) containing 64 squares, each about 1 inch in width arranged in 8 vertical and 8 horizontal rows (8 × 8). Mark an *E* in each of the two squares located at two opposite diagonal corners.

To solve the checkerboard puzzle, you must place part of a paperclip in every available square, i.e., those not marked *E*. (An *E* in a square signifies that it must be kept empty.) The only rule is that you must place each paperclip always in either a vertical or a horizontal position so as always to occupy two squares. You may not place a paperclip in a diagonal position.

We can reason arithmetically about the puzzle in this manner. Since each paperclip can cover 2 squares, 2 paperclips can cover 4 squares, and so forth, so that 31 paperclips can cover all of the 62 available squares. Such mathematical calculations, therefore, suggest that the puzzle can be solved, **but not if** this numerical relationship neglects significant attributes of the real situation.

---

* These problems are like the two-king, Take 1 or 3, and two-coin examples introduced in Chapter 1.

Research question: Can 31 paperclips be placed across each of the 62 available squares (not marked *E*) of the 8 × 8 checkerboard, according to the rule for covering two available squares with one paperclip? Can it be done? If so, how? If not, why not? What do you think?

You will need to search for some elusive attributes, which are not obvious. In fact, the attributes necessary to solve the problem are not observable until useful key attributes of a real checkerboard are recognized. Then, if you are "lucky" or can recall the solution of a similar problem, you may discover a numerical relationship, or law, that answers the puzzle, predicting new facts not now suspected.

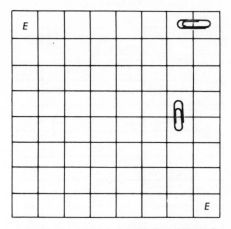

Fig. 2-1. The 8 x 8 checkerboard puzzle with two *E* squares (two paperclips shown).

In a recent test, about 1 out of 4 undergraduate non-science majors in college found the answer within 30 minutes, when given the same hints you have been given. If you want to test the strength of your scientific thinking, *do not read beyond this paragraph until you have tried to solve the puzzle.* If you cannot get the answer in a short period of time, do not be dismayed. Some professional scientists have been stumped on this puzzle for hours.

Here are some *results* produced by the kind of scientific thinking that will be taught in the tennis tournament problem. You can solve the puzzle if you imagine the 64 squares to be alternately "shaded" and "plain" squares, like the alternate colored squares of a standard checkerboard.* This creation of two significant quantifiable attributes ("shaded" and "plain" squares) makes possible the discovery of an *invariant* relationship about the checkerboard puzzle, stated below in the qualified law form.

QLF 2-1　　Law of Shaded and Plain Squares	
WHAT	It is **always true** that one paperclip must cover 1 "shaded" square and 1 "plain" square,
WHEN	**no matter** the number, sequence, or positions of the paperclips placed on the checkerboard, the number of available squares or how the available squares are arranged, the number or positions of the *E* squares that are kept empty,
WHEN NOT	**but not if** the rule for the placement of a paperclip is violated.

---

* You also can imagine each of the 64 squares to have alternate odd and even numbers. The key conceptualization is that there be two kinds of squares alternately arranged. Like the "shaded" and "plain" squares, almost all the significant scientific attributes studied in mechanics are useful concepts (e.g., moment, center of gravity, potential energy, velocity, acceleration, force, mass, etc.).

The law of "shaded" and "plain" squares gives you a conceptual tool that you did not have before.

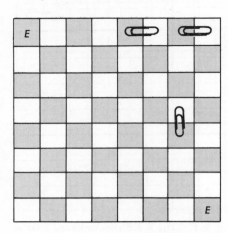

Fig. 2-2. The 8 x 8 checkerboard puzzle with imaginary shaded and plain squares. (Each of the three paperclips shown covers one square of each kind.)

1. You now can predict that **you can't** cover the 62 squares of the checkerboard with 31 paperclips, **no matter what.** Here is the proof. If you imagine the 64 squares to be alternately "shaded" and "plain", the two diagonal corners marked E are always the same kind of squares. For example, as shown in Fig. 2-2, you can imagine that the two E squares are both "shaded". Then there are two more "plain" squares to be covered than "shaded" squares. Count them. There are 32 "plain" and 30 "shaded" squares. But **you can't** cover the two extra "plain" squares, because each paperclip always must cover one "plain" square and one "shaded" square. We conclude for the 8 × 8 checkerboard puzzle that there always must be at least two squares that cannot be covered.

2. You now can predict the number of paperclips that cannot be exceeded (the upper limit) for *any* number or arrangement of A squares (available squares) and E squares. The 8 × 8 checkerboard puzzle is but one example of a class of checkerboard puzzles. For example, **you can't** place more than 8 paperclips and 27 paperclips in the triangular and rectangular arrangements of A and E squares shown in Fig. 2-3. The answers are easily obtained if you apply the theorem (logically deducible from the law of "shaded" and "plain" squares) that the *number of paperclips which can be placed in the A squares cannot exceed the lesser number of either "shaded" or "plain" squares.*

3. You now can predict an *invariant* numerical relationship that is **always true** at *any* time during the history of *any* single trial to cover *any* arrangement of squares: *The difference between the number of uncovered "shaded" and the number of uncovered "plain" squares remains constant.* For example, in the 8 × 8 checkerboard puzzle, there always will be two more uncovered "plain" squares than uncovered "shaded" squares, **no matter** whether you count the squares at the beginning, during, or at the end of any of the trials. *The number of uncovered "plain" squares minus number of uncovered "shaded" squares is continuously conserved.* **You can't** change this *invariant* relationship, **no matter** the number, sequence, and positions of the paperclips placed, the number and arrangements of the squares, or the number and positions of E squares to be kept empty.

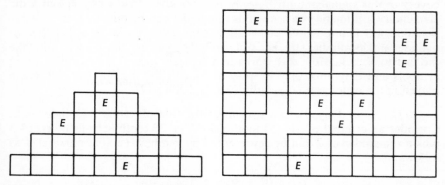

Fig. 2-3. You can't place more than 8 paperclips in the triangular figure and 27 paperclips in the rectangular figure. Why?

2-3 Take 1 or 4 Game

The *Take 1 or 4 Game* is a three-person game. Imagine that you are playing a game with Sally and John. You play first by taking either 1 or 4 toothpicks from a pile of 20 toothpicks. Then Sally takes either 1 or 4, then John, then you again, and Sally in turn, until all the toothpicks have been taken. The player who takes the last toothpick wins.

These are the rules of the game:

1. For each play, you have exactly two choices. Either you must take one toothpick or you must take four toothpicks. If there are only 2 or 3 toothpicks left in the pile, when it is your turn to play, you must take 1.

2. The player who takes the last toothpick is the winner. He can take the last toothpick by making a play that takes only one toothpick, or he can take the last toothpick as one of a set of 4 toothpicks.

Suppose that you play first, starting with a pile of 20, Sally second, John third, and so on. *We predict that Sally will win.* If you are alone and have no one to play with, make Sally's and John's plays however you like. Try to make Sally (who plays second after you start) lose. Do your worst for Sally. Sally will still win. **You can't** make Sally lose, **no matter** what!

Do you want to win? Then let John play first, you second, and Sally third. You will win. Another way for you to win is to start with a pile of 22 toothpicks, and you play first. You will win.

Why does it work? What is the *principle* for predicting the winner? Before reading the answers in the next paragraphs, you may want to try to discover on your own the principle that predicts the winner.

Here are some *results* produced by the kind of scientific thinking that will be described in detail in the tennis tournament example in the next section. The prediction stated above of the winner of the Take 1 or 4 game, whether the original number of toothpicks was 20 or 22, was made possible by the discovery of this significant attribute: *remainder after dividing by 3*. From the elementary arithmetic you know this remainder can be only 0, 1, or 2. A remainder of 3 is impossible and really means 0. If you know about this remainder and its number size, i.e., 0, 1, or 2, then you can predict who will take the last toothpick. How this works in a typical "game" is described, using symbols and diagrams, play by play as follows for the 20-toothpick game played in the order you (Y), Sally (S), and John (J):

Before First Play. Before you make the first play, the remainder is 2. Consider an original pile of 20 toothpicks. The 20 toothpicks as 6 sets of 3 plus a remainder of 2 can be represented by symbols (arabic numerals) as follows:

$$20 = 6 \times 3 + 2$$

We also can choose to represent the 20 toothpicks by a diagram of 6 sets of 3 marks, each mark representing a toothpick,* again showing the remainder of 2 like this:

$$
\begin{array}{ccccccc}
1 & 1 & 1 & 1 & 1 & 1 \\
1 & 1 & 1 & 1 & 1 & 1 & 1 \\
1 & 1 & 1 & 1 & 1 & 1 & 1 \\
\end{array}
$$

After First Play. After your first play, the remainder is reduced by 1 (from 2 to 1), **no matter** whether you take 1 or 4. First, consider what happens if you take 1. The number of toothpicks in the pile comes down to 19, which leaves 6 sets of 3 and a remainder of 1. This numerical relationship can be represented by our symbols and diagrams as follows:

$$
\begin{aligned}
19 = 20 - 1 &= (6 \times 3 + 2) - 1 \\
&= 6 \times 3 + (2 - 1) \\
&= 6 \times 3 + 1
\end{aligned}
\qquad
\begin{array}{ccccccc}
1 & 1 & 1 & 1 & 1 & 1 \\
1 & 1 & 1 & 1 & 1 & 1 & X \\
1 & 1 & 1 & 1 & 1 & 1 \\
\end{array}
$$

The X mark represents a toothpick that you take. The remainder has been reduced from 2 to 1 by this play.

On the other hand, consider what happens when you take 4 on your first play. It is the same as if you take 1 and a whole set of 3. But *taking a whole set of* 3 (the 3-part of $1 + 3 = 4$) *has no effect on the remainder;* taking 3 simply removes one of the sets of 3. In fact **no matter** how many sets of three you take, they **can't** affect the remainder. Thus, to take 4 reduces the remainder by 1. The effect of taking 4 from 20 can be shown symbolically like this:

---

* Which representation—the symbols (arabic numerals) or the diagram with its marks—is better to use depends on the experience or skill of the user. In this case, arabic numerals are neater. However, the marks may be easier to follow the first time; furthermore, you can actually arrange the toothpicks to correspond to this set of marks.

$$16 = 20 - 4 = (6 \times 3 + 2) - (3 + 1) \qquad\qquad 1 \quad 1 \quad 1 \quad 1 \quad 1 \quad X$$
$$= (6 - 1)\, 3 + (2 - 1) \qquad\qquad 1 \quad 1 \quad 1 \quad 1 \quad 1 \quad X \quad X$$
$$= 5 \times 3 + 1 \qquad\qquad 1 \quad 1 \quad 1 \quad 1 \quad 1 \quad X \quad 1$$

After Second Play. Just as you reduced the remainder by 1 for the first play, so does Sally reduce the remainder by 1 on the second play—and for the same reason—again **no matter** whether she takes 1 or 4. Consequently, Sally reduces the remainder to zero, and the pile of toothpicks remaining is an even multiple of 3. This is illustrated below for the example in which both you and Sally take 4.

$$12 = 20 - 4 - 4 = (6 \times 3 + 2) - (3 + 1) - (3 + 1) \quad 1 \quad 1 \quad 1 \quad 1 \quad X \quad X$$
$$= (6 - 2) \times 3 + (2 - 1 - 1) \qquad 1 \quad 1 \quad 1 \quad 1 \quad X \quad X \quad X$$
$$= 4 \times 3 + 0 = 12 \qquad\qquad 1 \quad 1 \quad 1 \quad 1 \quad X \quad X \quad X$$

After Third Play. The third play, which is made by John, removes 1 toothpick from a full set of 3 and produces a remainder of 2, again **no matter** whether he takes 1 or 4. The symbols and diagrams for the case of taking 1 from 12 are as follows:

$$12 - 1 = 4 \times 3 - 1 = (3 \times 3 + 3) - 1 \qquad\qquad 1 \quad 1 \quad 1 \quad X \quad X \quad X$$
$$= 3 \times 3 + (3 - 1) \qquad\qquad 1 \quad 1 \quad 1 \quad 1 \quad X \quad X \quad X$$
$$= 3 \times 3 + 2 = 11 \qquad\qquad 1 \quad 1 \quad 1 \quad 1 \quad X \quad X \quad X$$

Thus, after one round of three plays, the remainders begin to repeat. Starting with a remainder of 2 before the first play, the numerical values of the remainders (after dividing by 3) form an invariant three-term sequence of the form 2, 1, 0, 2, 1, 0, as play proceeds. This invariant sequence is a consequence of two key attributes: the definition of the *remainder after dividing by 3*, and the fact that *each individual play always reduces the remainder by 1*. Proving this with the postulate system of counting, which is the foundation of arithmetic, is like proving that the odd-even–odd-even sequence is an invariant relationship for the series of integers.

We can summarize this invariant 2, 1, 0, 2, 1, 0 sequence of remainders in the following qualified law form.

QLF 2-2	Law of Conservation of Remainders
WHAT	It is **always true** that a player in a Take 1 or 4 Game leaves the same remainder (after dividing by 3) each time he plays,
WHEN	**no matter** how many toothpicks he and his opponents take on the next plays,
WHEN NOT	**but not if** a player makes a mistake or cheats.

Notice how this law of conservation of remainders greatly expands our power to predict results.

1. The second player will always win in a Take 1 or 4 game of 20 toothpicks, because he is the only player who ever leaves a remainder of zero. If you make the first or third play, **you can't** win, **no matter** what, because you cannot leave a remainder of zero.

2. The first player will always win in a Take 1 or 4 game of 22 toothpicks. Before the first play, the original remainder after dividing by 3 is 1. After the first play, the first player leaves a remainder of zero. He will always leave a remainder of zero, which means that he will take the last toothpick and become the winner.

The law of conservation of remainders states that the numerical value of the remainders for each player remains invariant when the plays are either take 1 or 4. What if the rule changes and the players take some number other than 1 or 4; will the remainders still be conserved?

1. Suppose that we consider taking 7. We can reason that taking 7 is like taking 1 and two sets of 3. Since the two sets of 3 do not change the remainder, taking 7 is like taking 1 or taking 4. As far as the remainder is concerned, it does not matter whether the play is take 1 or 4 or 7. Hence, we predict that the second player in a Take 1 or 4 or 7 game of 20 toothpicks will always win. **You can't** win if you are the first or third player because you can never leave a remainder of zero, **no matter** how many toothpicks you or your opponent takes.

2. What about putting back 2 toothpicks? This play is like "put back a set of 3 and take 1." Because putting back 3 has no effect on the remainder, we can again predict that the second player is the only possible winner.

Thus, from a special case of the law of conservation of remainders dealing with a limited number of plays, we have generalized the law to include the two different kinds of plays of take 7 and put back 2. In other words, we have predicted other quantities that, when added or subtracted to the original number, cannot change the invariant 2, 1, 0, 2, 1, 0 sequence of remainders and do not alter the conservation of the remainder by 3 plays.*

This reasoning shows that the law of conservation of remainders is really a theorem for a three-person game that is based on a more fundamental postulate. This postulate, which itself is a theorem of arithmetic, is the QLF.

·	QLF 2-3 Reduction of Remainder Law
WHAT	It is **always true** that the remainder after dividing by three is reduced by one to produce the invariant sequence 2, 1, 0, 2, 1, 0,
WHEN	**no matter** whether the permitted play is take away 1 or take away 1 plus any whole multiple of 3,

---

* Remember this law of conservation of remainders for the special case of Take 1 or 4, and how the law was generalized to include other additive quantities of Take 7 and Put Back 2. This example will help you to discover in Chapter 7 the special law of conservation of potential energy and to predict the more general law of conservation of energy, in which other forms of energy, like the other plays of Take 7 and Put Back 2, can be included without altering the conservation law.

> **WHEN NOT**   **but not if** an object breaks in half to make two objects or is lost or someone cheats.

One of the major aims of theoretical science is to find the minimum number of the simplest, most basic postulates from which all the other laws, like conservation laws, can be deduced as theorems. The reduction of remainder law serves this purpose in the Take 1 or 4 game.

2-4 Tennis Tournament

The Green Hills Country Club is sponsoring a tennis tournament. The tennis committee has followed a standard set of rules and regulations, which are illustrated for a six-player tournament, as shown in Fig. 2-4.

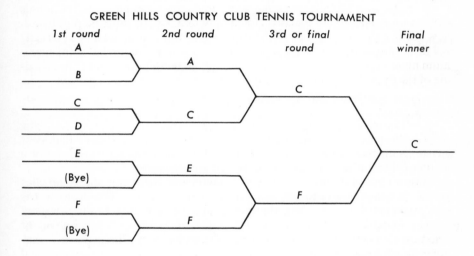

Fig. 2-4. Drawsheet showing a schedule of matches and possible results for a six-player tournament.

In the first round, two matches are scheduled. Player A plays a match with B, and C plays a match with D. As Fig. 2-4 shows, players E and F have no opponents in the first round, and they advance to the second round by having byes. The 4 players who advance to the second round play each other, and winners C and F advance to the third or final round. C is the winner of the final round and therefore the winner of the tournament. He has won three matches by defeating players D, A, and F.

The rules of the tennis tournament are as follows:

1. A *match* must be played between two players.
2. The *winner* of a match will continue in the tournament until there is one final winner, who is the champion of the tournament.

3. The *loser* of a single match will be eliminated from the tournament; thus this will be called a *single-elimination* tournament.

4. A player may receive a *bye* during any round, or more than one bye during the tournament. A bye is when a player is scheduled not to compete during a round of competition (he advances "bye" the round without playing a match).

To illustrate further how byes can be scheduled, note that if this were a five-player tournament (imagine that F is not playing), the rules permit E to have 2 byes, for both the first and second rounds. This, however, would be very poor scheduling because it would give E an unfair advantage over the other players.

2-5 Question: How Many Matches?

Suppose that 137 players are entered in a tennis tournament. The tennis committee needs to make plans. How many tennis balls must be purchased, how many umpires must be hired, how many tennis courts must be reserved? All these questions require the answer to one key question: What is the maximum number of matches that may be played, **no matter** the number or schedule of the byes. The following question now becomes a research project.

> *Question:* What will be the maximum number of matches to produce a final winner in a tennis tournament of 137 players?

Try to find an answer to this question, and also try to prove that your answer is correct. Then *compare* your solution and thinking with those of a theoretical scientist, as described in the sections to follow.

Several hunches may occur to you. Examples of frequently stated hunches are these, which you need not take seriously at this time: "The drawsheet is like a geometric progression; the final round has one match, the semifinal has two matches, the next four, the next eight, and so one. There is a way of summing geometric series. This must be the way to solve the problem." Another hunch for a mathematically experienced student is: "Use mathematical induction. Find a law for two players; next prove that if this law is true for n players, it will work for $(n + 1)$ players; and so forth."

Neither of these hunches turns out to be really useful. However, a very useful *hunch* can be obtained by a very straightforward procedure. This procedure, discussed in the next section, gives you enough detailed *familiarity* with the way the tournament works so that a certain relationship becomes obvious.

2-6 Use of Search-Thinking Tools to Discover a Law

When confronted with a seemingly complex situation, we can use an effective mental tool called **simplest cases** to search for the answers. The mental operation for using this tool is: *Think of the simplest case of the tennis tournament that retains most of the aspects of the 137-player tournament, and then try to solve it.* The simplest case of a tournament in which any matches are played is that involving only two players. We know the answer for this case: one match is required to produce a final winner.

How many matches are required for the simple case of a tournament of 3 players? Of 4 players, 5 players, and so on, up to 137 players? We could set up a real tournament (like real experiments) and study them, or we could imagine the tournaments and try to reason the results.

However, another powerful mental tool for scientific thinking is the use of *symbols and diagrams*. Fig. 2-5 shows how *symbols and diagrams* (a special use of *pencil and paper*) can be defined and used as *search-thinking tools* for finding an orderly relationship in the tennis tournament problem. The use of these mental tools involves this mental operation: *Invent a set of symbols that has a one-to-one correspondence to real attributes, and then manipulate the symbols and their relationships by logical reasoning and with pencil and paper to answer the questions*. As a dramatic illustration of the power of these mental tools to produce order from chaos, study carefully the contents of Fig. 2-5. Notice how manipulation of the invented set of *symbols and diagrams* suggested by the actual tennis tournament drawsheet has resulted in solutions for the *simplest cases* of tournaments involving 2, 3, 4, and 5 players.

Look at the *results* tabulated in Fig. 2-5. Four attributes of the tournament are considered. What we see is that the number of byes for a five-player tournament can be either two or three, depending on the schedule. Evidently, the three-bye case is less unfair than the the the two-bye case, because no player gets more than one bye.

However, one relationship is **always true, no matter** what schedule of byes occurs or how many players compete: *The number of matches M is one less than the number of players P who enter the tournament*. This law has been empirically established for P up to 5. This leads us to the *hunch* that there is a general law. The symbols of algebra enable us to express this law compactly. We shall refer to this law, which has not been proved, as a "Law-Hunch". Although it makes a statement like a law, we have a *hunch*, rather than a proof, that it is true for more players than 5.

$$Law\text{-}Hunch:\ M = P - 1$$

There is a *one-to-one correspondence* between these symbols and the attributes of Fig. 2-5. M is a symbol representing a number; that is, the number M equals the *number* of matches to complete a P-player tournament. Likewise, P is a symbol representing a *number:* the number of players entering the tournament.

2-7   Classes of Symbols and Qualified-Equations

The important subtleties of symbols cannot be overemphasized. We emphasize this by simple statements: Symbols *are* very powerful tools. *They* can help *you* think, but first *you* must think about *them*. If you do not think carefully about them, you can easily become very much confused. (See Sec. 3-3 and Chaps. 4 and 5.)

As an example of a mixup, consider the following: The tennis tournament denoted by the symbol T requires the playing of M matches by P players. Does this mean

$$T = M + P?$$

Definitions	Symbols
Players A and B are scheduled to play a match	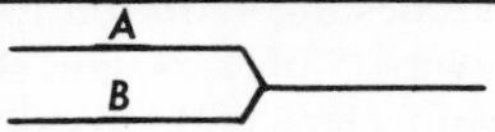 A / B
Player A has advanced to next round and B has been eliminated	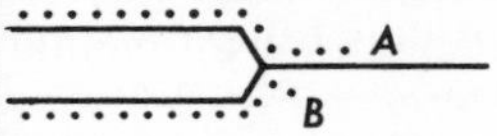 ....A / ....B
Player C has advanced to next round due to a bye	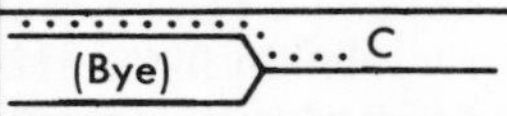 (Bye) C

Name–symbol of diagram	Solutions for simplest cases: 5 Tournaments	Number of players $=P$	Number of matches for tournament $=M$	Number of byes	Maximum number of byes for 1 player
T_2	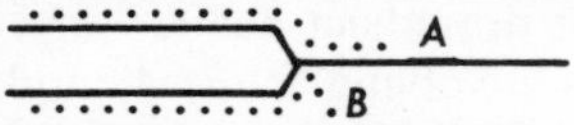 A / B	2	1	0	0
T_3	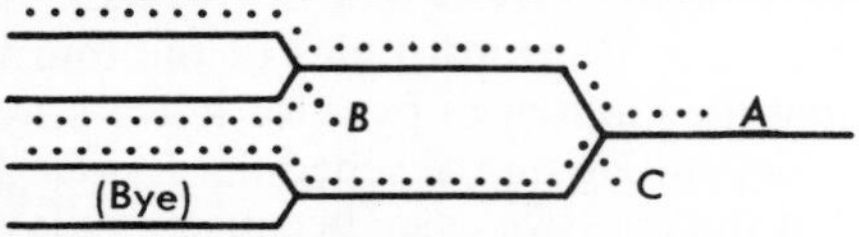 B, (Bye) → A, C	3	2	1	1
T_4	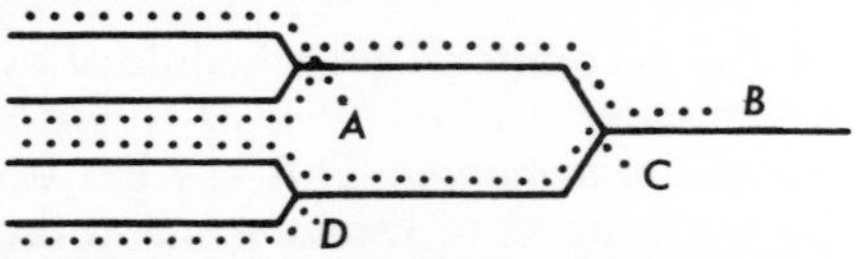 A, D → B, C	4	3	0	0
T_5	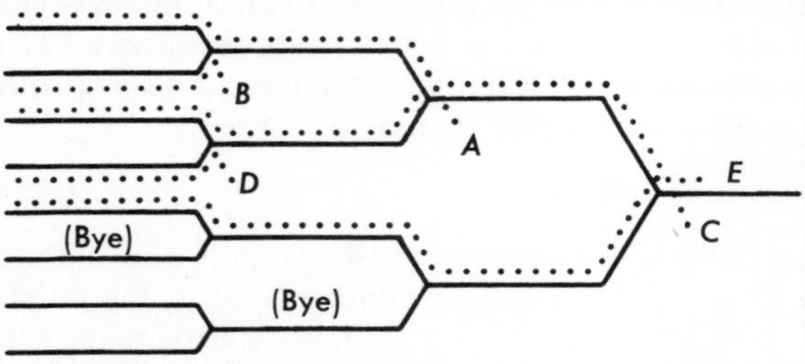 B, D, (Bye), (Bye) → A, C → E	5	4	2	2
T_5'	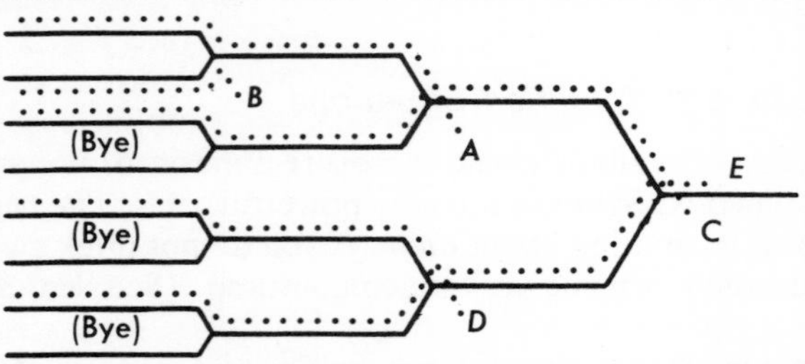 B, (Bye), (Bye), (Bye) → A, C, D → E	5	4	3	1

Fig. 2-5. Use of symbols to solve some examples of simplest cases of the tennis tournament.

This says that the tournament is the sum of the matches and the players. But does this equation make sense? Surely, we are considering only one tournament, so $T = 1$. But the symbolic equation can't be true because $P = 137$, and $M + P$ must be bigger than 137, so that T can't be 1.

Another mixed-up example expresses the idea that "2 players make a match" by the unreasonable equation $P + P = M$.

The discussion above is *nonsense*. In fact, it is *dangerous* nonsense, because confusion like it makes people feel that *they don't want to understand mathematics*. They *can't believe* that it will really *help them*.

One important use of mathematics involves setting up those one-to-one correspondences between symbols and ideas that *will* help you think. Another equally big part of mathematics is understanding that there are several different kinds of symbols. In this chapter we are using at least four kinds of symbols to represent words, things, qualifications, and numbers: (1) *abbreviation-symbols,* (2) *name-symbols,* (3) *adjective-symbols,* and (4) *number-symbols.* We shall also introduce another class of symbolism: (5) *qualified-equation* (QE). We introduce (5) before we get to (4), because it is easier to discuss them in this order.

(1) *Abbreviation-Symbols*

QLF are three letters standing for three words: "Qualified Law Form". This is not a mathematical use of symbols; it is the use of symbols for abbreviation. QLF is an **abbreviation-symbol.**

(2) *Name-Symbols*

When you see T, you think: "the tennis tournament with 137 players". T is a mathematical symbol that we have selected to name a tennis tournament. This is like selecting in geometry the symbol P to represent a point. In Fig. 2-5, T_2, (you say "tee two" or "tee sub two") is the **name-symbol** for the tournament with two players. Since there are two tournaments with five players, to tell them apart, one is marked T_5 and the other T'_5 (read "tee five prime" or "tee sub five prime").

(3) *Adjective-Symbols*

Subscripts like "sub two" and superscripts like "prime" are symbols that play the role of adjectives, like the "*third* man" or the "*new* concept".

How **adjective-symbols** are used in conjunction with *name-symbols* is a matter of personal preference and convenience. For example, if we wanted to keep an account of the byes, the tournament of 2 players (see Fig. 2-5) could have been called $T_{2,0}$ (read "tee two zero" or "tee sub two comma zero"). The symbol $T_{2,0}$ is then the name-symbol for the simplest case of 2 players and 0 byes. (The zero modifies the symbol T_2.) Another way to write $T_{2,0}$ would be $_2T_0$. You really have a wide choice.

When you are working on your own, the choice is up to you. When you are communicating with others, there may be some accepted conventions. Using these conventions simplifies communication.

Name-symbols for the last two different tournaments of 5 players (Fig. 2-5) would be $T_{5,2}$ and $T_{5,3}$. Does it make sense to say

$$T'_5 = T_{5,3}?$$

Not unless you really know what you mean. Here is a better way to put the idea in symbols:

$$T'_5 = T_{5,3} \quad \text{(for diagrams in Fig. 2-5)}$$

In the above line, the statement within the parentheses, (for diagrams in Fig. 2-5), is part of the equation. What this last part says is that T'_5 is equal to $T_{5,3}$ so far as naming diagrams on Fig. 2-5 is concerned. Both symbols mean one and the same diagram. Otherwise, saying $T'_5 = T_{5,3}$ might be just nonsense.

The equation above is this book's first example of a new way of expressing the precise meaning of equations in quantitative science. We have defined two important new concepts to explain what such equations mean. The name-symbols and the names of the concepts are displayed on a separate line below for emphasis and ease of reference:

(5) *Qualified-Equations and Equation-Qualifiers:*
(*QE*) and (*EQ*)

A **qualified-equation** concludes with a parenthetical phrase called an **equation-qualifier,** which specifies the attribute about which the symbols (on the two sides of the equal sign) are equal. We shall put the *equation-qualifiers* into the class of *adjective-symbols*, although they might be considered to be more like adverbs because they modify an equals sign, which is more like a verb than a noun.

Another example of a qualified-equation will illustrate how *qualified-equations* (QE) and *equation-qualifiers* (EQ) are used.

$$T_2 + T_4 = T_5 \quad \text{(in number of matches)}$$

This equation means the number of matches in T_2 added to the number in T_4 equals the number in T_5. This is true because the three numbers of matches are 1, 3, and 4 and it is true that $1 + 3 = 4$. This equation exhibits a rather clumsy way of dealing with the most important of symbols in science: *number-symbols*.

(4) *Number-Symbols*

Number-symbols are *the* most important thinking tools for any quantitative science. They are also the foundations of algebra.

The verbal statement that *number of matches in T_2 and T_4 together equals the number of matches in T_5* can be better stated by appropriate symbols. Again the choice of symbols is a matter of convenience. For example, we might define M_2, M_3, M_4, M_5, and M'_5, as the *number-symbols* for the number of matches in tournaments T_2, T_3, T_4, T_5, and T'_5. We would then represent the relationship as

$$M_2 + M_4 = M_5 \quad \text{(in number size)}$$

The *equation-qualifier* "(in number size)" means that both sides of the equation are ordinary numbers, actually integers in this case, and the equation means the two numbers are equal. We shall use "(in number size)" later to apply to positive and negative numbers, such as, for example, the three numbers in $3 - \pi = -0.414$.

Another way to define *number-symbols* for the number of matches would be by the symbols $M(T_2)$, $M(T_3)$, ..., $M(T_5')$. Each notation represents simply the number of matches for that particular diagram, shown on Fig. 2-5, whose *name-symbol* is in the parentheses after M.

Now let us return to our discovered law-hunch $M = P - 1$ about the tennis tournament. M and P are symbols for unspecified numbers. In Fig. 2-5, P may be 2, 3, 4, or 5; hence, the cases in Fig. 2-5 test the equation up to $P = 5$ and $M = 4$.

$$M = P - 1 \quad \text{(in number size)}$$

Almost all equations you will use ordinarily are equations about number size. The equations for numbers are so conventional that the parenthetical qualification is ordinarily understood without bothering to write it down. Consequently,

$$M = P - 1$$

is taken to mean that the number of matches in the tournament equals the number of the players less one. In this book, however, we shall often use the equation-qualifier "(in number size)" to insure that the meaning is clear.

Let this discussion warn you about a *terrible pitfall* that awaits the unwary in using *symbols*. M is not the *matches* themselves. M is a *number*. M cannot mean a hard-contested tennis set that was tied many times and would have ended in a tie if the rules permitted. M is the *number* of matches. M can only be 0, 1, 2, 3, 4, etc., up to the number we are trying to find. "You can't add apples and oranges," *nor* can you add *matches* and *players*. But you can subtract M, a *number*, from P, another *number*. These symbols stand *not* for *matches* and *players* but for ordinary *numbers*. M is the *number* that tells *how many matches*, and P is the *number* that tells *how many players*. The fact that M and P represent plain, ordinary, whole numbers enables you to reason about the tennis tournament by manipulating the M and P symbols according to well-established laws of mathematics. This feature of algebra is a consequence of the great power of the *number-symbols*.

Often the *number-symbols* are introduced for unknown numbers or, at least, unspecified ones. When we wish to emphasize this aspect, we shall refer to them as **unknown number-symbols** or **unspecified number-symbols.**

The most famous *unknown number-symbol* is x. The symbol x is most appropriately used where there is no particular association between the quantity it represents and some other important feature of the problem. In the tennis tournament, the unknown number of matches could be called x. However, using M has the convenience of reminding you that the unknown of interest is the number of matches and not some other number such as, for example, the number of byes, which would more appropriately be called B.

2-8 Is the Law-Hunch $M = P - 1$ True?

The word and the symbolic statements of the conjectured law, of course, are equivalent. The law asserts that a numerical relationship exists between two significant attributes which can always be counted. If the value of one attribute is known, then the law enables us to *predict* the value of the other quantity. For example, we can predict that 136 matches are required for a 137-player tournament.

But is the prediction of 136 matches proved? Or is it only a hunch?

At this stage of our reasoning in this chapter, the relationship $M = P - 1$ is a hunch, or a hunch about a law; it is not a proved law. Although the law works for up to five players, how do we know if it works for 137 players? The old saying "If something works three times, it is true" is not reliable. For example, the statement "all odd numbers are primes" works for 1, 3, 5, and 7; but it fails for the next odd number: 9 can be factored into 3×3 and is therefore not a prime number.

How can we find out if the law-hunch $M = P - 1$ is true for $P = 137$, and for that matter, larger numbers? As a next step, we shall formulate the problem more specifically by stating the law-hunch in a more complete and exact form.

2-9   Qualified Law Form of $M = P - 1$

A basic thinking tool is the *qualified law form*. The mental operation is: *Cite specific instances when an assertion is true and when it is not true.* The use of this mental tool, then, will force us to re-search the law $M = P - 1$ for factors that may affect its truthfulness.

How do byes affect the law $M = P - 1$? Is the law reliable for *any* number of players? These are still two bothersome questions. We do know that for the simplest cases of $P < 6$, it **is always true** that $M = P - 1$, **no matter** the number of players or the number and sequence of byes. But is this assertion true for 137 players, or even 13 players?

When we manipulate the symbols for the case of 13 players, we find that we **can't** find any exception to the law-hunch, **no matter** how we schedule the matches. The number of matches to produce a final winner **is always** equal to 12, or one less than the number of players, **no matter** the sequence of byes or whether the number of the byes is 1, 2, 3, or 4. Of course, we could continue to perform *conceptual experiments* with different numbers of players, but that consumes time and effort, and we can never try all the possible cases. At this point, our hunch is that probably the law is **always true, no matter** the number of players or the number and sequence of byes.

What if a player becomes ill and has to leave the tournament? (This is called a **default.**) Is the law $M = P - 1$ still true? This can easily be answered by trying the simplest case. Imagine a two-player tournament. The law predicts that one match is required to produce a final winner. When one player defaults, no match is played and the other player "wins by default". Hence, it is **always true** that $M = P - 1$, **but not if** there are defaults.

Our hunches about the law $M = P - 1$ can now be summarized in the qualified law form.

QLF 2-4   The $M = P - 1$ Law

WHAT   It is **always true** in a single-elimination tennis tour-
            nament that the number of matches required to pro-

duce the winner is one less than the number of
players at the start of the tournament, or $M = P - 1$,

WHEN   **no matter** the number of players in the tournament
or the number or sequence of the byes,

WHEN NOT   **but not if** there are defaults.

2-10 Discovery of Another Significant Attribute and a Logical Structure

The $M = P - 1$ law is still *only a hunch*, because our evidence for the law rests almost entirely on the results of a few simple cases. Our hunt now must continue for another law, ever for the same purpose: to make new predictions with increasing certainty. More specifically, we ask this question:

Can we prove that the law $M = P - 1$ is
always true, no matter what the number of
players or the number and sequence of byes?

The method of *deductive proof* has been taught for over 2000 years, since even before the time of Euclid, in countless geometry classes throughout the world. It is also a powerful mental tool used in scientific thinking to discover and to prove new laws. Recall that the mental operation is: *Find a logical relationship (proof) between true statements (postulates) and statements to be proved (theorems)*.

We now use the search-thinking tools to try to find a more fundamental law (postulate) than can be used to explain logically why the number of matches played always equals one less than the number of players. (If you have not yet found the more fundamental law, you will probably wonder why it eluded your search for so long.)

The most significant discovery of this creative search pattern is the finding of this key attribute of the tennis tournament puzzle, the postulate law, that brings order and meaning to our search efforts. What is this key discovery or **payoff hunch?** It happens when there is a sudden flash of insight, often described as an "inductive leap" or a "bright idea". This payoff hunch is that the significant attribute upon which to focus our attention is *not* the number of players in the tournament, nor the number of winners. The significant attribute is the *number of losers!**

There is a simple one-to-one relationship between number of losers and number of matches. The number of players eliminated (losers) equals the number of matches played, because one match eliminates one player. Thus, the *number of players remaining* in competition is always reduced by one after each match. When the tournament is over, there is only one player

---

* This payoff hunch that you should focus attention on the losers instead of some other attribute is logically similar to some of the great discoveries in science. It calls for looking at an old situation from a new viewpoint. For example, when Copernicus and Kepler focused their attention upon the position of the sun instead of the position of the earth, the new viewpoint ushered in a whole new science of mechanics.

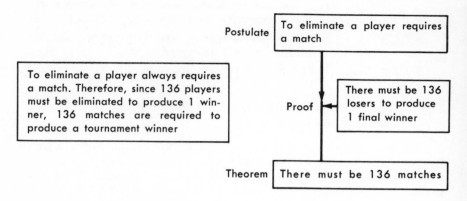

Fig. 2-6.   **Deductive proof for why there must be 136 matches played.**

remaining. Therefore, 136 players have been eliminated, and 136 matches have been played. This reasoning can be represented diagrammatically in Fig. 2-6.

This deductive proof of why there must be 136 matches permits us to make predictions with greater certainty. We now can say that for a tennis tournament of any number of players, say, 200 players, it is always true that the number of losers equals the number of matches; and since there must be 199 losers (and 1 final winner), there also must be 199 matches. Because a bye cannot produce a loser, it cannot affect the number of matches played. In addition, we have new attributes upon which to focus our attention: number of players eliminated (losers) and number of players remaining.

2-11   Discovery of a Conservation Law

Research means just that—search again and again for more understanding of old laws and the discovery of new laws. When we now research, with the aid of symbols and mathematical logic, the logical structure of the tennis tournament puzzle, we will discover a *conservation law* that is of the same form as the great conservation laws in science. The scientific conservation laws have great predictive capabilities and serve as foundational postulates for the deduction and explanation of other laws. The next law that we will discover will have these same capabilities for the simple case at hand.

We begin this part of the search by returning to the attributes and relationships just explored, which gave us new insights into the 137-player tournament. First, we notice that *"to eliminate a player requires a match"* is a key relationship. It is **always true, no matter** how many players enter the tournament or how the byes are scheduled. The only **but not if** of the law is when a player defaults. This observation is a basic postulate in our reasoning. It is analogous to the odd-even law of checkers of Sec. 1-3, the law of shaded and plain squares of Sec. 2-2, and the reduction of remainder law of Sec. 2-3. It is on such basic postulate laws that theoretical science is based. It is often very difficult to find the best way to put such a law into words. Here is one good way for the tennis tournament.

QLF 2-5	Law of Eliminations and Matches
WHAT	It is **always true** that to eliminate a player requires a match,
WHEN	**no matter** how many players or what schedule of byes,
WHEN NOT	**but not if** there is a default.

Next, we note another even more invariant relationship about the tennis tournament: The *number of players eliminated plus the number of players remaining equals the number of original players in the tournament* (a constant value). Can we use these two fundamental relationships as postulates from which to reason about the law relationships of the tournament?

Fig. 2-7 outlines the *results* of this systematic logical search. The important attributes of the tennis tournament have been carefully defined in Fig. 2-7. Note that the terms "winners" and "losers" have not been used. This is because "winner" is a confusing term. Before the tournament starts there are no winners; after the first match there is one winner; after the second match two winners; but finally at the end of the tournament there again is only one winner. Also, is a player who has won three times and lost once a winner or a loser? The classification based upon "eliminated players" and "remaining players" avoids this confusion.

The deductive reasoning based upon two selected postulates is represented in the diagram of Fig. 2-7; the proof can be understood in detail as follows:

Law 1

From Postulate 1, we can derive Law 1. The proof requires only the ability to count. If there is one loser for each match played, then there are 2 losers when 2 matches are played, 3 losers when 3 matches are played, and so forth for any number of matches played. Since each loser becomes an eliminated player, the number of eliminated players E equals the number of matches played M. (Remember! E is a number and so is M. *Players* can't equal *matches;* but *numbers* can be equal.)

Law 2

From Postulate 2, we can derive Law 2. Our proof is based on the theorem that the sum of the parts is equal to the whole. The whole can be classified into two groups: E players eliminated and R players remaining; if none of the players disappears (all players are conserved), then the sum of the parts (number of eliminated players plus number of remaining players) is equal to the whole (number of players in tournament).

Law 3

From the combination of Law 1 and Law 2, we can derive Law 3. The proof follows the theorem that an equation remains true when equals are

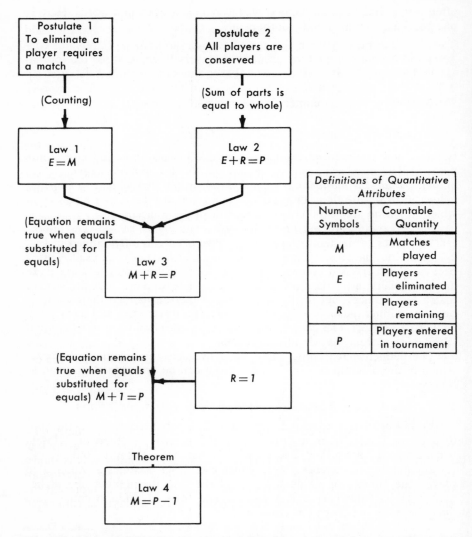

Fig. 2-7.   A postulate-proof-theorem structure of four laws relevant to the tennis tournament.

substituted for each other. Since $E = M$ (Law 1), we can substitute M for E in Law 2 to deduce Law 3.

Law 3, $M + R = P$, is a new law. It was theoretically deduced, and it predicts something quite amazing! **No matter** how complex the situation or how the sequence of the tournament unfolds, the sum of two countable quantities, $M + R$, will always be a constant number, equal to the number of original players in the tournament. We can easily check this prediction by referring to the history of the 2-, 3-, 4-, and 5-player tournaments recorded in Fig. 2-5. We conclude that it is **always true** if we count the number of matches played, M, and the number of remaining players, R, and then add these two numbers together; the sum of the quantities, $M + P$, remains constant and is equal to the total number of players P who entered the tournament, **but not if** there are defaults. Thus, from the invariant relationship $M + R = P$, we see that the sum of the two attributes M and R is conserved throughout the history of a tennis tournament.*

Law 4

From Law 3, we can deduce Law 4. Again the proof is based upon the theorem that an equation remains true when equals are substituted for each other. At the special time after the final match, there is 1 player who has never lost. He is the only remaining player so that $R = 1$. Therefore, if 1 is substituted for R in the general conservation Law 3, we arrive at Law 4. (Law 4 establishes our $M = P - 1$ law-hunch, because if we subtract 1 from each side of the equation, it is equivalent to $M = P - 1$.)

Our research of the logical structure with the aid of symbols and mathematical logic has yielded new knowledge: Law 4, $M = P - 1$, which started as a hunch from trying simplest cases, is a special case that predicts the number of matches at the *end* of the tournament. It is derivable from a general conservation Law 3, which predicts an invariant relationship that holds no matter how far the tournament has progressed. The conservation Law 3, in turn, is derivable by logical proof from postulate Laws 1 and 2. These postulate laws are intuitively self-evident: Postulate 2 has no **but not if,** except for extremes like deaths of players, and Postulate 1 fails only if there are defaults.†

2-12 *The Importance of Simple Symbolic Representations*

Now that we have at last produced a *result* in the form of an orderly relationship among the attributes of the tennis tournament puzzle, let us look at a really simple way to display the basic processes. This simple way is shown in the table below. Imagine that you list in column 1 word descriptions of the different stages of the tournament. Then in column 2, represent the stages in terms of M. Since one basic process is that a player is eliminated

---

* The scientific search for the invariants of nature dates back to the atomist Democritus (5th century B.C.), who asserted that matter was indestructible. Since then, the scientific search has established several widely encompassing conservation laws dealing with such quantities as mass, energy, and momentum. Stated as laws, these quantities are conserved; they remain changeless amidst many changes, thus permitting explanations of the past and predictions into the future of many observable facts. These conservation laws stand today as pillars of scientific knowledge.

† The next research step might seek to make the logical structure of the 4 laws to be **always true, no matter** the number of defaults. If so, we could let $D =$ number of defaults, and extend the logical structure to prove $M + R + D = P$ as a more general conservation Law 3. This extension of a more limited conservation law, $M + R = P$, is logically similar to the example that extended the law of conservation of remainders to include "Take 7 or Put Back 2." Also, it is like what has occurred with the energy concept in science. As new forms of energy have been discovered, it has been possible to include them in more complete laws of conservation of energy.

for each match, we can list the values for E in column 3. Another basic process is that each increase of one in eliminated players means a decrease of one in remaining players; hence, we can write in column 4 the values for R. When we examine the table, we see that the conservation law $M + R = P$ and the $M = P - 1$ law are inevitable arithmetic consequences of the tabulated numbers.

Column 1	Column 2	Column 3	Column 4
Stage of Tournament	$M =$ Number of Matches Played	$E =$ Number of Players Eliminated	$R =$ Number of Players Remaining in Competition
Before first match	0	0	137
After first match	1	1	136
After second match	2	2	135
. . . .	. . .	. . .	. . .
After 135th match	135	135	2
After 136th match	136	136	1

The finding of neat symbolic forms, like the above table and those of Sec. 2-3, to describe phenomena in nature has been one of the great accomplishments of science. The level of sophistication is, of course, much higher in science than in the tennis tournament. But the treatment of the orderly symbolic forms for the tennis tournament is analogous to the mysterious hieroglyphics

$$\frac{\partial^2 \varphi}{\partial x^2} + \frac{\partial^2 \varphi}{\partial y^2} + \frac{\partial^2 \varphi}{\partial z^2} = \frac{1}{c^2} \frac{\partial^2 \varphi}{\partial t^2}$$

that describe the propagation of electromagnetic waves, or the equation

$$x_{CG} = \frac{\Sigma W_i x_i}{\Sigma W_i}$$

that predicts center of gravity. The x_{CG} equation, which will be discussed in a later chapter, is much like the symbolic form that has resulted from the investigation of the complex tennis tournament puzzle. The attributes W_i and x_i are like E and R. In any case, the final *result* is again an *orderly relationship* of *key attributes* in a complex situation.

2-13   Summary of the Creative Search Pattern in the Tennis Tournament

We have spent this great amount of exposition on a relatively simple problem for a definite purpose. Although our intellectual journey through the maze of the tennis tournament may seem devious and inefficient, it does accurately represent typical aspects of scientific research.

1. The tennis tournament puzzle, although trivial in its subject matter, does attempt to convey correctly the frustrating, confusing aspects often

associated with creative thought. It illustrates how, when unfamiliar concepts and relationships are involved, even the best human minds often wander up blind alleys and spend much time exploring fruitless avenues. It is important for the reader to know that this is normal. The more original or difficult the problem, the more certain it is that these frustrating experiences will occur.

2. The tennis tournament example shows that the use of the *search-thinking tools* to increase *familiarity* with the details of the problem at hand does increase the chance that useful *hunches* will occur. Also, the more experience that the mind has had with *invariant relationships* and *conservation laws*, the more quickly it will discover and appreciate new ones. The excitement and joy in finding a new law is dramatized by the famous story of Archimedes leaping from his bath and running naked through the streets crying *Eureka!* ("I have found it") when he discovered his famous buoyancy principle. The history of science contains many examples of similar incidences of men who devoted years of effort and gained detailed *familiarity* with a particular problem before discovering the significant relationship. It is quite likely that these men went through a creative search like the one described here.

3. The tennis tournament puzzle illustrates how big a role chance may sometimes play, when someone is lucky enough to focus on a key attribute. For example, suppose that, out of all the possible countable quantities about the tournament, you focused on the *number of sets of tennis balls needed for the tournament*. Suppose that a fresh set of tennis balls was used for each match. Suppose that each loser, as a consolation prize, got to keep the balls from the match he lost. Obviously, everyone except the final winner gets a set of balls. Since "everyone but the winner" is $P - 1$ players and each gets a set of balls, there must be $P - 1$ matches to produce 1 final winner.

About one student in 50 or so will somehow chance on a quick, lucky answer and will say at once, "You must eliminate all the players but one, so it takes 136 matches." On the other hand, a first-rank professional scientist may work through most of the steps we have described. The big difference between the professional scientist and the lucky student is this: If the student is not lucky on his problem, he may become discouraged and not know how to proceed, whereas the scientist will go on. The scientist knows how to use a set of *search-thinking tools* effectively, he has experienced the expected frustrations of *creative search,* and he can recall some relevant *invariant relationships* previously mastered. He will produce in the end, with much greater certainty, new and useful invariant relationships.

Let us now review our intellectual journey through the maze of the tennis tournament puzzle by retracing the steps on the *creative search map* drawn in Fig. 2-8. This particular journey was planned for an optimum learning experience. A student on his own might have a lucky hunch, or he might follow parts of the same pattern, or he might simply bog down. Our plans, however, were to move continuously from chaos to increasing order made possible by the use of *search-thinking tools* that had the power to carry us to ever higher levels of understanding and prediction. Follow again the sequence and steps of the *creative search pattern,* as we summarize the significant attributes of this creative search in an orderly sequence, as shown in Fig. 2-8.

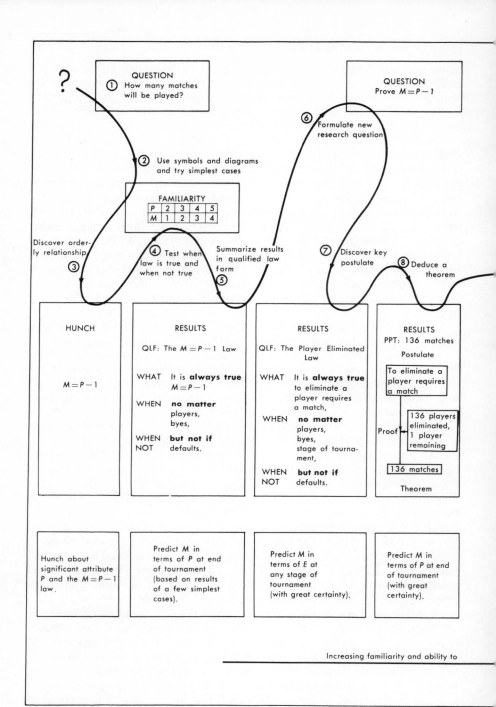

Fig. 2-8. **Creative search map showing journey**

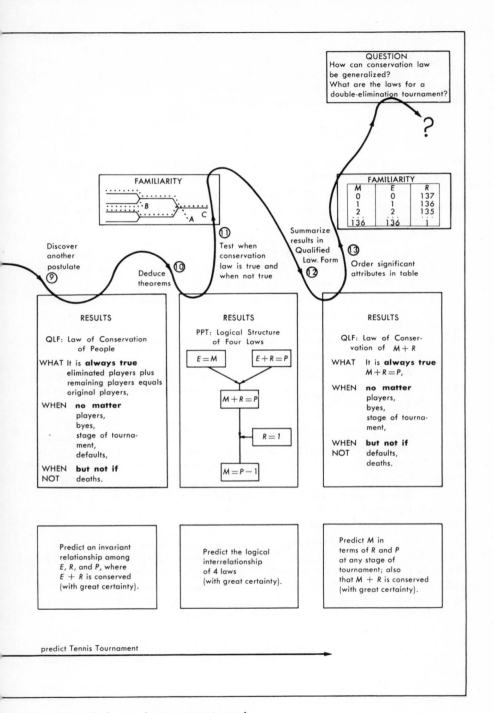

QUESTION
How can conservation law
be generalized?
What are the laws for a
double-elimination tournament?

FAMILIARITY

FAMILIARITY

M	E	R
0	0	137
1	1	136
2	2	135
...	...	...
136	136	1

Discover
another
postulate
⑨

Deduce
theorems
⑩

Test when
conservation
law is true and
when not true
⑪

Summarize
results in
Qualified
Law Form
⑫

Order significant
attributes in table
⑬

RESULTS

QLF: Law of Conservation
of People

WHAT It is **always true**
eliminated players plus
remaining players equals
original players,

WHEN **no matter**
players,
byes,
stage of tourna-
ment,
defaults,

WHEN **but not if**
NOT deaths.

RESULTS

PPT: Logical Structure
of Four Laws

$E = M$ $E + R = P$

$M + R = P$

$R = 1$

$M = P - 1$

RESULTS

QLF: Law of Conser-
vation of $M + R$

WHAT It is **always true**
$M + R = P$,

WHEN **no matter**
players,
byes,
stage of tourna-
ment,

WHEN **but not if**
NOT defaults,
deaths.

Predict an invariant
relationship among
E, R, and P, where
$E + R$ is conserved
(with great certainty).

Predict the logical
interrelationship
of 4 laws
(with great certainty).

Predict M in
terms of R and P
at any stage of
tournament; also
that $M + R$ is conserved
(with great certainty).

predict Tennis Tournament

line through the tennis tournament puzzle.

41

① We began our journey through the world of the tennis tournament when we decided to investigate the *question*, "How many matches will be played?" This was not really the question that finally brought order out of chaos. That question did not come until Step 6.

② We achieved new familiarity with specific features of the complex 137-player tournament, when we used *symbols and diagrams* to solve *simplest cases*. We studied the detailed histories of these simplest cases, performed *conceptual experiments* to examine selected attributes, and arranged the *results* in an orderly table.

③ Our journey was quickened when a key hunch occurred: The number of matches played is always 1 less than the number of players entered in the tournament.

④ We subjected this newly discovered relationship to further *conceptual experiments* to find out WHEN and WHEN NOT the relationship was true. In this manner, we gained more detailed *familiarity* about how byes, players, and defaults affected the relationship.

⑤ We used number-symbols to write the relationship as a *qualified-equation, $M = P - 1$* (in number size) and then summarized our results in one sentence in the qualified law form. At this point we classified and defined the four kinds of symbols and the qualified-equation we have used as *search-thinking tools* about the tennis tournament.

⑥ What was the meaning of the new hunch-law $M = P - 1$? The research *question* now was: "Can we prove it? Is there a more fundamental law from which it can be deduced?"

⑦ The proof was made possible when we made a key discovery of a more fundamental relationship that related number of matches to number of players eliminated (losers). It was like finding the key clue in a mystery story. The word statement of the relationship was: "To eliminate a player required a match".

⑧ This discovered relationship was used as a *postulate* to give a logical *proof* of the *theorem:* 136 matches must be played in a 137-player, single-elimination tournament, **but not if** there are defaults.

⑨ The success of this logical proof for a particular tournament suggested that a more general proof be attempted using algebraic symbols. "To eliminate a player requires a match" was selected as one of the *postulates* and expressed as a qualified equation, $E = M$ (in number size). A second *postulate* was selected when we noted an invariant relationship about two categories of players in the tournament; players eliminated and players remaining divided all the players into two classes. The number of players is not affected by this classification (see Sec. 3-2), so that the sum of the numerical values of these two categories equals the number of players entered in the tournament. Stated in number-symbols, the second postulate became $E + R = P$. When we reasoned from these two postulates, using the mathematical logic of arithmetic and algebra, we deduced new relationships in the form of mathematical *theorems*.

⑩ There were two significant results. One of the *theorems* produced in this **postulate-proof-theorem, PPT,** structure of algebraic equations was a fundamental conservation law, $M + R = P$. In addition, the empirical $M = P - 1$ law was seen as a theorem and special case of the more general conservation law.

(11) *Conceptual experiments* were conducted with previously recorded simplest cases to test the mathematically derived conservation law. New *familiarity* with the tennis tournament problem was achieved.

(12) This conservation law of the tennis tournament was summarized in the qualified law form.

(13) In Sec. 2-12, the most significant attributes of the 137-player tournament were placed in an orderly relationship with the aid of an appropriately organized table. The numerical values of E and R were tabulated after each match of the tournament, M. The table of three columns displayed the numerical relationships of the four discovered equations and how the equations are related to each other. This *familiarity* with the tennis tournament puzzle, in comparison with our initial familiarity at the $M = P - 1$ stage, is more certain, more comprehensive, more penetrating.

Thus, our detailed *familiarity* about the tennis tournament now has been compactly recorded in orderly forms—*qualified law forms, qualified-equations, postulate-proof-theorem* structures of mathematical equations, tables of significant attributes—as usefully done in theoretical science. As the search progressed, we focused our attention upon the players entered in the tournament, number of matches played, players eliminated, and players remaining. Buried in a footnote is the hunch that we should next look at the number of defaults. It is an attribute often placed in the **but not if** category. When a default occurs, it places restrictions on the general applicability of the $E = M$ law $M + R = P$ and its special case $M = P - 1$. How can the conservation law be generalized to include the new attribute D, the number of defaults? What would be the form of this more general conservation law for a double-elimination tournament ("To eliminate a player requires two matches")?

It is appropriate that our journey in scientific thinking about the world of the tennis tournament end at this point. It ends where it should end, and *where it began,* with a new *question* and a *hunch* and some *familiarity* and some *results* to research.

Chapter 3

Measurement of Weight and Conservation of Matter

3-1 Introduction

In this chapter and the next two, we shall discuss several of the basic concepts of mechanics: weight, force, tension, and the principle of "action is equal and opposite to reaction."

Although these concepts will be discussed on the basis of common experiences with simple equipment such as bathroom scales, soda bottles, and string, the logical development will make use of the concepts of invariance, conservation, postulate-proof-theorem reasoning discussed in Chapters 1 and 2, and the *logical structure of measurement* developed in this chapter.

To lay a foundation for discussing the properties of invariant relations particularly applicable to physical quantities such as weight and force, we shall discuss in the next section the simplest of all quantitative attributes of nature—the number of discrete objects in a set of objects; actually, we shall carry out *conceptual experiments* involving the counting of pennies. The "counting pennies" example permits you to commence exact quantitative scientific thinking in an area of concepts where you already have detailed familiarity with the key attributes, namely, the properties of ordinary whole numbers.

The discussion of counting forms a link between the invariant attributes discussed in Chapters 1 and 2, both of which involve counting, and the invariant attributes of measurement, such as are involved with weight. The important invariance principles apply to weight and force in the same way that they do to the purchasing power of pennies. We emphasize the properties of these invariant attributes by introducing a new word *conaddian;* this word is defined in terms of concepts explained in the next section.

Following the discussion of the invariance of weight in this chapter, we shall extend the concepts to vertical forces, and to action and reaction in Chapter 4, and to vectors and vector forces in Chapter 5.

Now for a problem that leads up to the invariance of weight: Suppose that Secret Agent 003 has a suitcase and an attaché case. He is packing prior to a transatlantic flight. He loads his clothes into the suitcase, and his papers and ray-gun into the attaché case. He has a baggage allowance of 40 lb for his flight. He weighs the suitcase and finds that it weighs 30 lb. Then he weighs the attaché case and finds that it weighs 15 lb. This 15 lb is 5 lb too heavy because it brings the total weight to 45 lb. He takes out the ray-gun, which weighs 5 lb, so as to lighten the attaché case. He puts it in the suitcase.

Because of your practical experience with weights, you will predict that his baggage is still 5 lb over the weight allowance. In fact, you are probably already convinced that **no matter** how he tries, he **can't change** the five pounds overweight—a situation that leads to the *hunch* that there is a *conservation law*.

In this chapter we shall put this problem into scientific terms. We shall show how it leads to making weight-measuring instruments. In the following chapters we shall extend the reasoning to reach several interesting and useful conclusions. One of these is the principle that *action* is equal and opposite to *reaction*. Another is Archimedes' buoyancy principle. This principle, mentioned in the beginning of Chapter 1, enabled Archimedes to tell whether or not the king's crown was pure gold.

3-2   "Counting Pennies" and the Concept of an Invariant Attribute of Nature

The purchasing power of pennies in a bag exemplifies several features of the important concepts in quantitative science. We shall discuss the determination, or measurement, of the purchasing power as if it were an example of measurement of a physical quantity, like energy or momentum. In fact, as we discuss later in this chapter, pennies, nickels, dimes, and quarters are to purchasing power much as atoms of hydrogen, lithium, boron, and aluminum are to weight.

The measurement or evaluation process can be divided into three parts. The results of measurement fit into an orderly relationship that constitutes a fourth part. In this money example of the logical structure of measurement, the parts are as follows:

Part 1. The *quantitative attribute* is the *purchasing power:* in this case, simply what the pennies are worth—for example, 15 cents.

Part 2. The *standard unit* is a representative *penny* you might have obtained from a bank.

Part 3. Carry out the *comparison operation* as follows: Reach into the bag and take out an object (it always turns out to be a penny); compare it with the standard (it always has the same value); lay it aside as you count "One cent"; do the same with the next penny counting "Two cents" and so on until the bag is empty; at this point you will have reached "15 cents."

Part 4. Concerns orderly relationships. We return to it later.

The phrase "15 cents" is the symbol that represents the *purchasing power* of the pennies. This "15 cents" is an **invariant attribute** of the bag of pennies. All experimenters, i.e., anyone who can count, will get the same value. It never *varies*. It is *invariant*.

If you did not know how much money was in the bag, you could call the unknown value x. You would then find that $x = 15$ cents; or would you find that $x = 15$? Which you decide on depends upon the **one-to-one correspondences** you choose to set up between symbols and ideas. For example, you may choose to define x as follows:

    x corresponds to purchasing power measured in standard units
    of the U.S. cent;

or you may define another *x*, call it $x^\sim$, which you read aloud as "ex till-de"
with the last "e" pronounced as in "end":

    $x^\sim$ corresponds to the purchasing power.

You might even choose to introduce still one more symbol:

    d corresponds to the purchasing power measured in U.S. dollars.

These definitions mean that in terms of the qualified-equation of the
notation of Section 2-7,

$$x \;= 15 \quad \text{(in number size)} \tag{3-1}$$
$$x^\sim = 15 \text{ cents } = \$0.15 \quad \text{(in purchasing power)} \tag{3-2}$$
$$d \;= 0.15 \quad \text{(in number size)} \tag{3-3}$$

These equations emphasize the difference between the two unspecified
number-symbols *x* and *d* and the purchasing-power symbol $x^\sim$.

The purchasing-power symbol $x^\sim$ is a new kind of symbol, which we shall
call a **quantity-symbol** to distinguish it from a *number-symbol*. The next
section discusses in detail unspecified quantity-symbols and their relationship to number-symbols and pure numbers.

The *quantity-symbol* is the fifth class of symbols we have considered.
The other four listed in Sec. 2-7 are abbreviation-symbols, name-symbols,
adjective-symbols, and number-symbols. By introducing it, we expect to
avoid many ambiguities. These ambiguities are practically never cleared up
in other texts. Experienced students and teachers are often not bothered by
these ambiguities. They hold enough details in their heads so that they do
not mix things up. But their apparent competence is sometimes merely rote
learning. Here, we are trying to develop mental tools that will enable you to
understand more thoroughly and to learn more quickly.

Accordingly, we shall use the *tilde symbol* $\sim$ to distinguish *quantity-
symbols*. The tilde is easy to write and to pronounce.

Part 4 in our logical structure of measurement is **orderly relationships.**
One of the great powers of orderly relationships is that they often enable you
to make **predictions** (as you did about the 45 lb of luggage in Sec. 3-1);
this we shall illustrate after putting Part 4 in words:

    Part 4. There are *orderly relationships* between quantitative values of
    the purchasing-power attribute. These *orderly relationships* permit you to
    make *predictions*.

Predictions in regard to numbers of pennies are so natural that you probably are scarcely aware that you often make them. You ordinarily take
for granted the *relationships between numbers* obtained by counting. Analyze
your thinking, however, so that you can transfer your experience to science
later. In particular, do you not predict how much change you will get when
you buy something? Don't you, or shouldn't you, predict one-to-one correspondence between your check stubs and the balance they show and your
bank statement, with all its withdrawals, deposits, and balance?

The invariant property of number of pennies has other features of great simplicity, in addition to the invariance. You use these when you make predictions. Very similar features occur in many important laws of nature. The two features of greatest importance are the *relationships* of being *additive* and *conservative*.

Additive can be understood from this example: If you take two bags of pennies, one worth 15 cents and the other worth 10 cents, and pour them both into a new empty bag, what will be the value in the new bag? Obviously, 25 cents, because everybody knows that $15 + 10 = 25$. This relationship between pure numbers holds true **no matter** what objects you count to get the numbers, or even if you count nothing except your own mental images—for example, the fence-jumping sheep that are supposed to put you to sleep.

The numbers of the pennies in several bags are additive because if you make up a new "total" bag of pennies out of any collection of pennies in other "subtotal" bags, the new number is the sum of the parts.

Additivity is an obvious result for pennies because everyone is used to counting objects like pennies, matches, paperclips, kittens, luggage, etc. Everyone knows by experience that *numbers of discrete* **objects** *add*. Remember this simple additivity law when in later chapters you think about weights, moments, and energies. The importance of these scientific concepts is due primarily to the fact that they also have the additive property.

The number of pennies also has a *conservative* property because **no matter** how you divide them up in bags, you still have the same number.

Conservation and *additivity* usually go hand in hand, but not always; you can have additivity without conservation. For example, if you are in a penny arcade, the number of pennies you have is the sum of the number in each pocket. But if you spend pennies, the total number you have is not conserved. The same distinction applies to that famous and elusive concept of thermodynamics—*entropy*. Entropies add, but unlike pennies in the arcade, the total always increases rather than decreases with the passage of time.

These *relationships between numbers of pennies* (or other objects) are what you use when you predict how much change you expect or what your bank balance is. The relationships can be stated in qualified law form. This is left as an exercise for the reader.

Many of the most important concepts in physical science involve attributes of nature having properties like numbers of objects. Sometimes the properties are not perfect and the WHEN NOT situations must be watched for.

The attributes we shall discuss in this chapter are also *con*served under the proper circumstances; they are *add*itive; and they are *in*variant *at*tributes of *n*ature for which all observers get the same values under a great variety of conditions. Attributes with these features can be described by the new word mentioned in Sec. 3-1:

conaddian

Connaddian is an abbreviation for "**con**servative" "**add**itive" "**in**variant" "**attribute of nature.**" This one word is an important thinking tool. It should remind you of a whole logical structure pattern useful in quantitative science whenever you think of it. Conaddian is pronounced to rhyme with "con" "bad" and "ee-an", accent on "add".

The subject matter of *Mechanics* as discussed in Chapter 1 is concerned almost exclusively with conaddians. The law of conservation of objects is the prototype of all these conservation laws:

QLF 3-1 Law of Conservation of Objects	
WHAT	It is **always true** that the number of objects in a set of objects is a fixed invariant number,
WHEN	**no matter** in what order you count them or how many there are,
WHEN NOT	**but not if** some divide into two or more or combine or evaporate like drops of water.

This law can be summed up by saying that number of objects is conaddian. It is the basis of arithmetic and even of such measuring instruments as rulers; each $\frac{1}{16}$-in. division may be regarded as a little object so that measuring consists in effect of counting the objects along the ruler and estimating the fraction left over. These concepts underlie many instruments—in particular the direct-reading, weight-measuring instrument at the end of this chapter.

3-3   Quantity-Symbols and Classification of Symbols

The symbol $x^{\sim}$ is, as mentioned above, a member of a new class of symbols. The *tilde* ($^{\sim}$) itself is an adjective-symbol, the third of the four classes discussed in Sec. 2-3, namely: (1) abbreviation-symbols, (2) name-symbols, (3) adjective-symbols, and (4) number-symbols. The *symbol* $x^{\sim}$ adds a fifth class to this list. Since $x^{\sim}$ stands for *purchasing power* of a *quantity* of money, we shall call symbols of this new class **quantity-symbols.** Two other examples of the many quantity-symbols that we shall use are the weight $W_A^{\sim}$ of an object A and the length $L_A^{\sim}$ of a lever arm. With the introduction of the quantity-symbol, we are in a position to make a broad classification of symbols in general.

Symbols are the most important thinking tools in science. But they are often misunderstood and poorly explained. The difficulties arise because the user often does not take the trouble to say precisely what he means by a symbol, and sometimes he unwittingly uses the same symbol to represent several different ideas. In other words, he does not set up a one-to-one correspondence but, instead, uses a two-to-one or a three-to-one correspondence between ideas and symbols. Sometimes the confusion causes no problems, but in any event it often represents sloppy thinking. On the other hand, when the meaning is made precise, sometimes quite difficult ideas can be quickly understood and new results easily obtained.

In this section we shall present a classification that comprises seven different classes of symbols. Almost every one of these seven classes appear in all books that use mathematical equations to describe physical science. Most of these symbols will be familiar to you. However, you have probably never taken time to analyze them before. You will find that if you become familiar with the classification of symbols, it will help your thinking in other parts of this book and in any other book on physical science or on applied mathematics.

In order to show the power of symbols to work out new results, we shall give at the end of this section two examples of changing units. These examples are not intended to be self-evident on a first reading; however, they should give you an idea of what you can easily do when you become well acquainted with quantity-symbols and their associated standard units.

One thing that you can do with quantity-symbols appears at first to be the forbidden operation of adding apples and oranges. However, such seemingly improper operations can be quite correct when you are adding the same kinds of quantities. Some examples of qualified-equations (see Sec. 2-7) will make this clear. The first example equates purchasing powers:

$$3 \text{ nickels}^\sim + 1 \text{ dime}^\sim + 3 \text{ quarters}^\sim = 20 \text{ nickels}^\sim = 10 \text{ dimes}^\sim$$
$$= 4 \text{ quarters}^\sim = 1 \text{ dollar}^\sim \quad \text{(in purchasing power)} \qquad \textbf{(3-4)}$$

We use the tilde $^\sim$ to show that all the standard units of money are quantity-symbols for purchasing power consistent with the equation-qualifier (in purchasing power). The second example equates lengths and uses equation-qualifier (in length):

$$6 \text{ in.}^\sim + 3 \text{ ft}^\sim + 2 \text{ yd}^\sim = 114 \text{ in.}^\sim$$
$$= 9.5 \text{ ft}^\sim = 3\tfrac{1}{6} \text{ yd}^\sim \quad \text{(in length)} \qquad \textbf{(3-5)}$$

These equations obviously make sense in a quantitative way quite differently from a set of symbols such as

$$\text{circus ticket} + \text{ice cream cone} = \text{happiness}$$
$$\text{(in six-year-old emotions)} \qquad \textbf{(3-6)}$$

The famous **"you can't** add apples and oranges" fits into our symbolic scheme as follows:

$$3 \text{ apples}^\sim + 2 \text{ oranges}^\sim = 6 \text{ tangerines}^\sim \quad \text{(in peaches)} \qquad \textbf{(3-7)}$$

is obviously nonsense. However, if we choose as a standard unit any fruit from a tree and let the tilde $^\sim$ mean "amount of tree-fruit attribute", the equation

$$3 \text{ apples}^\sim + 2 \text{ oranges}^\sim = 5 \text{ tangerines}^\sim \quad \text{(in tree fruit)} \qquad \textbf{(3-8)}$$

makes at least a little sense.

Quantity-symbol equations can be treated like algebraic equations with ordinary numbers. For example, when you buy a 25-cent$^\sim$ magazine with a dollar bill, how much change should you get? *Solution:* Let $x^\sim$ stand for the purchasing power of the change. Then a law of conservation of purchasing power requires that change plus purchase equals the dollar bill in purchasing power (at least until you take your purchase off the counter). Consequently, you can use symbols to write

$$x^{\sim} + 25 \text{ cents}^{\sim} = 1 \text{ dollar}^{\sim} = 100 \text{ cents}^{\sim}$$
$$\text{(in purchasing power)} \qquad \textbf{(3-9)}$$

Now subtract 25 cents$^{\sim}$ from both sides and you get

$$x^{\sim} = 75 \text{ cents}^{\sim} \quad \text{(in purchasing power)} \qquad \textbf{(3-10)}$$

If we had used not the quantity-symbol $x^{\sim}$ for the unknown quantity of purchasing power but, instead, the number-symbol p standing for the number of pennies you would get in change, the equation would be

$$p \text{ cents}^{\sim} + 25 \text{ cents}^{\sim} = 1 \text{ dollar}^{\sim}$$
$$\text{(in purchasing power)} \qquad \textbf{(3-11)}$$

so that

$$p \text{ cents}^{\sim} = 75 \text{ cents}^{\sim} \quad \text{(in purchasing power)} \qquad \textbf{(3-12)}$$

The only way this equation can be true is for p to be the ordinary number 75.

This relationship between the $x^{\sim}$ and p equations is an example of a relationship that occurs repeatedly in physical science. It involves conversion of a quantity-equation to a number-equation. We emphasize its importance by stating it as a QLF.

QLF 3-2 A Quantity-Equation Can Convert to a Number-Equation	
WHAT	It is **always true** that you can convert a quantity-equation with every term expressed in the same standard unit (or units if several kinds of quantities are involved) into a number-equation by dividing out the units,
WHEN	**no matter** what units are involved or how many terms are included,
WHEN NOT	**but not if** (no exceptions known except plain mistakes).

An example is as follows:

$$p \text{ cents}^{\sim} = 75 \text{ cents}^{\sim} \quad \text{(in purchasing power)} \qquad \textbf{(3-12)}$$

then

$$p = 75 \quad \text{(in number of cents}^{\sim}) \qquad \textbf{(3-13)}$$

The equation-qualifier used here in Eq. (3-13) is the first example of the most important equation-qualifier in science. It specifies that the equation applies to number of standard units of the cent found on the two sides of the equal sign. All the important equations in science and engineering are most useful when they are put in this class, but to the best of the authors' knowledge, no *adjective-symbol* of the form (in number of cents$^{\sim}$) has been printed before Eq. (3-13). This new adjective-symbol applies to both the equation and the number p.

Equation (3-13) is an example of a qualified-equation with an equation-qualifier of a general class of the form (**in number of standard units**). This adjective-symbol can be represented by **NSU** as an abbreviation-symbol. We shall discuss these NSU qualifiers more fully in Sec. 3-8. One of the important mental tools in quantitative scientific thinking is the process of conversion from a quantity-equation to an (in number of standard units)-equation.

The great value of NSU qualified-equations is that they are simply the ordinary equations of algebra. The symbols in the equations are simply number-symbols. They stand for known numbers like 2, 4, 0.265, or 3.414 . . . $= \pi$, or unknown numbers like x. However, NSU numbers differ from **pure numbers** like π and $\sqrt{2} = 1.414$ which have values that are determined from their definitions alone. For example, consider the two NSU numbers that describe a desk-top four feet long. We denote them by $L_{in.}^D$ for the NSU in inches and L_{ft}^D for the NSU in feet. Then we can write

$$L_D{}^\sim = L_{in.}^D \text{ in.}^\sim = L_{ft}^D \text{ ft}^\sim \quad \text{(in length)} \qquad \textbf{(3-14)}$$

where $L_{in.}^D = 48$ and $L_{ft}^D = 4$. This example shows how NSU numbers differ from pure numbers: in particular, the value of the NSU number depends not only on what specific quantity it describes but also on the standard units that are used; the pure number does not depend on standard units. This example also exhibits a common phenomenon with NSU numbers that at first seems puzzling. The desk seems to be smaller in feet than in inches, but the foot is bigger than the inch. How can this be? The answer is that because the foot is twelve times as big as the inch, it takes only one twelfth as many feet to make the desk top; hence, L_{ft}^D is twelve times smaller than $L_{in.}^D$.

As discussed above quantity-symbols are the fifth class of symbols that we have considered. Two additional familiar classes of symbols are used in mathematical equations, namely: *relationship-symbols* and *operation-symbols*. They will be clear from their definitions in Table 3-1.

Table 3-1   Table of Seven Classes of Symbols

Class	Example	Section
Abbreviation-symbols	QED, QLF	2-7
Name-symbol	T_2, B_1, J_2, ECE, E_A	2-7, 3-4, 5-4
Adjective-symbol	$\sim$, $'$, $_2$, (in purchasing power)	3-2, 3-5
Number-symbol	P, E, R, π	2-7
Quantity-symbol	$x^\sim$, $W_2{}^\sim$	3-3, 3-6
Relationship-symbols	$=$, $>$, $\geqq$, $\equiv$, $\neq$	2-7, 3-5
Operation-symbols	$+$, $-$, $\times$, $\div$	3-4

The relationship symbols include the "greater than" sign: $3 > 2$; the "greater than or equal to" sign: $x^2 \geq 0$, which is true for all values of x (real values, not imaginary); the definition- or identity-symbol: $\pi \equiv$ circumference/diameter of a circle, or $\$ \equiv$ dollar; and the inequality sign: $3 \neq 2$.

---

* See inside back cover for table including vector-symbols.

Symbols like $T, B, J, P, E, R,$ and X may be appropriately called *noun-symbols* since they represent the main idea that is modified by the adjective-symbol. Sometimes pairs or triplets of letters may be used as noun-symbols such as ECE in Chapter 5.

From Table 3-1, it is evident that many classes of symbols inevitably occur in any exposition of physical science that contains any equations. Classifications like the one above are published in books so rarely as to be practically nonexistent; the authors of this book had never seen one before. Usually the authors of science books simply hope that the readers will not be confused, and do not analyze the variety of symbols they use. Often they use one and the same symbol for several classes of meaning. We believe it will help the reader to be aware of the fact that almost every book in physical science uses all the above seven classes of symbols and even an eighth class, vectors, which we shall discuss in Chapter 5.

We shall conclude this section with three examples of the use of symbols. The first two illustrate that symbols and their manipulations can be very useful with the difficult problem of changing units. These two examples, which you may not understand on a first reading, are presented to encourage you to continue your attempt to become more familiar with the ideas of this section by applying them as you read farther in this book. The third example illustrates an actual problem with symbols that occurred while this book was being written.

*Example 1. Changing Units for Gasoline Prices**

How does the price $P_F{}^\sim$ of gasoline in *F*rance compare with the price $P_A{}^\sim$ of gasoline in *A*merica? Suppose that gasoline in France costs 0.53 franc$^\sim$ per liter$^\sim$ and in America 30 cents$^\sim$ per gallon$^\sim$. These quantity-symbols for prices can be put into qualified-equations as follows:

$$P_F{}^\sim = 0.53 \text{ franc}^\sim/\text{liter}^\sim$$
(in purchasing power per unit volume) †   **(3-15)**

$$P_A{}^\sim = 30 \text{ cents}^\sim/\text{gallon}^\sim$$
(in purchasing power per unit volume)   **(3-16)**

Now we also know, from foreign exchange rates‡ and from standard units of volume, that

$$5 \text{ francs}^\sim = 100 \text{ cents}^\sim \quad \text{(in purchasing power)}$$

$$1 \text{ liter}^\sim = 0.265 \text{ gallon}^\sim \quad \text{(in volume)}$$

These are the key attributes of the problem. What orderly relationship can be set up?

---

* This example is illustrative of methods that need not be mastered before the survey of Chapter 9.

† The different purchasing power of money in different countries is discussed briefly in connection with Fig. 3-4.

‡ Par value is 1 franc$^\sim$ = 20.41 cents$^\sim$ and 1 gallon$^\sim$ = 3.785 liters$^\sim$. We "round-off" these values to simplify the arithmetic in this example.

The quantity 5 francs~ is the same as 100 cents~ in purchasing power. Divide by 5 so that we compare 1 franc~ with one-fifth of 100 cents~. Symbolically:

$$5 \text{ francs}^{\sim} \div 5 = 100 \text{ cents}^{\sim} \div 5$$
$$\text{(in purchasing power)} \tag{3-17}$$

so that we obtain

$$1 \text{ franc}^{\sim} = (100 \div 5) \text{ cents}^{\sim} = 20 \text{ cents}^{\sim}$$
$$\text{(in purchasing power)} \tag{3-18}$$

Consequently, in $P_F{}^{\sim}$ you can substitute 20 cents~ for the unit symbol franc~. You can also substitute 0.265 gallon~ for the unit symbol liter~. These substitutions of equals for equals (in purchasing power) and (in volume) work out as follows:

$$P_F{}^{\sim} = 0.53 \times 20 \text{ cents}^{\sim}/0.265 \text{ gallon}^{\sim}$$
$$= (10.6/0.265) \text{ cents}^{\sim}/\text{gallon}^{\sim}$$
$$= 40 \text{ cents}^{\sim}/\text{gallon}^{\sim}$$
$$\text{(in purchasing power per unit volume)} \tag{3-19}$$

On the other hand, $P_A{}^{\sim} = 30$ cents~/gallon~. Consequently the ratio of gasoline costs is

$$\text{Ratio of costs} = P_F{}^{\sim}/P_A{}^{\sim} = 40/30 = 1.33$$
$$\text{(in number size)} \tag{3-20}$$

This is a number and not a quantity, because the purchasing power and volume quantities cancel out. If we consider $P_A{}^{\sim}$ as a standard unit, then 1.33 is the NSU value of $P_F{}^{\sim}$.

These operations consist simply of replacing equals by equals for the same kind of quantities. They may seem mysterious and arbitrary, to begin with, but they will seem quite natural once you have become accustomed to thinking in terms of quantity-symbols and the standard units they use.

*Example 2. Expressing Automobile Acceleration in "g" Units**

As another everyday example, consider the acceleration of a car on a drag strip compared to $g^{\sim}$, the acceleration of gravity. The acceleration of gravity, $g^{\sim}$, as discussed in Chapter 9, is 32.2 ft~/(sec~)², or 32.2 feet~ per second~ per second~. The drag-strip car accelerates from 0 to 60 miles~ per hour~ in 6 seconds~. How do these compare? The answer is that the **average acceleration** $a^{\sim}$ for the car is

$$a^{\sim} = (60 \text{ mi}^{\sim}/\text{hr}^{\sim}) \div (6 \text{ sec}^{\sim}) = 10 \text{ mi}^{\sim}/\text{hr}^{\sim}\text{-sec}^{\sim}$$
$$= 10 \times 5280 \text{ ft}^{\sim}/3600 \text{ (sec}^{\sim})^2$$
$$= 14.7 \text{ ft}^{\sim}/(\text{sec}^{\sim})^2 \quad \text{(in acceleration)} \tag{3-21}$$

This can be compared with $g^{\sim}$ as follows:

---

* See footnote for Example 1 on p. 52.

$$a^\sim/g^\sim = 14.7/32.2 = 0.46 \quad \text{(in number of } g^\sim \text{ units)} \quad \textbf{(3-22)}$$

Again the standard units cancel out, giving an NSU number. In other words, the car accelerates with about ½ $g^\sim$. The 180-lb$^\sim$ driver will press back into his seat with about 90 lb$^\sim$ of force. These conclusions depend on the reasoning formulated by Newton and discussed in Chapter 9.

These examples of changing units and quantitative symbols show the great power that symbols and algebra possess. Although the processes may seem to be mysterious, in principle they are essentially the same as converting purchasing power from francs to dollars. This is why we discuss purchasing power and counting so fully. This is intended to help you transfer your familiarity with the conaddian-like aspects of purchasing power to the new concepts of weight, force, density, potential energy, etc., of mechanics.

Example 3.   Confusion Resulting from Poor Symbols

We end this section with a final example of problems with symbols. This example shows that *you* must *think carefully* about *symbols* before *symbols* will help *you think*. This example of difficulty actually occurred while this book was being written. Some teachers who were using the tennis tournament problem of Chapter 2 for high school students tried to simplify the symbols by using W for winners and L for losers. Then they said that every player is either a winner or a loser, so that

$$W + L = P \quad \text{(they didn't qualify the equality)} \quad \textbf{(3-23)}$$

Next, since each match produces a loser, $L = M$, substituting equals for equals gives Law 3 of Fig. 2-5:

$$W + M = P$$

When some university professors reached this point in reading the material, Dr. Shockley, one of this book's authors, asked: "Is Law 3 **always true** during the tournament? Does it apply just before and also just after the first match is played?"

Can you answer this? Can you see what was fuzzy about the discussion above? The professors had a very difficult time. If you can't answer this, go back and read Secs. 2-7 and 2-11 again to see how the symbols should have been carefully defined.

In the rest of this chapter we shall deal with symbols very explicitly so that you can see how easy and safe they are to use. But you must always ask yourself, "What do I really mean by this symbol? Is it a name-symbol? A number-symbol, unspecified or not? A quantity-symbol?"

In Sec. 3-4, which follows, we shall show the one-to-one correspondence of unspecified number-symbols for integers and for numbers of things. Then, in Sec. 3-5 we shall start with the invariant aspect of weight.

3-4   Number-Symbols, Arithmetic Laws, and Diagrams

In the tennis tournament problem of Chapter 2, symbols were used to represent numbers of matches, eliminated players, and so on. According to the principles of algebra, the symbol M for the 137-player tournament might represent any number from 0 to 136. The way we use these symbols in equations is a consequence of the experimental fact that numbers of objects add.

For example, the arithmetic law of commutation says that

$$a + b = b + a \quad \text{(in number size)} \qquad \textbf{(3-24)}$$

These unspecified number-symbols, and for that matter, the $+$ and $=$ signs, can be put into a *one-to-one correspondence* with facts about bags of pennies. Suppose that the correspondences are as follows:

$$a \quad \text{with 4¢ bag}$$
$$b \quad \text{with 3¢ bag}$$

Then a stands not for the 4¢ bag nor for copper (the metal from which pennies are made) but for the *number* 4, which is the *purchasing-power attribute* measured in *penny standard units*. Clearly, a is a number-symbol. Then, the quantity $a + b$ evidently represents the number you get when you make a total bag with all the pennies in the following order: a followed by b. It is as if we can interpret the $+$ operation-symbol in $a + b$ to mean: pour the pennies from bag a into a total bag; then pour the pennies from b into the same total bag; then count the pennies in the total bag and call the resulting number $a + b$. If you poured b into the total bag first and then a, you would write it $b + a$.

Thus, the one-to-one correspondences we have set up are the following:

$a + b$ means the number you get by first taking a,
then adding b to it, and then counting the total;

whereas

$b + a$ means the number you obtain by using b for
the first operation.

Because of the fact that numbers of pennies (and of all discrete objects) are additive, $a + b$ is the same number as $b + a$ so that we write

$$a + b = b + a \quad \text{(in number size)}$$

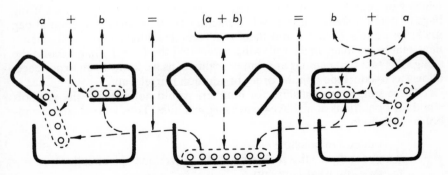

Fig. 3-1. One-to-one correspondences represented by dashed lines between symbols and diagrams.

(A pure mathematician would *not* say that the two numbers were *equal*, but that they were *the same* number. But this is a more precise bit of logical elegance than we need; our emphasis is on facts and clarity rather than on perfection of expression.) This equality is addition's **commutative law.**

Diagrams representing these addition operations are shown in Fig. 3-1. The one-to-one correspondences between the symbols a, $+$, b, and $=$, with proper portions of the diagrams, are represented by dashed lines. The diagrams in turn have a one-to-one correspondence with the reality you might set up on your desk using bags and pennies or paper cups and paperclips.

The invention of suitable diagrams having appropriate one-to-one correspondences with measurable observable aspects of reality has led to the fame of many scientific thinkers. Figure 3-2 shows several of these: Pascal's triangle helps to understand the binomial coefficients in algebra and probability theory. Descartes' discovery of cartesian coordinates (the "carte" in cartesian comes from Des(carte)s' name) is the foundation of modern geometry and physics; coordinates also give an operational meaning to the assertion that space is three dimensional, because you can specify the location of any point in a room with three number-symbols: x, y, and z, or alternatively the vector symbol $\vec{R}$ that is discussed in Chapter 5. Mendeleev laid a cornerstone in chemistry by making the diagram showing his periodic table of the chemical elements. Feynman shared the 1965 Nobel Prize in physics partly because of his famous Feynman diagram for describing nuclear processes in atoms.

Mechanics and, in fact, all branches of physical science depend extensively on diagrams. This will be illustrated for forces in the next two chapters, particularly for vector forces in Chapter 5.

Counting pennies presents one of the simplest examples of using symbols and diagrams to interpret reality. We shall continue to illustrate the one-to-one correspondences between symbols and reality by considering the **associative law** of addition

$$(a + b) + c = a + (b + c) \qquad \text{(in number size)}$$

which can be put into one-to-one correspondence with the operations using bags of pennies shown in Fig. 3-1. Evidently $(a + b)$ means a subtotal bag made by putting in first a and then b. When c is added to $(a + b)$, then a *new* total bag is made in the following order: first the $(a + b)$ bag, second the c bag. The fact that pennies are simply additive, as we know from experience, allows us to conclude that the order of addition is irrelevant.

These simple relationships for numbers would not apply if the symbols stood for operations at a coffee dispensing machine. Thus let c, d, and s symbolize as follows:

c put cup in machine
d put in dime (this makes machine deliver one cup of coffee)
s swallow what is in cup

Then you will drink your coffee only for the operation $c + d + s$. For opera-

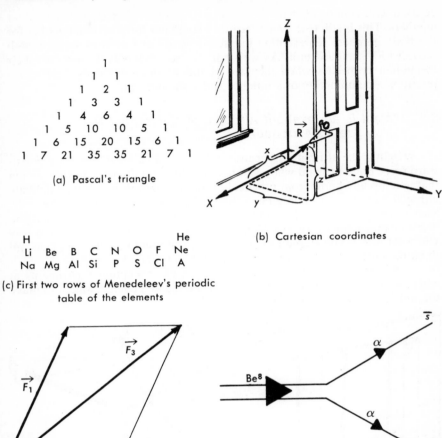

(a) Pascal's triangle

(b) Cartesian coordinates

(c) First two rows of Menedeleev's periodic table of the elements

$$\vec{F_1} + \vec{F_2} = \vec{F_3} \quad \text{in vector force}$$

(d) Feynman diagram

(e) Parallelogram of forces diagram

Fig. 3-2.   Five famous diagrams of science and mathematics: (a) Pascal's triangle; (b) Cartesian coordinates of the tip of a coat hanger and a vector $\vec{R}$; (c) First two rows of Mendeleev's periodic table of the elements; (d) Feynman diagram; (e) Parallelogram of forces diagram.

tions $c + s + d$ and $d + c + s$, the coffee runs down the drain and you swallow from an empty cup.

Weights and forces that we shall consider in this chapter are conaddians, and symbols representing their quantitative values in standard units are ordinary numbers. We shall discuss in Chapters 4 and 5 the *one-to-one correspondences* between symbols representing quantities of weight and diagrams showing directions of forces. As discussed in Chapter 2, symbols may be used with confidence when it is remembered that they stand for familiar numbers. This is still true even when they stand not for pure numbers but for the NSU numbers representing measured values of forces or weights with respect to a standard unit. As we shall also see, symbols do not lose their conaddian properties when they are of the $x^\sim$ quantity-symbol class representing a combination of a number and a standard unit.

3-5 Weight Is an Invariant Attribute of Nature, but Not If You Are an Astronaut

Weight is the attribute that causes a book or a suitcase to exert a downward force on your hand when you hold it. You will discover in this section that you already know from practical experience that weight is a conaddian, although you have probably never had occasion to think of it in this way. Sometimes, you may think that weight isn't a connadian, especially when you discover that your nearly invariant, personal body weight changes the way you want it to if you step on the right scale. But you know it is only wishful thinking—the sad truth is that the scale is inaccurate.

In this section we shall carry out a series of conceptual experiments in which we use a bathroom scale, several springs, and a counterweight to make the weight-sensing devices shown in Fig. 3-3.

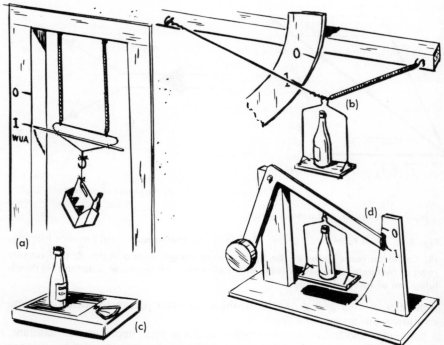

Fig. 3-3. Some weight-sensing devices. In every case bottle B_1, which weighs 1 wua$^\sim$, is shown on the platform. Devices (a), (b), and (c) use springs for the resisting forces, and (d) uses a counterweight.

Each piece of apparatus has a part that serves as a pointer, and a scale against which its position can be observed. One chief objective of this chapter will be to see how the scale can be marked so that the quantity of weight on the platform can be directly on the scale. To start with, a zero mark is placed where the pointer stands when no weight is on the platform. Figure 3-3(a) represents a weight-sensing device the student can make at home by using springs obtainable from most hardware stores. It is shown hanging in a doorway. The horizontal pointer can be a bicycle spoke or a coat hanger wire scotch-taped to the other coat hanger. (This is further described as an experimental problem for this chapter.) Figure 3-3(b) has variable sensitivity. The two screw hooks are in a beam, and when no weight is on the platform, the spring pulls the wire out nearly straight. The first, relatively light weight placed on the platform produces a relatively big deflection. For heavier loads, the wire carries more of the weight. The wire acts as the indicator, and you put the zero mark on the scale board just behind the wire. As more weights are added to the platform, the wire moves to lower positions. These positions, which will then be marked at the other places on the board, serve as a scale of weight.

Three devices shown have springs to resist the downward force of the weights. In device (d) the resistance is furnished by a counterweight. But for our purposes we need not consider what resists the downward force so long as deflection of the weight-sensing device obeys the following law:

QLF 3-3	Reproducible, Increasing Deflection Law
WHAT	It is **always true** that the weight-sensing device deflects to a certain particular position when a particular object is placed on it and always deflects more for two objects together than for either alone,
WHEN	**no matter** whether the object is placed on it exactly the same way,
WHEN NOT	**but not if** you overload the device so that it becomes distorted or damaged.

The fundamental invariant feature of weight is like the invariance of money at the poker table in Chapter 1. From the viewpoint of modern physics, the reason is much the same. **No matter** how the coins or paper money is distributed among the players, the total purchasing power remains invariant. The weight of some combination of matter on the hanging platform of the weight-sensing device **doesn't** change **no matter** how the matter is rearranged, **but not if** you lose or gain matter. The interpretation is that the matter, whether it be chunks of ice, sugar cubes, water glasses, or what-not, is made up of atoms. Effectively, the atoms are like the coins in the poker game, and the weight is like the purchasing power. According to modern theoretical physics, every atom on earth attracts every other atom with a gravitational force. This gives a down-pull for each atom on the hanging platform. This gives each atom its own weight (just as each piece of money in the poker game has its value) and the weights all add up to an invariant total. We shall discuss these ideas more in Chapter 9.

In mechanics, however, we do not start with ideas of atomic theory; we start with experimental facts that you can prove to yourself with desk-sized equipment. What are the facts about invariance of weight?

Another aspect of the invariance of weight is also like the purchasing power of the money at the poker table. This purchasing power **doesn't** change **no matter** to *what new and different poker table* the money is taken. A similar invariance applies to weight. Many experiments using a wide variety of weight-sensing devices and many rearrangements of matter lead to a law of invariance of weight. You can test this law on your home bathroom scale and on one you borrow from your neighbor. This law is:

	QLF 3-4 Law of Invariance of Weight
WHAT	It is **always true** that if a first collection of matter produces on one weight-sensing device the same deflection as a second collection of matter, then the two collections will produce equal deflections on any weight-sensing device,
WHEN	**no matter** how the matter is rearranged (for example, ice melting or sugar dissolving in water) in either collection, or how it is arranged on the hanging platform, or what is producing the resisting force in the weight-sensing device (for example, springs, or weights, or magnetic or electric forces, or compressed gases, or bending fishing poles),
WHEN NOT	**but not if** the resisting force is produced by something fragile which is permanently distorted by being overloaded (a rubber band may show this trouble), or if in one case the platform is in air and in another case it is submerged in water, or if the experiment is done in a space capsule in orbit, or if atomic energy is involved.

The WHEN NOT situations reflect important scientific effects. The atomic energy problem arises from the fact that in a nuclear explosion or an atomic power plant, matter is actually turned into electromagnetic energy.* The WHEN NOT situation for the space capsule is a consequence of loss of weight. Loss of weight has become very real to all of us since 1961 and 1962, when Gagarin, Titov, Glenn, and Carpenter orbited the earth a total of 24 times. Weightlessness in spacecraft is a real problem. If liquid is spilled, you can't wipe it up. It floats around. It can produce short circuits in electrical equipment. It exerts no down-force on whatever it is placed. In fact, there is no "down" or "up". How to think of these problems was made clear by Newton as discussed in Chapter 9. In this chapter we shall stay in an ordinary earth laboratory.

---

*Basic concepts are discussed in two other books in the Merrill Physical Science Series: *Electricity and Electromagnetic Fields* by Francis E. Dart, and *Modern Physics* by Isaac Maleh.

In our desk-sized experiments, we need not be concerned with earth orbits or atomic energy, but we are concerned with weighing objects under water. The reason for the WHEN NOT situation for the platform under water can easily be seen: Suppose, for example, that the two objects pushing down equally on a platform in air are a flatiron and a piece of firewood. Then the flatiron will still push down on the platform in water, but the buoyancy of the water will support the piece of firewood so that the firewood will not push down at all. The exact relationships of bodies in water will be discussed with Archimedes' buoyancy principle in Chapter 8.

The need for the hanging platform has to do with moments and centers of gravity as discussed later in Chapter 7.

The thinking tool of idealized limiting cases will now be brought into use. This important thinking tool leads us to conceptual experiments with apparatus in which the springs are never damaged. We shall also keep out of water and shall neglect any buoyancy effects due to the air. These idealizations are quite realistic, considering, for example, what goes on with a good scale in a grocery store.

Accordingly, we shall assume that by our experiments in our laboratory, *we have established the fact that if two weights produce equal down-forces on one weight-sensing apparatus, they will exert equal down-forces on any other weight-sensing apparatus. We have also established the fact that internal rearrangement or divisions into parts of one weight has no effect. The equality of the down-forces produced by the two weights is therefore an* **invariant relationship** *between the two weights.*

The reader will find it helpful to consider the many one-to-one correspondences that relate features of the invariance principle for weight to corresponding features for the invariance of purchasing power for money, **no matter** whether the money be coins or printed certificates. In practical terms, the invariance of purchasing power of money means that when you count your change, it is **always true** that the total is all that matters **no matter** whether you get it in pennies or dollar bills **but not if** you plan to use your purchasing power in slot matchines that will accept only dimes.

The invariance principle for both money and matter is that two collections of money that have equal purchasing powers in one situation have equal purchasing powers in any other situation **no matter what (but not if** the exceptional situations discussed below arise). Precisely corresponding statements are true regarding the weights of two collections of matter. The relevant one-to-one correspondences are displayed in Fig. 3-4. The particular examples of matter, the bottle B_1 and the jar J_2, referred to by their name-symbols with adjective-symbol subscripts, are used because they play a major role in the next section.

Figure 3-4 also shows the correspondences between the laws that underlie the invariance principles. These laws fall into a hierarchy of abstractness. They can be discussed in terms of postulates of different levels of abstraction. (The reader is referred to Fig. 1-3 for a similar discussion.) The laws of Fig. 3-4 are classified at three levels, with the degree of abstraction increasing with the adjective-symbol subscripts, PP referring to purchasing power laws, and W to weight laws. One could go further with the PP series. PP_4 would

ONE-TO-ONE CORRESPONDENCES BETWEEN THE KEY ATTRIBUTES OF PURCHASING POWER FOR MONEY AND THE KEY ATTRIBUTE OF WEIGHT FOR MATTER

Name-Symbols and Definitions

C is the name-symbol for a bag of coins containing 20 pennies, 2 nickels, 2 dimes, and 2 quarters.

P is the name for a paper dollar bill.

B_1 is the name-symbol for a pint milk bottle containing enough water so that it weighs altogether 17 oz.

J_2 is the name-symbol for a mason jar containing enough salt so that it weighs altogether 17 oz.

WHAT: Qualified-Equality Relationship

$C = P$ (in purchasing power)

$B_1 = J_2$ (in effect on weight-sensing device)

WHEN: Qualified-Equality Relationship Holds

Anywhere, any time in U.S.A.

On any hanging-platform type weight-sensing device

WHEN NOT: Qualified-Equality Relationship Fails

If you are in a phone booth with pennies only, or if you take your money abroad where a bank may not accept C while it will accept P so that

$P > C$ (in purchasing power: French francs in France)

If weight-sensing device has a platform under water, and buoyancy is different for B_1 and J_2 so that

$B_1 \neq J_2$ (in influence on "wet", weight-sensing device)

Superficial Basis of Equality Relationship

PP_1: 20 cents   + 1 nickel
   + 2 dimes   + 2 quarters
   = 100 cents   = 1 dollar

W_1: Qualified Law of Invariance of Weight (Sec. 3-5)

More Fundamental Law

PP_2: U.S. law requires that coins up to $1.00 be legal tender.

W_2: Newton's discovery of mass and gravitational attraction (see Chapter 9)

Most Fundamental Law

PP_3: To simplify life by replacing barter with standard units of purchasing power; people make laws about money.

W_3: ? Einstein attempted to formulate a general theory based on mathematical description of space, not complete today?

Fig. 3-4. Purchasing power and weight compared.

probably be very philosophical and would involve the fundamental nature of man. In physics, the most basic postulates are still being sought. The hope that clues will be found in the innermost parts of the nucleus is one of the motives for making the enormous atom smashers of modern physics.* The new laws, if they are found, cannot be simple explanations in the same way that the eliminated-player key attribute explained the $M = P - 1$ law-hunch of Chapter 2. The new laws will probably take the form of neat mathematical formulations that have a one-to-one correspondence with observed facts of nature. A satisfying one-to-one correspondence of this sort is a fundamental aim of theoretical science, and has been a very satisfactory accomplishment of mechanics. Our use of familiar, purchasing-power concepts to explain the logical structure of invariance-of-weight concepts is an example, on a simplified level, of a theoretical structure in physical science.

One last comment should be made on the philosophy of Fig. 3-4. There is a big difference between laws of science and laws of economics. The laws of science are invariant with respect to the politics or religion of the observer. Once told what experiments to carry out, all observers get the same result. This is not so true for man-made laws about human affairs.

The invariant attribute of weight, although it is a very fundamental feature of the world of our laboratory, is not so fundamental as newer discoveries. The invariance of weight is more like "king A can't lose to king B" and "the number of matches is one less than the number of players" in Part I. Both of these empirical laws were found to be theorems from more basic postulates: "the odd-even law of checkers" and Postulate 1, "To eliminate a player requires a match." The invariance of weight is also a theorem from more basic laws about nuclear particles, electrons, and gravitational fields. The invariant aspect of weight for an electron has recently been a subject of experimental research at Stanford University. Perhaps a new WHEN NOT situation will be found if the research is successful.

These advanced topics show that weight, dull and prosaic as it seems, is a manifestation of deep and mysterious aspects of nature. This is one of the reasons it was selected as the first conaddian of mechanics to be discussed in this book.

To return to the conaddian aspect of weight, we shall now assume, from the discussion of this section, that the law of invariance of weight has been established. This justifies the -*ian* in conaddian. It also justifies *con*servative in the sense that dividing a weight into parts and weighing the parts together conserves the original deflection. What remains to be established is the basic feature of conservation defined in Sec. 1-4, namely, that the sum of the parts remains constant. This requires that we develop methods to measure the parts separately. Then the individual values can be added together. In the next two sections, we shall discuss conceptual experiments that reach this objective.

3-6   A Standard Unit of Weight and a Binary Set of Multiple Weights

Now we are ready to start a series of conceptual experiments that will end up in measuring weight. You may ask, "Why all this bother? We already

---

* See Isaac Maleh, *op. cit.*

know that we can measure weight on a scale." The answer is that by understanding not only *how* but *why* you can measure weight will help to show *how*
you can measure moments and energies in later chapters.

Figure 3-3 represents a "pop" bottle with a tight stopper. It is shown sitting on all three platforms of the figure. This, we imagine, is the same bottle
that we name B_1 (pronounced "bee one" or "bee sub one"). The adjective-
symbol "sub one" means that it is the first bottle we shall consider. The symbol
B_1, as we shall use it in this section, is a name-symbol; it is not a number-
symbol or a quantity-symbol.

Now carry out the following conceptual experiments. Make B_1 into *your*
standard weight unit by adjusting the amount of water in it until it reads one
pound on the bathroom scale.

Actually this is very inaccurate—bathroom scales are not sensitive; the
zero may be off; the scales may stick—but do the best you can. To be definite,
suppose that you get a bad standard—one that actually weighs 17 oz instead
of 16 oz. This standard unit of weight of yours is called "**wua~**". (Wua~ is
pronounced "woo′ah til′-dĕ".) This stands for **weight unit *a*.** The tilde reminds you that wua~ is a symbol representing a quantity. (To be consistent,
we shall also write oz~ in this chapter.) If we wish to compare this with a
second weight unit "*b*", we shall refer to the latter as "wub~" (to rhyme
with "cub").

Now go to the other more sensitive devices of Fig. 3-3. Place B_1 on each,
and on the scale where the pointer stops, put a line labeled 1 wua. Do this for
all three devices (a), (b), and (d).

Now duplicate the weight of your wua~ by taking as your second weight a
one-pint mason jar; put it on the platform (b) which is the most sensitive
and pour salt in it. Adjust the salt, teaspoon by teaspoon, until it pushes the
pointer down just to the same 1-wua mark. This new jar has the same effect
on the spring as did B_1. By our invariance-of-weight QLF, B_1 and the jar will
have equal down-forces in all our conceptual experiments.

Let us give this jar a name: J_2 (pronounced as "jay two" or "jay sub
two"). The symbol J_2 is again a name-symbol. The adjective-symbol "sub
two" reminds us that it is our second member of a set of weights. Since J_2
produces the same weight effect as B_1, which we have chosen as our standard
weight unit wua~, we can write a qualified-equation

$$(\text{Weight of } J_2)^{\sim} = 1 \text{ wua}^{\sim} \quad (\text{in weight}) \qquad \textbf{(3-25)}$$

with the adjective-symbol (in weight) as the equation-qualifier. This qualified-equation is strictly analogous to a more familiar qualified-equation of
the type discussed in Sec. (3-3):

$$\left(\begin{matrix}\text{Purchasing power of a} \\ \text{book of trading stamps}\end{matrix}\right)^{\sim} = 1 \text{ dollar}^{\sim} \quad (\text{in purchasing power}) \textbf{ (3-26)}$$

in which the key attribute of purchasing power plays the same role as weight,
and dollar~ replaces wua~. In the J_2 situation, you are dealing with the *key*
attribute of weight and you are measuring it in units of *your standard unit*,
the wua~. The number 1.0 is what you have obtained by the *comparison*
operation of measurement. J_2 pushes down on the spring exactly as hard as

1.0 wua~. We shall use the symbol W_2~ to represent the *weight* of J_2. This symbol is pronounced "double-you sub-two tilde". Next write

$$W_2\text{~} = 1.0 \text{ wua~} \quad \text{(in weight)} \tag{3-27}$$

(Maybe you are justified in saying 1.000 wua~; this is a question of accuracy, which we shall discuss later. Accuracy is what separates measurement from counting. Counting is 100 per cent accurate, **but not if** you only estimate.)

As discussed in Sec. 3-3, our use of the tilde in W_2~ is intended to overcome one of the pedagogical shortcomings of modern scientific symbolism. It calls to your attention that W_2~ stands for a quantity of weight and not a number. It is like the quantity-symbol x~ $= 15¢ = \$0.15$ (in purchasing power) in Secs. 3-2 and 3-3. When you are used to the two kinds of symbols, numbers and quantities, you can keep straight by keeping the difference in mind instead of expressing them carefully with precise symbols. In this chapter, we shall be meticulous in distinguishing between quantity- or tilde-symbols and number-symbols.

To illustrate once more the importance of precise use of symbols, consider the silly equation

$$B_1 = J_2 \tag{3-28}$$

This says that bottle B_1 with its water is equal to jar J_2 with its salt. This is like adding apples and oranges. There is precisely *one* easily recognized attribute which is the same for B_1 and J_2; that one thing is the magnitude of their weight attribute, or the ability to push down on a weight-sensing device. They are not equal in any other obvious way. In keeping with the quantity-symbol notation, we write this relationship:

$$(\text{Weight of } B_1)\text{~} = (\text{weight of } J_2)\text{~} \quad \text{(in weight)} \tag{3-29}$$

but W_2~ is the quantity-symbol for the (weight of J_2)~ and 1 wua~ is defined as the weight of B_1. Substituting equals for equals and introducing a number-symbol W_2, we can write

$$W_2\text{~} = W_2 \text{ wua~} = 1.0 \text{ wua~} \quad \text{(in weight)} \tag{3-30}$$

What we mean is that J_2 is equal, so far as weight comparison is concerned, to W_2 wua~ weights. Since J_2 equals B_1 in weight, within the accuracy of our experiment, $W_2 = 1.00$. By 1.00 we really suggest that it is nearer to 1 than to 1.01 or 0.99 and might be 1.005 or even 0.995; we shall discuss accuracy more fully in Sec. 5-4.

The symbol W_2 is simply a number. In other words, W_2 is a number-symbol. The quantity-equation

$$W_2\text{~} = W_2 \text{ wua~} \quad \text{(in weight)}$$

can be converted to a (numerical: standard unit)-equation by comparing both sides to the wua~. This comparison operation is represented symbolically by dividing both sides by wua~. The result is

$$\frac{W_2\text{~}}{\text{wua~}} = \frac{W_2 \text{ wua~}}{\text{wua~}} = W_2 \quad \text{(in number of wua~)} \tag{3-31}$$

This comparison operation is the basis for the conversion of a quantity-equation to a number-equation discussed as a QLF 3-2 in Sec. 3-3. The (in numbers of wua~) means that we have obtained a numerical value by comparing the weight of J_2 with the wua~.

We could also write an equation for B_1 alone:

$$\text{(Weight of } B_1)^{\sim} = W_1 \text{ wua}^{\sim} = 1 \text{ wua}^{\sim} \quad \text{(in weight)} \qquad \textbf{(3-32)}$$

Because 1 wua~ is exactly the same as the weight of B_1, by definition, W_1 is exactly 1 by definition. (The symbols 1 or 2 or 3 with no decimal point or zeros conventionally mean a perfect integer. This means that $W_1 = 1$ is the same as saying that $W_1 = 1.000000$, etc., never stopping the zeros.) To be completely precise, we should use the identity or definition sign ≡ and write $W_1 \equiv 1$. The corresponding weight-comparison equation would be a definition also:

$$\text{(Weight of } B_1)^{\sim} \equiv W_1^{\sim} \equiv 1 \text{ wua}^{\sim} \quad \text{(in weight)} \qquad \textbf{(3-33)}$$

A diagram representing the equality of the weights B_1 and J_2 is shown in Fig. 3-5. In this diagram we represent, for the first time in this book, the down-force of the earth's pull on weights B_1 and J_2. These are represented by the down-pointed arrows of Fig. 3-5. These arrows are the simplest cases of representing forces by **vectors**. *Vectors* are one of the great symbolic concepts of mathematics and science. Many of the most important attributes of

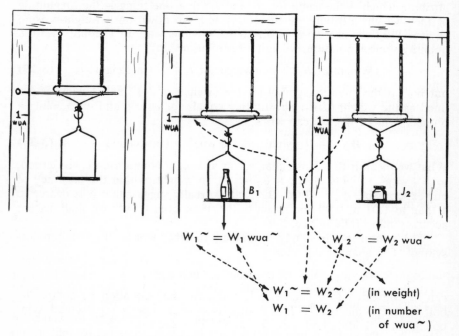

Fig. 3-5. **Diagram representing equality of weight, down-forces of gravity, and one-to-one correspondences with qualified-equalities.**

nature are found to be reliably described by vectors. The important qualified laws about conservation of linear and angular momentum are most succinctly and elegantly expressed in terms of vectors. The key attributes involved are conaddian vector quantities. We shall explain vectors in Chapter 5.

The quantity equation for the two weight quantities

$$W_1{}^\sim = W_1 \text{ wua}^\sim = W_2{}^\sim = W_2 \text{ wua}^\sim \quad \text{(in weight)} \qquad \textbf{(3-34)}$$

can be converted to a number-equation, as was done first for Eqs. (3-13) and (3-14), by comparing all expressions with wua$^\sim$. The symbolic operation consists of dividing by wua$^\sim$. The new equation is

$$W_1 = W_2 \quad \text{(in number of wua}^\sim) \qquad \textbf{(3-35)}$$

This looks very much the same as $W_1{}^\sim = W_2{}^\sim$, but the ideas are really different. This is an example of the conversion of a quantity-equation to a number-equation. The equation-qualifier (in number of wua$^\sim$) reminds us that the equation is numerical and that the numbers are weights expressed in terms of our standard unit, the wua$^\sim$. We shall discuss more fully this very important form of qualified-equation in Sec. 3-9.

The bothersome weakness of present-day scientific symbolism is that it frequently does not make itself clear. For example, when you see the length symbol L, it may really be $L^\sim$, a quantity-symbol for a physical length, or L in.$^\sim$, where L is an NSU symbol for number of inches. The same comments apply to the often-used symbol t, which may stand for $t^\sim$ a time, or t sec$^\sim$ in which t is the number that might result from a measurement. Often it does not make any difference in the reasoning. When it does, we shall try to make it clear by using the tilde and the ( ) that qualifies the equality sign.

To be consistent with the tilde notation, one should always write wua$^\sim$, in.$^\sim$, and sec$^\sim$. However, the usage of science is such that when symbols like "in." for inch or "ft" for foot or "lb" for pound are used, we know that these do not stand for numbers but are quantity-symbols representing standard units for attributes such as weight. The tilde is thus not needed to avoid confusion on quantity-symbols for standard units. We shall use the tilde only occasionally with standard unit symbols to remind you of the nature of the quantity-symbols for standard units.

A weight like $W_2{}^\sim$ is a down-force exerted by an object on whatever is holding it up by exerting an up-force on it. We shall explain this *force concept* in detail in Chapter 4. When you take the up-force away, the object has nothing to push down on; thus, it loses its weight and falls. The same situation occurs in a space capsule as discussed in Sec. 3-5 and explained by Newton's laws in Chapter 9.

If we wish to show that weight is a conaddian, in our ordinary earth laboratory we must show its conservative and additive properties. In order to do this, we must show that the whole is the sum of the parts so far as weight is concerned, just as is the case for the purchasing power of the bags of pennies. One way to do this is to take some object, a log of firewood, for example, and divide it into several parts by using a hatchet to split it into kindling. If the log is weighed before splitting, and then the parts are weighed afterward, the sum of the weights of the individual parts should add up to the original weight, if weight is a conaddian. But how shall we conduct these conceptual weighing experiments?

Obviously, with the three pieces of apparatus of Fig. 3-3 available, we use the bathroom scale. But using the bathroom scale is not practical for weighing anything less than one pound. But more important *in this chapter* is that *it is cheating*. It is not in keeping with the conceptual experimental program we are carrying out. We are pretending that we only have a *hunch* that weight is a conaddian. We want to set up a plan of experiment that does not depend on all the knowledge possessed by the industry that manufactures bathroom or other scales.

For the moment then, forgetting that we have the bathroom scale, let us use the other spring devices of Fig. 3-3. We may supplement these with stiffer or more flexible ones if necessary, or ones that use completely different resisting forces.

The way we prepare to weigh any reasonable-sized object is to make an extensive set of weights based on *your standard unit weight,** the wua, defined as the weight attribute of B_1. Using this set of weights, we shall mark on the scales the positions for 2 wua, 3 wua, etc. Later we shall also mark divisions at all the ½-wua and ¼-wua positions, and so on. In this way, we shall convert the *weight-sensing device* into a *direct-reading instrument*.

But how to get the set of weights? We already have a start with two weights, each of 1 wua: bottle B_1 and jar J_2. B_1 is our primary standard, and J_2 is our secondary standard. We show them in Fig. 3-6 along with a photograph of a real weight standard.

Hunch: We can make a 2-wua secondary standard. How? Find out how far 2 wua will push down the platform by putting both B_1 and J_2 on at the same time. This will produce a down-push of 2 wua *if weight is additive*, in keeping with our *hunch* that weight is a conaddian. We shall act on this hypothesis in our conceptual experiments. (Actually, you should be convinced that weights are additive and conservative from your practical experience; for example, you know that weights of meat have a one-to-one correspondence with the pennies that they cost, and you are familiar with the fact that purchasing power is a conaddian.) Accordingly, we shall proceed on the hypothesis that amounts of weight obey the additivity and conservation laws, as does the purchasing power of pennies in bags. But we shall remember that this hypothesis is not proved, and we shall discuss suitable experiments to verify it.

We now take our next step in producing a set of weights. We put B_1 and J_2 on the platform and make a 2-wua mark for the resulting indicator position as represented in Fig. 3-7. As the diagram shows, we assume additivity by combining the down-pulls on B_1 and J_2 end to end to make a combined down-pull force $W_1{}^{\sim} + W_2{}^{\sim}$. The proof that this procedure of using symbol-diagrams actually does represent nature is based on establishing that weight is a conaddian. This is completed in Sec. 3-8, and is extended to force vectors in Chapters 5 and 6.

Next, we make a 2-wua weight. To do this, we get a big enough jar called

---

* We shall now drop the tilde in wua$^{\sim}$ in keeping with the abbreviation convention for standard units discussed in the preceding paragraphs.

Fig. 3-6. Some standard units of weight. (a) The bottle B_1, our wua, kept in a safe. (b) The secondary standards J_2, kept in a laboratory. (c) The secondary standard, a platinum kilogram, kept at the U.S. Bureau of Standards. Photographs are courtesy of Dr. Allen V. Astin (shown), Director of National Bureau of Standards.

J_3 in keeping with our previous name- and adjective-symbol notation. We put in enough salt so that it also brings the pointer to the 2-wua position. Our set of weights can now be represented symbolically:

$$W_1^{\sim} = 1 \text{ wua} \quad \text{(in weight)} \tag{3-36}$$
$$W_2^{\sim} = 1.00 \text{ wua} \quad \text{(in weight)} \tag{3-37}$$
$$W_3^{\sim} = W_1^{\sim} + W_2^{\sim} = 2.00 \text{ wua} \quad \text{(in weight)} \tag{3-38}$$

The relationships are shown in Fig. 3-7.

An instrumental problem is illustrated in Fig. 3-7. When either B_1 or J_2 is put on an empty platform, the resulting stretch of spring is greater than when either is added to the other. The cause of this diminishing effect is that the spring is overly stretched by 2 wua. This causes the distance between the 1-wua and 2-wua marks to be less than the distance between the 0-wua and 1-wua marks. This inequality does not prevent matching the combined effect of B_1 and J_2 by the jar J_3. To go to still heavier weights, however, we would have to use a stronger spring. The qualified law of invariance of weight permits us to make these changes; in fact, this law is based on the experimental observation that if B_1 and J_2 produce two equal deflections on any one weight-sensing device, then they will also produce a pair of equal

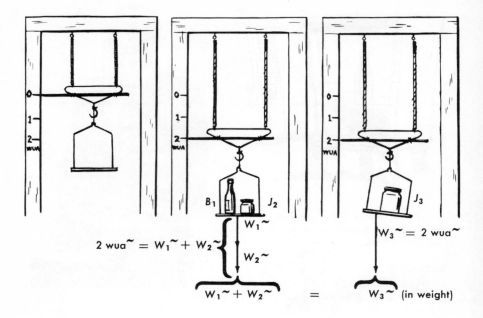

Fig. 3-7. Method of making a 2-wua weight, J_3, that weighs as much as B_1 and J_2 combined.

deflections on any other weight-sensing device, but these deflections will be smaller than the first pair if the second device is stronger than the first device.

Figure 3-7 also shows vector arrows representing the addition of the two down-forces exerted on the platform by B_1 and J_2 to give the same down-force exerted by J_3. We shall return to these force vectors in Chapters 4 and 5.

We can double the 2-wua weight by putting all three weights on the platform of a suitable device to obtain a 4-wua mark. Then we can make a 4-wua weight. Using this and the first three weights, we get an 8-wua mark and can make an 8-wua weight, and so on. This gives what is called a **binary scale** because the sizes double.

To see how a set of binary weights can be used, observe that the numbers 1, 1, 2, 4, and 8 (these are all powers of 2) will enable you to get combinations that cover all numbers from 1 to 16, inclusive. Adding the number 16 to the set permits you to cover everything up through 32. Adding 32 will cover everything up through 64, and so forth.

With the set of weights represented in Fig. 3-8, we can now make marks on the wooden scale to show the indicator or pointer position for various weights on the hanging platform. In this way, we can make marks for 2 wua, 3 wua, 4 wua, etc., up to twice the largest weight.

Now a question of symbols: Suppose that someone takes a group of your weights and puts them in a black (but weightless) bag. The symbol that is

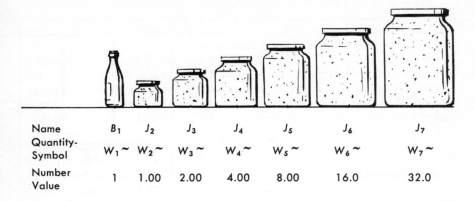

Name	B_1	J_2	J_3	J_4	J_5	J_6	J_7
Quantity-Symbol	$W_1 \sim$	$W_2 \sim$	$W_3 \sim$	$W_4 \sim$	$W_5 \sim$	$W_6 \sim$	$W_7 \sim$
Number Value	1	1.00	2.00	4.00	8.00	16.0	32.0

Fig. 3-8. **A binary set of weights based on additivity. (The similarly proportioned mason jars are hypothetical: actual standard sizes do not progress in the binary steps shown here.)**

used to represent this unknown weight is traditionally your old friend x, the unknown. But should it be x or $x^\sim$?

This is the question that the new symbolism in this book was especially designed to answer. The answer is that both x and $x^\sim$ are appropriate if you think about your symbols. Here is the equation you need:

$$(\text{Weight of bag of unknown weights})^\sim$$
$$= x^\sim = x \text{ wua} \quad (\text{in weight}) \qquad \textbf{(3-39)}$$

We have even put a tilde on the first parentheses, even though the words tell us that it means a quantity. A concrete numerical example will help make the difference between x and $x^\sim$ clear: Suppose the black bag contains the three weights J_2, J_4, and J_5, corresponding to 1, 4, and 8 wua. Then the pointer will stand at the 13-wua mark. This means that

$$x^\sim = 13 \text{ wua} \quad (\text{in weight}) \qquad \textbf{(3-40)}$$
$$x = 13 \qquad (\text{in number of wua}) \qquad \textbf{(3-41)}$$

It is in situations precisely like this that confusion between symbols may occur.

Now, to check additivity and conservation of weights, imagine the following experiment. Put two jars on the platform and adjust by pouring sand into one so that the two together bring the pointer just to 13 wua. Next, take the full jar off and pour sand from it into the other until the pointer reads 5 wua. Now put the first, partly emptied jar back on with the other. Where will the pointer stand?

The answers can be predicted because of a theorem from QLF 3-4: the qualified law of invariance of weight. All we have done is to rearrange the matter consisting of the two jars and the sand; this rearrangement must leave the 13-wua deflection of the weight invariant. (This relates directly, of course, to what the traveler of Sec. 3-1 found he **couldn't do, no matter what** with his overweight luggage.)

But now there is one more question. What does the deflection read if you remove the 5-wua jar, leaving only the other jar? You know from experience that the pointer will stand at the 8-wua mark. You couldn't prove this result without experiment, but it *is* what experiment shows.

You may doubt if it could be any other way. But it could. For example, suppose that the down-pull of the weights was not really weight, but that the weights contained magnets which were attracted down to a sheet of magnetic material below the platform. Then additivity would fail, because the down-pull of two equal magnets put together would be more than twice the down-pull of each one alone.

But we shall now assume that we have done so many experiments with jars weighing 13 wua, 19 wua, 63 wua, etc., all of which show additivity, that we no longer doubt that weight is a conaddian so far as whole-number weights are concerned. Can we then be sure that we shall obtain conaddian results for weights that do not come out to even numbers of wua?

3-7   The ½-Wua Weight and Other Binary Fractions

The making of fractional weights such as ½ wua and ¼ wua depends on the *conservative property of weight*. Here is one way to do it: Obtain two nearly equal smaller jars. (We shall not need to use name-symbols for these, but J_{s1} and J_{s2} or S_1 and S_2 would be suitable symbols. Why?) Put both small jars on the platform of a sensitive weight-sensing device as shown in Fig. 3-9. Add salt equally to both until the combined weight puts the pointer at 1 wua. Now take one jar off and make Mark 1 lightly with pencil along the new pointer position. Then replace that jar with the other one. Suppose it is a little heavier. Mark the pointer position for it. This is Mark 2. Now estimate a point halfway between these two marks. Put a mark there, labeled "Est 1". This is your first estimate for the ½-wua mark.

Next, try to equalize the two jars by transferring salt from the heavier to the lighter. When you get the pointer to your estimated ½-wua mark, take the other jar and try it. If the jars are not yet quite equal, put on a new, second estimate mark halfway in between as shown in Fig. 3-9(d). Then readjust the weights again. In this way you will redistribute the salt until the two jars are equal, as accurately as you can tell. Mark this position. It is ½ wua, as close as you can get it.

But how do you know that it is ½ wua? Because the two jars are equal in weight, and they add to 1 wua. The only two equal numbers that add up to 1 are ½ and ½. But how do you know that the two jars add up to 1 wua after you have redistributed the salt between them? You know this for the same reason that you knew the traveler could not take 5 lb off his luggage weight by moving his ray-gun from attaché case to suitcase—in other words, it is a theorem from the qualified law of invariance of weight. Thus, we are safe in concluding that the two ½-wua weights, when added together, produce 1 wua.

Next we match the ½-wua mark by making two equal ¼-wua small jars. These give us the ¼- and ¾-wua marks in Fig. 3-9(f). We then continue to ⅛ wua, and so on. At some stage we may have to shift to very delicate weight-

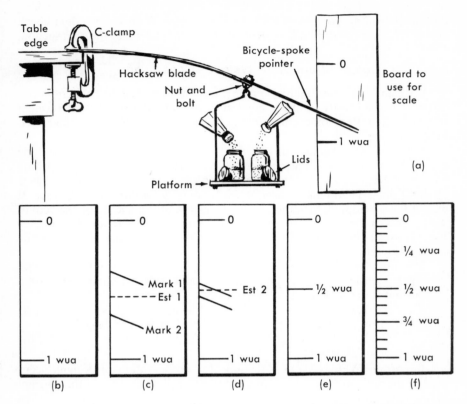

Fig. 3-9. A direct-reading fractional binary scale constructed by using the conservative property of weight. Errors in (c) and (d) are greatly exaggerated.

sensing apparatus. But we cannot, even in principle, go as far as we like; eventually we get down to atom sizes. (This would require halving about 70 times!)

Having obtained a set of weights from, say, $\frac{1}{64}$ wua on up, we can then make up sums to get everything in $\frac{1}{64}$-wua steps from zero to 64 wua, provided that our largest weight is 32 wua.

By placing a series of marks on the scale next to the spring, we can make a *direct-reading instrument*. This is what the manufacturer has done, at least in principle, in making the bathroom scale. His standard unit, however, is a platinum weight kept at the U.S. Bureau of Standards in Washington, D.C., or else a secondary standard derived from it. The scale in your grocery store has also been checked against a national official standard. Such scales are required by law to be checked regularly in order to make certain that they are accurate. You can probably find an inspection tag attached to each scale in your town showing when it was last tested.

In the last two sections, we have performed conceptual experiments that demonstrated the *-ian* from *in*variant *a*ttribute of *n*ature and the *con-* from the *con*servation of weight, and we have used *add-* from *add*itive in making the direct-reading instrument. What we need now is an independent check of *add*. This, and its symbolic representation, is the subject of the next section.

3-8   The Logical Structure of Weight—Conaddian

With our conceptual, direct-reading, weight-measuring instrument at our disposal, we can easily eliminate any last worries about our hunch that weight is a conaddian. Remember, this means a *con*servative *add*itive *in*variant *a*ttribute of *na*ture.

Just take any old collection of stable, permanent objects. (Do not include a piece of dry ice that evaporates, unless you are an expert on a *safe,* strong container that lets no gas escape and doesn't explode.) Weigh these objects one at a time. Then make a new object by putting two or more together. If weight is a conaddian, then the weight of the new object should be the sum of the weights of the individual objects. You know that it is. If you doubt it, try it out on your own scale. (In the next two chapters, we shall describe some closely related experiments.)

The invariant aspects of weight become evident when we realize that the object measured has the same value **no matter** what scale it is measured on, **but not if** the scale is out of adjustment.

The fact that the traveler with 45 lb of luggage could not cut down its weight at all **no matter** how he divided it between his two bags is a consequence of the law of conservation of weight for his luggage as well as for the objects in your laboratory.

Important WHEN NOT situations for conservation of weight occur often, especially in space ships. In Chapter 9 we shall show how the concept of mass replaces weight. Mass, which is what pushes back on your hand when you throw a baseball, is more invariant than weight; a body does not change its mass when it flies in a satellite. But even mass is not as invariant as an Einstein relativity concept called *rest mass.* However, that is a subject for modern physics, and not for this mechanics book.

But back to our earthbound laboratory and the problems we can investigate with our set of weights and our weight-measuring instruments. We can now use our symbols to describe what is meant by the statement: "Weight is a conaddian." Consider a set of three objects with name-symbols A, B, and C. When all three are put together, we shall call them set S, another name-symbol. Suppose that we measure their weights by putting them on our direct-reading instrument for measuring weight. Let the measured values, as read on the scale, be represented by the NSU number-symbols W_A, W_B, W_C, and W_S. These number-symbols stand for the number read by observing where the pointer stands in the scale of the instrument.

The quantity-symbols for the weights are $W_A{}^\sim$, $W_B{}^\sim$, $W_C{}^\sim$, and $W_S{}^\sim$. Since the scale reads weight in comparison with the standard unit of the wua, the relationships between quantity-symbols and number-symbols are the qualified-equations

$$W_A{}^\sim = W_A \text{ wua}, \quad W_B{}^\sim = W_B \text{ wua}, \quad \text{etc.} \quad \text{(in weight)} \quad \textbf{(3-42)}$$

Then if weight is a conaddian, we must have

$$W_S{}^\sim = W_A{}^\sim + W_B{}^\sim + W_C{}^\sim \quad \text{(in weight)} \tag{3-43}$$

But this equation is the same as

$$W_S\,\text{wua} = W_A\,\text{wua} + W_B\,\text{wua} + W_C\,\text{wua} \quad \text{(in weight)} \tag{3-44}$$

and again, if weight is a conaddian,

$$\begin{aligned} W_A\,\text{wua} &+ W_B\,\text{wua} + W_C\,\text{wua} \\ &= (W_A + W_B + W_C)\,\text{wua} \quad \text{(in weight)} \end{aligned} \tag{3-45}$$

Since this is also equal in weight to $W_S{}^\sim = W_S\,\text{wua}$, this leads to the prediction that if weight is a conaddian, it must be true that

$$W_S\,\text{wua}^\sim = (W_A + W_B + W_C)\,\text{wua}^\sim \quad \text{(in weight)} \tag{3-46}$$

where we have again added the tilde to get wua$^\sim$ so that we emphasize that this equation is a qualified-equation with "(in weight)" as the equation-qualifier.

Now we are finally at the point to make the conversion, discussed in QLF 3-2 in Sec. 3-3, from a quantity-equation to a number-equation involving those numbers obtained from our direct-reading, weight-measuring instrument. This resulting number-equation is typical of the most important contributions of quantitative science to society; it is a prototype of the equations used to predict a space capsule's journey to the moon, the amount of gold in the crown of Archimedes' king, or the power of an atomic-energy power plant. All of these cases involve number-equations in which one or more unknown numbers can be predicted from the other known numbers and the equations themselves.

The new qualified-equation is obtained by noting that if two weights are equal, they must both weigh the same number of wua$^\sim$. In other words, we can cancel wua$^\sim$ by dividing Eq. (3-46) by wua$^\sim$:

$$\begin{aligned} W_S\,\text{wua}^\sim \div \text{wua}^\sim &= (W_A + W_B + W_C)\,\text{wua}^\sim \div \text{wua}^\sim \\ &\text{(in weight)} \div \text{wua}^\sim \end{aligned} \tag{3-47}$$

where we have even suggested that we can divide the adjective-symbol "(in weight)" by wua$^\sim$. The result is, of course, as we have already discussed in Eqs. (3-13), (3-14), (3-31), (3-34), and (3-35), that the number of wua$^\sim$ on each side of the equal sign must be the same. We write the new qualified-equation as follows:

$$W_S = W_A + W_B + W_C \quad \text{(in number of wua)} \tag{3-48}$$

where the equation-qualifier "(in number of wua)" means that all the number-symbols in the equation are obtained by comparing weight quantities with our standard unit, the wua$^\sim$; this NSU, i.e., (in number of standard unit), qualifier is suggested correctly by the symbolic operation, (in weight) $\div$ wua$^\sim$, which does imply ordinary numbers for weight measured in wua$^\sim$ standard units. Experimentally, what is found to be **always true** for weight is that Eq. (3-48) works **no matter** what standard units or instruments are used, **but not if** we have the exceptional conditions of QLF 3-4 in Sec. 3-5.

The (*in number of standard unit*) *qualified-equation,* abbreviated NSU-QE, has truly enormous power for scientific and engineering purposes. These equations are the ones that are most useful in the interpretation of nature and in predictions of new untried experiments. For our "weight-is-a-conaddian" law, we can make predictions about Secret Agent 003's luggage (see Sec. 3-1): Let A be a name-symbol for his suitcase, B for his attaché case (without the ray-gun), and C for the ray-gun. Then, from Sec. 3-1,

$$W_A = 30, \quad W_B = 10, \quad W_C = 5 \quad \text{(in number of lb)} \qquad \textbf{(3-49)}$$

so that we predict for his whole set S of luggage

$$W_S = W_A + W_B + W_C$$
$$= 30 + 10 + 5 = 45 \quad \text{(in number of lb)}$$

and he will be 5 lb over his 40-lb baggage allowance. This prediction is a consequence of the conaddian property of weight.

The conaddian property of weight is a qualified law based on experiments of the sort we have discussed in this chapter. We know these experiments work because the W numbers of the (in number of standard unit of weight) or NSU-form always do show the additive property.

Is there some deeper reason why weight is a conaddian? That is a problem at the very forefront of modern physics—it depends on the basic nature of the parts of the atoms and how they interact. Perhaps it is to be understood in terms of the nature of space itself and its odd-even properties discussed in Sec. 1-5. But these are topics in other areas of physical science; particularly, modern physics, astronomy, and electricity and magnetism.* In these subjects, also, the basic scientific laws are quantitatively stated in qualified-equations with NSU equation-qualifiers.

To summarize the logical structure of this discussion, we see that, as is the case for determining purchasing power by counting pennies, measuring weight has four main parts, two of these being the measurement itself. These are as follows:

The Logical Structure of Weight Measurement

1. *Key attribute.* This is the down-force or weight that the object exerts on whatever holds it up. (Caused by the pull of the earth.)
2. *Standard unit.* We used the wua to show that in the last analysis, the standard unit involves an arbitrary choice.
3. *Comparison operation.* This started by comparing the effects of putting known and unknown weights on a weight-sensing device and ended by making a direct-reading, weight-measuring instrument. This instrument permits us to obtain measured numbers of the (in number of standard unit) or NSU-class represented by number-symbols like $W_2 = 1.00$, $W_3 = 2.00$, W_S, W_A, W_B, etc., in contrast to weight quantity-symbols like $W_2\tilde{\ }$.

---

* The other books in the Merrill Physical Science Series (Columbus, Ohio: Charles E. Merrill Books, Inc., 1966) adequately cover these topics.

4. *Orderly relationships* among measured numbers. These are NSU qualified-equations expressing the conaddian result that weights (except for being measured, which involves measuring rather than just counting) act like bags of pennies. (In fact, from the point of view of modern physics, the reason is that the atoms and their weight are like coins and their purchasing power). **Prediction** of useful results comes from these relationships in the form of NSU qualified-equations.

Parts 2 and 3 should be thought of as *measurement operations* or, in general, as *comparison operations* between an unknown example of the key attribute and the standard unit of the key attribute.

You will see that this four-part logical structure is a very important scientific thinking tool. It is common to all the important conaddian properties of mechanics and also of electricity and magnetism. In the next chapter we shall extend it to conaddian force vectors. In Chapter 7 we shall apply the same logical structure to moments.

We may sum up the considerations of this chapter in a QLF.

QLF 3-5 Law of Conservation of Weight	
WHAT	It is **always true** that collections of matter have weight and this weight is a conservative and additive and invariant attribute of the matter (i.e., conaddian),
WHEN	**no matter** whether the matter is solid or liquid or gas or divided into big or little pieces,
WHEN NOT	**but not if** buoyancy effects and changes of volume are important or if some parts of the matter are in different gravitational fields from other parts.

Chapter 4

Force, Tension, and the Action-Reaction Law

4-1 Contact Forces and Action-at-a-Distance Forces

The influence that the one wua~ weight B_1 has on a platform of a weight-sensing device in Fig. 3-3 is called a **force.** The word *force* describes the influence transmitted to the platform by the bottom of the bottle through its contact with the top of the platform. In this case the force owes its existence to the fact that the matter composing the bottle is attracted by gravitational forces toward the matter composing the earth. The important laws governing this attraction were discovered and stated by Newton. His theory of gravitation is discussed in Chapter 9. In this chapter we accept weight as a con-addian, as discussed in Chapter 3.

The weight-sensing platform is equally well a down-force-sensing platform. You can exert 1.00 wua~ down-force on the platform by putting your hand on it and pushing down until it stands at 1 wua. You have a *hunch* that the spring doesn't know the difference, and from the point of view of science you are right. If the platform is hidden behind a screen, as shown in Fig. 4-1, there is no measurement that science has discovered that can tell from the condition of the spring whether the spring is being stretched by B_1 or by a hidden person pushing with his hand or by another spring pulling down toward the floor.

It is evident that at least two kinds of force are involved in Fig. 4-1. One is a long-range, or *action-at-a-distance,* force; this is Newton's gravitational force. The bottle B_1 is being pulled by matter as far away as the opposite side of the earth. The other kind of force is a *contact* force; each of the three possible forces represented as acting on the platform in Fig. 4-1 are contact forces.

In addition to gravitational forces, there are two other well-known action-at-a-distance forces; magnetic and electric.* If you bring two magnets close together, they exert forces on each other long before they come in contact. The same is true of electric forces. The electric forces that you are likely to encounter in everyday experiences are associated with sheets of plastic material. When you remove a shirt from a plastic laundry wrapper, often the wrapper is attracted toward the shirt. This is caused by frictional electricity:

---

* See Francis E. Dart, *Electricity and Magnetic Fields,* Merrill Physical Science Series.

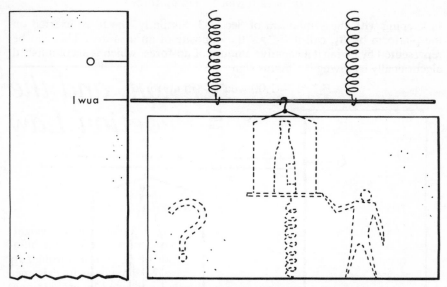

Fig. 4-1. A force is a force, no matter what produces it.

friction, or rubbing of the cloth on the plastic, transfers electrons from one to the other so that the one that gets the electrons acquires a negative charge while the other, having lost negative charge, becomes positively charged. This is an example of the algebraic law that a minus times a minus is a plus. The laws of electricity show that unlike charges attract.

Actually the contact forces are electrostatic in origin. All materials are composed of atoms and these atoms are bonded to each other by the electrical forces that exist between their negative electrons and the positive protons contained in their cores, or atomic nuclei. For our purposes, however, we shall deal with directly observable forces such as the ones we feel if we put our hand on the platform of Fig. 4-1 and push down with 1 wua. We shall show that these forces are conaddian vectors. The deeper understanding of the nature of contact forces is a subject for atomic physics and chemistry.* Still further inside the atom there are other kinds of forces within the nucleus; these are a subject for modern physics.*

In order to describe forces and the laws governing them, we need to introduce appropriate, clearly defined symbols and diagrams. Here algebra, with the power it derives from the minus sign, is of enormous help. We shall call upward forces *plus,* and downward forces *minus.* For example, suppose that you put B_1 on the platform of Fig. 4-1 and then pushed up on the platform from below with an exactly equal up-force so that the pointer indicated 0 as shown in Fig. 4-2. Then the upward force of your hand, denoted by $F_{yh}{}^{\sim}$ would be represented as follows:

---

* See Isaac Maleh, *Modern Physics*, and John McAnally, *Chemistry*, Merrill Physical Science Series.

$$F_{yh}{}^\sim = +1.00 \text{ wua}^\sim \quad \text{(in up-force)}$$

in keeping with the symbolism of Sec. 3-3. Similarly, the force exerted on the platform by B_1, call it $F_1{}^\sim$, is the opposite of an up-force. This can be represented by giving it a negative amount of up-force, which is accomplished algebraically by giving it a minus sign:

$$F_1{}^\sim = -1.00 \text{ wua}^\sim \quad \text{(in up-force)}$$

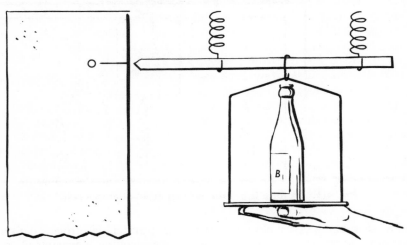

Fig. 4-2. Cancellation of an up-force and a down-force acting on a weight-sensing platform in static equilibrium.

The total up-force $F_T{}^\sim$ is the *algebraic* sum of these two forces, the positive up-force of your hand plus the negative up-force of B_1:

$$\begin{aligned}F_T{}^\sim &= F_{yh}{}^\sim + F_1{}^\sim = 1.00 \text{ wua}^\sim + (-1.00 \text{ wua}^\sim) \\ &= (1.00 - 1.00) \text{ wua}^\sim = 0 \text{ wua}^\sim = 0^\sim \quad \text{(in up-force)}\end{aligned}$$

Here $0^\sim$ is a symbol we shall not ordinarily use. In this case we use it to call attention to the fact that what vanishes is not simply a number but the quantity up-force specified by the equation-qualifier, (in up-force). We make this distinction because there are other aspects of the forces that do not vanish. Although the sum of the forces is $0^\sim$, forces are really acting on the platform and if the material of the platform were very weak, for example, if it were made of cardboard, F_{yh} and F_1 might bend or wrinkle it. Consequently, the two forces would not add up to zero so far as a qualifier such as (in distortion of platform) is concerned. Only when we wish emphatically to identify the particular quantitative attribute that vanishes in a given situation shall we use a tilde on the zero.

4-2   The Action-Reaction Law as a Theorem from Conservation of Weight

In this experiment it is seen that the weight of a collection of things on a bathroom scale is always the same **no matter** how they are arranged or pull and push on each other, **but not if** any up or down forces are exerted between them and anything else not on the scale platform.

To test this law, you will use a slab of concrete (such as a garden-walk paving stone) or a heavy plank and an 8 ft length of cord or light rope.

First weigh the block on the scale. Then weigh yourself and the rope in your pocket. Then put the block on the scale and step on it. If the scale is accurate, the law of additivity of weights should work to an accuracy of about 1 lb. (See Sec. 5-4 for accuracy and per cent accuracy.)

You will find that it is **always true** that the scale reads the sum of the block weight plus your weight, **no matter** whether you:

(1) Hold the slab in your hands and stand on the scale or

(2) Put the slab on the scale and stand on it or

(3) Put the middle of the rope under the slab and pull on the two ends (this is called "trying to lift yourself by your bootstraps")

but not if the reading of the scale is very inaccurate when you move all the way to one side or the other, or when you put one foot on the floor and push a little, or when a classmate puts his hand on your shoulder and pushes down.

These observations are an example of the law of conservation of weight of Sec. 3-8. Take note that forces exerted by the objects on each other (such as your pushing down or pulling up or holding the concrete block) do not affect how hard the entire collection pushes down on the scale. We shall

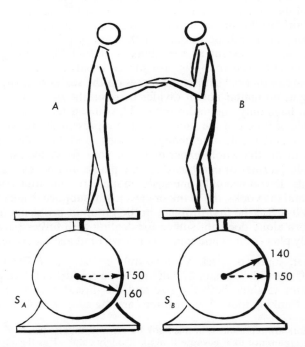

Fig. 4-3. Student *B* exerts an "action" by pushing down on *A* with a 10-lb force, and *A* pushes back with an exactly "equal and opposite reaction" of 10 lb up on *B*.

pursue the interpretation of this simple fact to the action-reaction law, one of the most basic of all the principles of physical science.

As the next step in studying the action-reaction law, take two bathroom scales and put them next to each other. Stand with one foot on each. If you stand evenly, each scale will read half your weight. The harder you push with your right foot, the more the right scale reads and the less the left one reads, but the sum of the two readings will stay constant.

The downward push of your foot on the scale is a force. The reading of the scale is the measurement of this force. *The scale exerts*, you will learn, *an exactly equal and opposite up-force on your foot.*

This famous and important law of equal and opposite action and reaction can be dramatized by using two scales and two students. Put the scales next to each other. Student *A* stands on one scale and holds out his hands palms up towards the other scale as shown in Fig. 4-3. Student *B* stands on the other scale and puts his hands on top of *A*'s and pushes down. Student *A* pushes back up to keep his hands from being pushed down. The students are exerting forces on each other.

If the students can exert a really steady force, the two scales will show equal changes. For example, if *A*'s scale reads 10 lb more, then *B*'s will be found to read 10 lb less.

The same situation of Fig. 4-3 can be produced with steadier conditions by replacing human muscles with inanimate bodies. Fig. 4-4 represents a plank, a concrete block, and a rubber ball. The rubber ball represents the yielding of the students' palms. The smaller board is used to keep the push on scale S_B fairly well centered on the platform so as to improve the precision of the experiment. It will be found that the sum of NSU numbers read on S_A and S_B remains constant as the plank is shifted from being balanced on S_B to the position shown in Fig. 4-4 so that it puts a down-force of 10 lb on S_A. This shows that the sum of the forces on the scales is always equal to the total weight, **no matter** how it divides between the two scales.

If you have only one bathroom scale, you can repeat the experiment by using a pile of books of the same height to represent the missing scale. After you have read the scale, interchange the books and the scale, and read again. Or you can do the whole experiment on your desk, by using one or two postal scales, a ruler or cardboard for the plank, and pencils or pocketbooks for weights. If you use only one scale, make sure that after you interchange the scale and the books, the plank or card is still supported at exactly the same points. Why? See the first problem in the group of problems for Chapter 7.

Algebra alone does not suffice for dealing with forces because they can be not only plus (or up) and minus (or down) but also sidewise, for example,

north, east, south, or west. Vector-symbols* such as $\vec{F_1}\sim$ (which you call "vector eff one tilde", or simply "eff one" if no confusion is likely) and arrows on diagrams to show both the size and the direction of forces are the appropriate thinking tools. Vector forces are the subject of Chapter 5.

---

* Vectors are represented in this book by arrow symbols such as $\vec{F}$. This symbol is selected in preference to **F** because it more strongly emphasizes the vector aspect. The simpler symbol **F** is used, for example, in Dart's *Electricity and Electromagnetic Fields*, Merrill Physical Science Series.

Fig. 4-4. System *B*, the concrete block and the plank, pushes down with 10 lb of force on system *A*, the 1-lb rubber ball.

An example of additivity of forces is shown in Fig. 4-5. The forces exerted on student *A*'s forward and back foot for the situation of Fig. 4-3 are shown. The vector symbol $\vec{F}_{AF \text{ by } S}$~ means the force exerted on *A*'s front foot (subscript *AF*) by the scale *S*, and $\vec{F}_{AB \text{ by } S}$~ is the force on *A*'s back foot. The force $\vec{F}_{A \text{ by } E}$ is the gravitational attraction of the earth *E* on *A*. The last force, $\vec{F}_{A \text{ by } B}$, is the 10-lb~ force exerted downwards on student *A* by student *B*.

Again, all these forces add up to zero. In Chapter 9, which is concerned with laws of motion, we shall see that if the sum of the forces is not zero, then the body will not stay at rest.

To establish that up- and down-forces are conaddians, we would in principle have to carry out a set of conceptual experiments, like those of Chapter 3, involving weight. We could make force-producing devices—for example, a pogo stick compressed to a standard amount—to push up or down on a bathroom scale used as a direct-reading instrument. Alternatively, some rubber bands or light spring devices could be used with postage scales. Then invariance and additivity would be established just as was done for weight.

Such experiments have been carried out in physics laboratories, and even more sensitive ones involving individual atomic or subatomic particles have been done. There are interesting parallels between these cases and the logical structures of Chapters 1 and 2. The nuclear experiments deal with conservation laws for energy and momentum.* These laws are of the **you can't, no matter what** class. They are like the **you can't** do it conclusions of the two-king problem, the two-coin problem, the checkerboard problem, the Take 1 or 4 Game, and the $M = P - 1$ law in the tennis tournament. In all these cases, the laws are really theorems that can be understood in terms of

---

* See, for example, Isaac Maleh, *op. cit.*, especially the discussions of conservation laws and invariance.

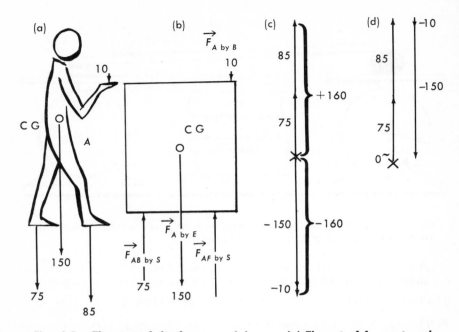

Fig. 4-5. **The sum of the forces on A is zero. (a) The set of four external forces applied at different places to A. (The action of the pull of the earth on A's center of gravity will be discussed in a later chapter.) (b) A mixed diagram representing the student schematically and the forces as vectors. (c) The addition of the up-forces represented as the sum of the plus (upward) forces and the minus (downward) forces. (d) All the forces added up as directed lengths or vectors so that the sum is zero.**

still more basic postulates. The law of action and reaction is a more basic postulate in the laws of mechanics and nuclear physics than are the conservation laws. The action-reaction law is in turn regarded as a theorem based on postulates about the nature of space itself.

In the logic of our presentation, however, we infer the more general action and reaction law from the far less general conservation of weight law of Sec. 3-8, which can be established using desk-sized experiments. This law is combined with the observation that **you can't** change your weight on the bathroom scale by pulling up on the rope under the block on which you are standing. What this means is that the down-pull on your hands exerted by the rope exactly equals the up-pull on the block exerted by the rope. The same would hold true for the students of Fig. 4-3 if they both stood on one large scale. Conservation of their total weight says that the NSU number indicated by the scale **doesn't change, no matter** how hard they push on each other. Again the simplest explanation is that the forces are equal and opposite so that they cancel out.

The action-reaction law may be stated as follows:

QLF 4-1 The Action-Reaction Law	
WHAT	It is **always true** that if a first body exerts a force on a second body, then the second body exerts an exactly equal and opposite force on the first body,
WHEN	**no matter** whether the forces are contact forces or electric, magnetic, or gravitational forces,
WHEN NOT	**but not if** the bodies are far apart and change their motion rapidly so that appreciable forces result from radiating energy or momentum as wave motion.

The WHEN NOT qualification can be eliminated by including the "waves" in the theory. But this lies beyond the scope of mechanics, and the reader is referred to electricity and magnetism, astronomy, and modern physics.*

The action-reaction law was stated by Newton as his third law, see Chapter 9.

4-3 The Zero Total Force Law of Statics and the Invariant Tension Principle

In addition to the action and reaction law, we have used another law for bodies that remain at rest. This law and the action-reaction law will be the key postulates of the developments of this chapter and the next. Because of its importance, we express this "zero force" law in the following QLF:

QLF 4-2 The Zero Total Force Law of Statics	
WHAT	It is **always true** that the sum of all the up and down forces including that of gravity on a body is zero if the body is static (i.e., is remaining at rest),
WHEN	**no matter** how the forces are caused,
WHEN NOT	**but not if** "at rest" is confused with at rest in an accelerated space capsule or if appreciable effects arise from energy and momentum being radiated, in a laser beam, for example.

(This law is a special example of Newton's first and second laws, which are discussed in Chapter 9. We shall return to it in Chapter 5 and remove the limitation which restricts it to up and down forces; the "zero force" law of Chapter 5 applies to vector forces and thus is applicable to all directions of force. But here we shall combine it with the action-reaction law to derive some theorems.)

Consider a chain of rubber bands and paperclips as shown in Fig. 4-6. The authors urge you to make such a chain with at least four identical, preferably brand new, rubber bands that have never been stretched. Put some paperclip links in the chain; also a six-inch length of string with loops at both ends. Next stretch the chain so that the rubber bands double their

_____
* See other books in the Merrill Physical Science Series.

Fig. 4-6. A chain of rubber bands and paperclips (method of linking indicated).

length. Keep it stretched by (1) scotch-taping two ends to the desk; (2) stretching it vertically by attaching a weight, such as a book, to the bottom end, and fastening the top end to a high support, such as a ruler extending from under a book on a book shelf; or (3) using a loop of string under a table so as to stretch out the chain on top of the table (like a buckle in a belt). You will find that all the rubber bands are stretched by about the same amount. Verify this approximate equality of stretching by comparing them with a ruler; or mark the length of them all, one at a time, on a piece of paper so that you can compare them. You will find that each rubber band has stretched approximately the same. Something related to the amount of stretch does not vary along the chain. The invariance principle involved is the QLF that we state at the end of this section.

Now, while the ends remain fixed or the weight still hangs, grasp one rubber band at both ends and pull it out to about four times its length and then let it come back. It will not come back to the length of the others. It has become **deformed.** If you release the load, however, the super-stretched band will pull back to only a little longer than the others. Pulling it out to four times its length has broken some of the chemical bonds that hold the polymer chains of atoms, which are rather like atom-scale rubber bands, together in vulcanized rubber.* We shall return to rubber bands when we measure vector forces in Sec. 5-9. What we need for our purposes now is simply the concept of **tension** as an invariant attribute of a string or a chain.

Figure 4-7 shows the chain hanging vertically and being stretched by a weight (not shown) which exerts a down-force $W^{\sim}$ on the bottom of the chain. This down-force exerted on the bottom B of the chain by W is represented on the diagram by the vector symbol $\vec{F}_{B\,by\,W}{}^{\sim}$ (meaning force on B by W) and by the associated arrow, which represents the direction and magnitude of the force.

Now consider any link—for example, the paperclip that is being pulled upward by the rubber band at the top of part (a). It is shown on a larger scale in (b). The force due to the rubber band is denoted by the vector symbol $\vec{F}_{C\,by\,R}{}^{\sim}$ and by the associated arrows. The arrows are considered to represent the forces that are applied to the paperclip at the point where the printed arrow in the diagram touches the printed paperclip. The length of the arrow is proportional to the magnitude of the force, and the arrowhead shows its direction. These arrows are vector symbols used in diagrams and are the main item in Chapter 5. Similarly the force due to the string is $\vec{F}_{C\,by\,S}$.

---

* For the chemical theory of rubber, see John McAnally, *Chemistry,* Merrill Physical Science Series, Fig. 11-3.

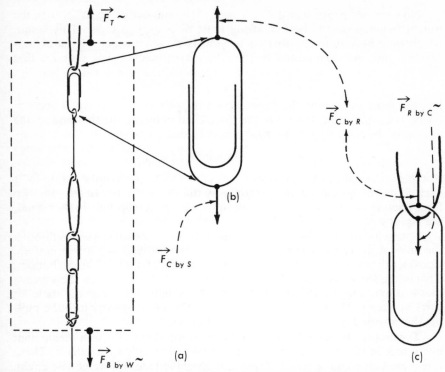

Fig. 4-7. Action and reaction forces in a chain. Two alternative ways of representing forces on a paperclip are shown in (b) and (c).

We shall express the forces by their NSU symbols $F_{C \text{ by } R}$ and $F_{C \text{ by } S}$ in up-forces in lb~ or in "up-lb~". Suppose that the magnitude of the string force is 2 lb~ so that

$$F_{C \text{ by } S} = -2 \quad \text{(in number of up-lb~)}$$

since down-forces are identical to negative up-forces. If the weight of the paperclip is W_C lb~, then the zero total force law of statics requires that the sum of all the up-forces on the paperclip be zero:

$$0 = F_{C \text{ by } R} + F_{C \text{ by } S} - W_C \quad \text{(in number of up-lb~)}$$

Consequently, by combining the last two equations, we obtain

$$F_{C \text{ by } R} = -F_{C \text{ by } S} + W_C = +2 + W_C \quad \text{(in number of up-lb~)}$$

Now W_C is less than 0.002 so that it hardly affects the 2.

In order to avoid the labor of keeping track of the paperclip weight, we use the important thinking tool of **idealized limiting cases** and assume that hypothetical clips, string, and rubber bands are weightless but strong enough to support the 2 lb~. For this idealized limiting case, $F_{C \text{ by } R} = -F_{C \text{ by } S}$ so that in general the up-force acting on the top of each link is equal to minus the up-force acting on the bottom of the link.

Now we can prove that if $F_{C\,by\,R} = 2$ (in number of up-lb~), then the weight hanging on the bottom string must be a 2-lb~ weight. This result, which may be intuitively obvious to you, is a consequence of the action-reaction law. As represented in (d), the action-reaction law requires that

$$\vec{F}_{R\,by\,C}{}^{\sim} = -\vec{F}_{C\,by\,R}{}^{\sim} \text{ (in force)}$$

i.e., the force exerted by the paperclip on the rubber band is equal and opposite (i.e., minus one times) to the force exerted by the rubber band on the paperclip. In NSU up-lb~ we then conclude that

$$F_{R\,by\,C} = -2 \text{ (in numbr of up-lb}^{\sim})$$

But this is the same as the down-force $F_{C\,by\,S} = -2$ (in number of up-lb~) exerted on the bottom of the paperclip by the string. Consequently, the two forces acting on the bottoms of both links, i.e., paperclip and rubber band, are equal with -2 for the NSU.

Following this reasoning leads to an invariant up-down sequence through the links of the chain. Every link has $+2$ at the top and -2 at the bottom. Consider the bottom string. It will have $+2$ at the top and -2 at the bottom. That is, the force exerted on its bottom end is -2 lb~ of up-force. This means that it is exerting $+2$ lb~ of up-force on the weight. The weight is static (it stays in place). The total force on it is zero. Therefore, gravity must be pulling down with 2 lb~. It is a 2-lb~ weight. Q.E.D.

Tension is the name for the condition in the chain. Tension means that every link in the chain has forces at its two ends trying to stretch it. These forces are equal and opposite. Tension is conserved along a weightless chain. A string can be thought of an an infinite number of infinitely short chain links.

In Fig. 4-7(a), the conservation of tension along the chain leads to the theorem that $\vec{F}_T{}^{\sim} = -\vec{F}_{B\,by\,W}{}^{\sim}$. This is not true if the chain has appreciable weight. Then the tension in the top link will be greater than the tension in the bottom link by a force equal to the weight of the chain.

The concept of conservation or invariance of tension along a chain or rope or string is so important that we state it as a QLF. It is a theorem, as we have just shown, based on the zero force law of statics and the action-reaction law:

QLF 4-3   The Invariant Tension Principle

WHAT	It is **always true** that the force exerted by any part of a chain, rope or string on the next part will be measured to be the same size,
WHEN	**no matter** how far you go along the chain, or whether the links are the same or different kinds,
WHEN NOT	**but not if** the weights of the link are large enough to be detected by the means of measurement or if other forces including friction act on the chain.

One way of measuring tension is to insert a spring as one link of a chain. The stretch of the spring can be calibrated to make a direct-reading tension-measuring instrument. Such a spring can also be used to measure *negative* tensions or **compression.** The concept of the idealized limiting case of such a tension-gauge as a weightless, rigid link that can be inserted in a chain or in a string or a rope is a valuable thinking tool for conceptual experiments. Such gauges will be used in this way in Chapter 5.

Chapter 5

The Vector Force Concept

5-1 The Equal Length Law

"You can't change the equality of $L_A{}^\sim$ and $L_B{}^\sim$ **no matter** how you hang the weights" in Fig. 5-1 is a clue to one of the most important principles in all of science. *Forces are vector conaddians.* You will have learned a major component of mechanics when you understand this sentence and can set up the effective one-to-one correspondences between (1) the reality of two unopened soft drink bottles hanging on strings from two door hinges, (2) vector diagrams representing the forces, and (3) quantity-vector-symbols in qualified-equations.

Two sets of desk-sized experiments have been devised to put you in a position to speak with authority about vector forces and to prove your point to a fellow student or in a court of law if need be. You will be able to show that the concept of force as a vector conaddian can bring order out of complex situations. You will be able to demonstrate the power of your knowledge by letting someone during your absence replace the two bottles in Fig. 5-1 by two opaque paper bags containing different numbers of identical bottles not exceeding three in either bag. Without lifting either bag, you will be able to tell how many are in each bag.

The apparatus you need may already be in your home or laboratory. If not, you can easily obtain it, probably all of it at the nearest drugstore or supermarket. Here is the list; the sizes are only suggestions, and substitutes will work as well:

(1) String (a small ball of good quality, not fuzzy or stiff, No. 24)
(2) A six-pack of one kind of 6 or 8 oz., unopened, carbonated beverage bottles
(3) A pad or sheets of ruled paper ($8\frac{1}{2} \times 11$ in. with about 34 lines)
(4) A pencil and a pen or a porous tip-marker
(5) Paperclips (a box of No. 0 or larger)
(6) Scotch tape ($\frac{3}{4}$ in.)
(7) Rubber bands (3 in. by $\frac{1}{8}$ in. wide, about 2 doz)
(8) A desk top or table on which to work

Before you get them, you may wish to glance at Secs. 5-2 and 5-9 to see how the supplies are used.

Here is the first action you take to acquire an important aspect of familiarity with forces.* Select two supports, preferably 5 to 8 feet apart. Make

---

* Do the experiment now, if you like, for preliminary orientation. Or if you prefer, first read Sec. 5-2, which presents detailed suggestions you will follow in Sec. 5-3.

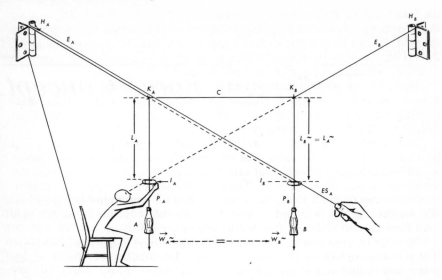

Fig. 5-1. The "you can't change it, no matter what" invariant equality of $L_A{}^\sim$ and $L_B{}^\sim$. (Note that C is usually not horizontal.)

an H-shaped piece of string long enough so that the two upper end segments, name-symbols E_A and E_B, can reach to two hinges or other supports. Using two full soda-pop bottles, name-symbols A and B, hang one from each of the two down-strings or *plumb lines*, name-symbols P_A and P_B. The remaining cross bar of the H corresponds to the center segment C that runs between the two *k*nots, name-symbols K_A, and K_B. We shall refer to the assembly of segments E_A, C, and E_B as *ECE*.

Adjust the string lengths by moving the chair or lengthening or shortening P_A and P_B until you can indicate the lengths $L_A{}^\sim$ and $L_B{}^\sim$ by adjusting the paperclips as shown in Fig. 5-1. This adjustment is accomplished in either of two ways:

Line-of-sight method: By stooping or sitting, line up your eye with the imaginary straight line in space occupied by segment E_B, which runs from K_B to the attachment point on the hinge H_B. This puts your eye on the dotted extension of E_B shown in Fig. 5-1. You will find this extension of E_B intersects P_A. Indicate the location of this intersection with the upper edge of a paperclip used as an indicator I_A. The name-symbol I_A is used for three ideas, the intersection point itself, the upper edge of the paperclip and the paperclip. Adjust I_A (meaning the paperclip) so that it lies on the E_B line when you do not disturb the strings by touching them with your hands. The length between K_A and I_A is given the quantity-symbol $L_A{}^\sim$.

Preferred ES method: An alternative method, and one you will actually use in the three series of measurements in Sec. 5-3, is shown in Fig. 5-1 for locating I_B. The **extrapolation string,** name-symbol ES_A, is an extra length of string which is attached to H_A at the same point as is E_A. While this ES_A string is pulled out straight, it can be held parallel to E_A so that it passes from H_A and touches K_A and extrapolates E_B to P_B; where the string touches P_B is then the location of I_B. ES_A serves another purpose: When it is held lightly against P_B, it acts as a brake to stop any swinging of W_B. When the motion has stopped, P_B can be grasped so that a fingernail locates the crossing point I_B. This point can then be marked with a paperclip. Use a similar ES_B string to locate I_A. Usually, segment C will not be level.

Both the line-of-sight method and the ES (extrapolation string) method permit you to make a very significant observation about a geometrical relationship among the five strings of the H. Can you guess what it is? We shall state it as QLF 5-2 later in this section.

Next compare $L_A{}^\sim$ and $L_B{}^\sim$ as follows: Take an extra piece of string and tie a knot or make an ink mark near one end. Hold this knot or mark against K_A with one hand and with your other hand grip the lower end so that the thumbnail comes adjacent to I_A. Then without letting go with your thumb, move the knot or mark to K_B and compare I_B with your thumbnail position. We predict that you will find it very close (probably within ⅛ inch if you have been careful and your pop bottles are matched).

Now let us urge you to take **action.** Do the experiment. The *familiarity* that you acquire will enable you to recognize **key attributes** of forces much better and to understand the simplicity (even beauty, to the science lover) of the *orderly relationships* resulting from vector concepts if you have first-hand familiarity with the experimental facts. Also you will learn something of great significance in science: *Most of the effort to do a good experiment is spent in becoming organized.* In the course of learning how to carry out an original experiment *you inevitably make many false motions. Do not be discouraged by these. Most competent scientists also make false moves when they extend themselves to try something that is new and original for them.* The experience with your errors gives you familiarity with the key attributes of the situation so that you steadily improve your hunches about how to set up useful orderly relationships both with the apparatus and with the concepts. *Take action and learn from what goes wrong.* (A reasonable time to allow for doing the experiments and working through the theory of this chapter is 16 hours.)

You can probably find enough string and two equal weights wherever you are when you reach this point in your reading. Use these if you have not already obtained the items listed at the beginning of this section. But do try the experiment at this point if you possibly can.

As you will find, $L_A{}^\sim$ will equal $L_B{}^\sim$ in length if $W_A{}^\sim = W_B{}^\sim$ in weight. If $W_A{}^\sim$ is greater than $W_B{}^\sim$, then $L_A{}^\sim$ will be less than $L_B{}^\sim$. In fact, there is a very simple relationship between the four quantities $W_A{}^\sim$, $W_B{}^\sim$, $L_A{}^\sim$, and $L_B{}^\sim$ which we shall derive later in this chapter as a theorem from the postulate that force is a vector conaddian. We shall present the relationship in this section as a QLF so that you will be aware of one target toward which the discussion of this chapter is aimed.

If you measure $L_A{}^\sim$ and $L_B{}^\sim$ and express the results as NSU values L_A and L_B in number of appropriate units (see Sec. 5-3) then you can calculate the ratio of lengths. We denote this ratio between L_A and L_B with a double-adjective number-symbol, L_B^A pronounced "ell super a sub bee" and meaning ratio of the length attributes associated with A and B:

$$L_B^A = \frac{L_A{}^\sim}{L_B{}^\sim} = \frac{L_A}{L_B} \quad \text{(in number size)}$$

L_B^A is a pure number since it is a ratio of the same kinds of quantities. If you repeat the experiment and get a second set of values, distinguished from the first set by a prime ' as an adjective-symbol, so that

$$(L_B^A)' = \frac{L_A'}{L_B'} \quad \text{(in number size)}$$

you will find that **no matter** how you hang the weights, it is **always true** that $(L_B^A)'$ will be equal to L_B^A within the accuracy of your experimental technique.

Furthermore, if object B is replaced by object B_2 which consists of two soda bottles so that B_2 weighs twice as much as A (i.e., $W_{B2}{}^\sim = 2\,W_A{}^\sim$), we predict that $L_{B2}^A = 2$. In general, we predict that you will find a QLF as follows:

QLF 5-1	Reciprocity Law of Length and Weight Ratios
WHAT	It is **always true** that if two weights $W_A{}^\sim$ and $W_B{}^\sim$ hang from the bottom strings of an H as in Fig. 5-1, then the pure number ratio $W_A{}^\sim/W_B{}^\sim$ and the pure number ratio $L_A{}^\sim/L_B{}^\sim$ are reciprocals so that they satisfy the two equivalent relationships. $$\frac{L_A{}^\sim\,W_B{}^\sim}{L_B{}^\sim\,W_A{}^\sim} \text{ or } \frac{L_A\,W_B}{L_B\,W_A} = 1 \quad \text{(in number size)}$$
WHEN	**no matter** where the weights hang on the strings or which is higher or lower or whether the strings stretch or not or are even replaced by rubber bands (see Sec. 5-9 regarding rubber bands),
WHEN NOT	**but not if** one weight touches the floor or touches the other weight or if the string is so heavy compared to the weights that its own weight makes a difference or if a breeze blows enough on the strings to keep them from hanging freely.

Earlier we asked if you could make any other observation about a geometrical relationship of the experimental situation of Fig. 5-1. Here is the answer: *the five strings E_A, C, E_B, P_A, and P_B all lie in a common vertical plane.* This plane is determined by two imaginary vertical lines through the two points of support H_A and H_B: These two lines, like edges of a door, determine a vertical plane. All five string segments lie in this plane. You can verify this conclusion by sighting past P_A to H_B in Fig. 5-1. The pupil of your eye (in effect, a geometrical point) and P_A (in effect, a geometrical line) determine a vertical plane. You note that P_B, E_B, and C all lie in this plane. The same conclusion applies to E_A when sighted past P_B.

The *ES* method also leads to the same conclusion. H_A and P_B determine a plane. When the string ES_A touches P_B, it lies in this plane. But by moving it up and down along P_B, you can make it touch also any point on E_A or C and the top part of P_A. This again proves that E_A, C, and P_A all lie in the plane determined by H_A and P_B.

These observations lead us to a very significant orderly relationship about vector forces when we focus our attention on relatively inconspicuous features of Fig. 5-1, namely the knots K_A and K_B. Consider the tension forces exerted on each knot by the three string segments it joins together:

	QLF 5-2 The Three Coplanar Forces Law
WHAT	It is **always true** that the three tension forces exerted by the three strings which meet at a knot in a static equilibrium lie in the same plane,
WHEN	**no matter** what produces the tensions in the strings or whether the plane is vertical or not,
WHEN NOT	**but not if** the knot is itself a heavy twist of soldering wire and the strings are slack or are replaced by heavy sagging chain.

The WHEN condition involving a plane that is not vertical can be checked by pushing weight A out of the plane with a chair. Then hold a flat object, for example a phonograph record or a breadboard, behind knot K_A where three strings meet and move it close to the three strings and the knot. In this way you will check that all three strings lie in a plane so that the tension forces, acting along the strings, are coplanar.

All these results, as we shall show in Sec. 5-8, are derivable from two postulates: the zero force law QLF 4-2 extended to vectors; and the vector conaddian law of forces QLF 5-5, the key concept of this chapter. In the next two sections we shall experimentally verify the weight-length reciprocity law. Then in Sec. 5-7 the concept of vectors will be developed and applied to forces in Secs. 5-8 and 5-9.

5-2   Introduction to the Length Ratio Experiment

The General Nature of Experimental Science

This section is an introduction to the experiments you should carry out according to the instructions of Sec. 5-3. These experiments involve many of the essential features of any serious scientific experiment: (1) apparatus preparation, (2) measurement techniques, (3) systematic variations of conditions, (4) establishment of an orderly relationship in the results.

The experimental techniques have a resemblance to those involved in modern physics, like making a billion-volt atom smasher for example. You must carry out engineering considerations to make sure you find a suitable site. If you try to carry out the experiment with the best china cups as weights, you may run into the difficulties with public reaction similar to those that the Atomic Energy Commission has whenever it wants to set up a new facility: someone is sure to object, often with good reasons. You must engineer your experiment after you have selected the site so that you don't do damage, like filling the bath tub with broken pop bottles.

You must bring not one but several skills to bear on the experiments. You must be able to tie reliable knots. You must be able to attach weights so that they can conveniently be added or removed. You must be able to locate I_A and I_B without disturbing the apparatus. And you must construct length-measuring instruments.

In an atom-smasher project, many more difficult skills are involved but the principle of diversity is similar. Some engineers must be experts on vacuum, some on electronic circuits such as radio transmitters, others on electronic measurements, and so on.

Once the equipment is working, the experiments are first done crudely and then everything is refined and perfected. After all this, good scientific data is at last obtained. You can have the similar experiences with the length ratio experiment.

Experimental Technique Hints

Here are some hints that are intended to help you with the series of experiments discussed in the next section. First read them quickly, and then return to them for details as you do the experiments in Sec. 5-3.

Points of Support. The points of support are preferably chosen to be 5 to 10 feet apart. Door hinges as suggested in Fig. 5-1 are one of the easiest supports to use. Other possibilities are: (1) braces holding shelves, for example book shelves, (2) lighting fixtures, (3) bathroom shower heads and shower-curtain supports, (4) radiator pipes (tie with a clove hitch shown in Fig. 5-2), (5) screw eyes that you buy and screw into wood for the purpose.

Caution. You can exert large forces with weights hanging from nearly horizontal strings. Pinup lamps will be torn off the wall. Glass bottles break easily over bath tubs. You can easily do damage or make an unpleasant mess if you don't think about what you are doing.

String. White wrapping string is good. No. 24 is a good weight of string. The results you get will be invariant to the kind of string you use. You will have more fun if you buy 100 ft or more of string so that you can throw away your mistakes without worrying about running out of string. But it is **always true** that the experiments will work **no matter** whether you make your H from bits and pieces tied together, including shoe laces, fishline, electrical wires, rubber bands, and dental floss **but not if** you tie bad knots that pull out or use weak strings that break.

Making and Hanging the "H". Part (a) of Fig. 5-2 shows an adjustable H. It has one long string that makes E_A, C, and E_B of Fig. 5-1. The name-symbol of this string is ECE. Its length can be adjusted using the simple loops L_1, L_2, L_3 and L_4 tied in E_B. The right-hand support should be arranged so that different loops can be hooked over it as shown in (a) or (h). Five plumb-lines hang down from it.

Knots. A good knot is a wonderful thing. In Fig. 5-2 we show several knots that may help with these experiments. The simple overhand knot in a doubled string in (b) makes the loops. The bowline (c) is the "king of knots": it never slips and never jams so tight that you can't untie it. Books on scouting and sailboat handling have good descriptions of knots. A neat way of tying a plumb-line onto ECE is shown in (d): a piece of string about 3 ft long has an overhand loop (see part (b)) in one end and a figure-eight knot (part (d)) in the other and both are pulled tight. A simple overhand knot as shown in (d) is tied in the ECE string around the plumb-line just below the figure-eight knot and drawn tight. The plumb-line is pulled through the knot until the figure eight stops against the overhand knot. In this way (or any other if you prefer) you should put five plumb-lines along string ECE when you prepare apparatus for Sec. 5-3. A clove hitch (e) further secured with a half hitch (f) and a hook (h) can be used with a water or steam pipe to replace H_B.

Weight Attachment. A bottle is illustrated for a weight. It is attached in (g) by putting a slip noose around its neck and drawing it tight. It is provided with a paperclip hook secured with scotch tape as shown in (h). 4 in. of string from bottle neck to hook works well. Scotch tape (not shown) also helps keep the slip noose on the bottle's neck in (g).

Locating I_A and I_B. Use the extrapolation-string method to locate I_A and I_B, the intersection of the extrapolated E lines with the plumb lines as discussed in Fig. 5-1, and shown in detail in Fig. 5-3. You can attach strings ES_A and ES_B to H_A and H_B in various ways. Be careful that ES_A, for example, lies very close to the proper ends of E_A and that pulling on it does not exert forces that move the ECE string from its natural free-hanging configuration. Next consider a refinement in locating I_B: You may find that when ES_A is made parallel to the E_A string, the knots hold it as much as $\frac{1}{8}$ in. away from E_A. Also when you try to locate the paperclip, you miss by $\frac{1}{8}$ in. *You do not need to eliminate these discrepancies;* you can instead *allow for them* by performing a *conceptual experiment.* Imagine that you could move ES_A so that it penetrated E_A without disturbing E_A, and thereby became a true geometrical extension of E_A. Then visualize where this line would strike P_B. Perhaps it is $\frac{1}{16}$ in. below the paperclip. Imagine that you mark this correct I_B point with an imaginary pen. Then when you measure the length from K_B to I_B, shown as $L_B{}^\sim$ on Fig. 5-1, measure to the imaginary indicator mark that exists only in your mind as a result of the two conceptual experiments just described: (1) replacing the real ES by an *idealized limiting case* of an intangible, perfectly straight string that runs down the center of E to the correct I_B position, and (2) replacing the ink mark you imagine you have placed on P_B to show just where I_B should be. *Just one precaution:* if you use imaginary ink, then actually measure L_B between K_B and I_B before you set up I_A. The imaginary ink on P_B fades very fast; use I_B while you can still imagine the imaginary ink is wet. (Of course, if it helps, use real ink—probably cheaper than imagination, anyway.)

Measuring $L_A{}^\sim$ and $L_B{}^\sim$. In this experiment you are to make your own instruments to measure $L_B{}^\sim$ and $L_A{}^\sim$: Take some ruled composition or scratch paper and cut some one-inch strips along the length of the paper and fasten them end to end so that the intervals between ruled lines line up. This unit of length we shall call the length unit for lines (on a ruled pad), or the lul$^\sim$. Then number the lines to make a length scale about four sheets of paper long, or about 130 lul$^\sim$ long. A set of heavy marks at 0, 5, 10, 15, etc. lul$^\sim$, together with numbers 0, 5, 10, etc., will make it easy to read. For typical ruled paper one finds:

$$\text{¼ in.}^\sim < 1 \text{ lul}^\sim < \text{⅜ in.}^\sim$$

You can check the accuracy of the paper itself by sliding an extra sheet of paper along your scale after it is made; you will find that **no matter** where you put it, the marks **can be made** to line up within about 0.1 lul$^\sim$ in 30 lul$^\sim$. This means an accuracy of 1 part in 300 or $\frac{1}{3}$ of 1 percent, i.e., 0.33 percent, which is better than you need for this experiment. (See Sec. 5-4 on percent accuracy. If your paper is much less accurate than this, devise a way to replace or improve it.)

You can use your paper ruler like a tape measure, but it will last longer if you scotch tape it lightly at several points on a table top and transfer your measurements with a string. This can be done by (1) tying a knot in a piece of string, (2) holding this knot against K_A, (3) grasping the string with your thumbnail next to I_A, (4) moving the string to your scale, and (5) holding one end at zero and measuring the other, estimating fractions to the nearest 0.1 lul$^\sim$.

5-3 A Set of Three Series of Measurements

You are next expected to carry out a set of three series of measurements intended to establish the reciprocity law QLF 5-1 within certain limits of accuracy. The discussion and the experiment are both planned so that you should understand the meaning of experimental accuracy. This experience is planned to put you face to face with a fundamental objective reality in nature.

To do the experiment, prepare the *ECE* string as discussed in Fig. 5-2(*a*) with at least three adjustment loops, L_1, L_2, and L_3 and five plumb-lines P_1, P_2, P_3, P_4, and P_5. Mark all of these with scotch tape labels so that you won't mix them up.

Prepare three weights *A*, *B*, and *C*. The example described below used weights as follows (you may use different weights but choose identical manu- factured items for *A* and *B*, something different for *C*, and attach hooks as shown in Fig. 5-2):

Weight *A* is a 6 oz unopened pop bottle; weight *B* is another bottle of the same size and brand; weight *C* is a different object (a book the World Almanac was used); weight *D* is the assembly of *B* and *C* hanging together as one weight, i.e., $D = B + C$ (as weight object).

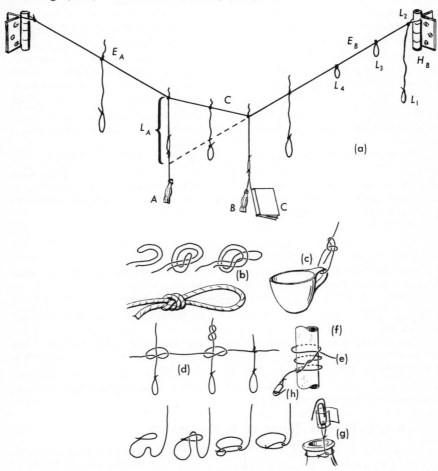

Fig. 5-2. Useful knots.

Altogether at least nine experiments are performed; for each of these, L_A and L_B are measured. The nine experiments are divided into three series. In each series the plumb-lines used or the end loops are varied so that no duplicate experiments are performed.

Outline of the Three Series

Outline of AB measurements: This series comprises three experiments using weights *A* and *B*. For each experiment, measure $L_A{}^\sim$ and $L_B{}^\sim$ and calculate $L_B^A = L_A{}^\sim/L_B{}^\sim$, and finally estimate, as explained in Sec. 5-4, the experimental accuracy in per cent for the series of three measurements.

One measurement of the first series is shown in Fig. 5-3. The figure represents weights *A* and *B* hanging from two plumb-lines, P_1 and P_3 which are called P_A and P_B for this experiment. Line *ECE* is supported from loop L_3 on hinge H_B. Further details are given in the figure legend.

Outline of AC Measurements: As before, with *C* replacing *B*.

Start of AD Measurements: Replace *C* by *D,* which is *B* and *C* hanging together as one object. *Do not do the whole series.* Instead, prove to yourself the power of prediction of QLF 5-1 as follows: Make first one measurement of $L_A{}^\sim$. *Next predict $L_D{}^\sim$ before you measure it.* If your technique is good, your prediction should miss by less than ¼ in. if $L_D{}^\sim$ is about one foot long.

The third series is deliberately interrupted to make a prediction as instructed in Sec. 5-5 to dramatize in this simple case the predictive power of orderly relationships. Your prediction of your first $L_D{}^\sim$ measurement before you make it is logically similar to putting a satellite in orbit using a two-stage rocket. The rocketeers know what stage *B* does by itself and also what second stage *C* does when shot from the ground. Now to make the space shot, they put *C* on top of *B* to make the space rocket assembly *D*. They must predict what *D* will do before they fire it. Similarly, they have predicted how jet motors would act to let Surveyor land on the moon.

In the third series you, like the rocketeers, will predict $L_D{}^\sim$ before you measure it. In your experiment you have never tried anything with the new assembly *D* made by hanging *B* and *C* together. How can you predict what $L_D{}^\sim$ will be? Your prediction as made in Sec. 5-5 should miss by less than ¼ in., provided that $L_D{}^\sim$ turns out to be less than 1 foot.

A miss of ¼ in. is terrible accuracy compared to that required for a moon shot. Why? Because ¼ in. in your experiment, when $L_D{}^\sim$ is 1 foot, is 1 part in 48 or 2 parts in 96 or practically 2%. A 2% error is satisfactory for your desk-sized demonstration, which is intended to develop concepts, but for a moon shot it would be terrible. The moon is 239,000 miles away so that 1% is 2,390 miles and 2% is 4,780 miles. Since the moon's diameter is 2,160 miles,* a 2% error would miss the whole moon by a wide margin. The importance of expressing errors in per cent is so great that we devote an entire section to it and to other advantages of the per cent concept.

Having predicted $L_D{}^\sim$ before you measure it as instructed in Sec. 5-5, you then complete the third series:

Outline of AD Measurements: Objects *A* and *D*. [D $\equiv$ B + C (in nature of objects)]. Measure $L_A{}^\sim$ and $L_D{}^\sim$ and calculate L_D^A and its accuracy.

---

* See E. G. Ebbighausen, *Astronomy*, Merrill Physical Science Series.

The check of the reciprocity law for length and weight ratios is based on the comparison of the L_D^A value with the prediction, derived in Sec. 5-5, that $L_D^A = L_B^A + L_C^A$.

First Series of Actual Measurements

Instructions for AB Measurements: This series is intended to add accuracy to your observations of Sec. 5-1 that the two lengths $L_A{}^\sim$ and $L_B{}^\sim$ **always have** a fixed ratio, **no matter** how you hang them, **but not if** certain problems arise. The law really applies only to the *idealized limiting case* shown as an insert in Fig. 5-3. Here there are only five strings, E_A, C, E_B, P_A, and P_B, and two knots K_A and K_B. The strings are assumed to be weightless and infinitely thin. Lines P_A and P_B are vertical and motionless. The knots are mathematical points. The weights are compressed into points (really their centers of gravity are represented, see Chapter 7). Perfect geometrical dotted lines extend E_A and E_B to their intersections I_B and I_A, which are idealized geometrical points. $L_A{}^\sim$ and $L_B{}^\sim$ are the straight-line lengths from point K_A to I_A and from K_B to I_B. The actual experiment attempts to approach this idealized case, but only to a certain degree of perfection. It suffers, therefore, from the limitations of all experimental science, even after the best possible work is done. One can only say that the law has been found to be **always true** only within the limits of the accuracy of measurement. The entire theory of relativity[*] could not exist if Newton's laws were absolutely true. However, the laws of vector forces that we shall develop in this chapter are thought to be **always true.**

Put A on one line and B on another with ECE hanging on a loop so selected that E_A and E_B slope down at about $45°$ from vertical. This angle leads to good accuracy. In Fig. 5-3 the plumb-lines chosen for A and B are lines P_1 and P_3 and are called P_A and P_B for the first experiment. Remember that P_3, for example, is a name-symbol with adjective-symbol "sub three" that represents one particular string. So that you can keep the correct one-to-one correspondence between name-symbols and strings throughout the experiment, label each string with ink dots, one for P_1, two for P_2, three for P_3, etc., or with scotch tape labels. Do the same with loops L_1, L_2, etc. When you enter your data in the table, record which loops and strings were used so that you can go back to the same arrangement and check any one of your experiments in case it seems to be badly out of line with others in the series.

Use the preferred *ES* method as discussed in Sec. 5-1 and Sec. 5-2 and Fig. 5-3 to locate I_A and measure $L_A{}^\sim$ and enter the value in a table like that shown below. Repeat for I_B and $L_B{}^\sim$.

It does not matter if P_B has splices in it provided you can locate I_B accurately and measure $L_B{}^\sim$ from K_B and I_B. The following table is a record of an actual experiment. Notice that adjacent plumb-lines are not used. The reason is that the lengths $L_A{}^\sim$ and $L_B{}^\sim$ are larger when more distant lines are used and this decreases the importance of errors made in placing I_A or I_B and measuring $L_A{}^\sim$ or $L_B{}^\sim$. On the other hand, if you pick the lines too far apart, the E_S strings may reach the floor before they intersect P_A or P_B. You

---

[*] See Isaac Maleh, *op. cit.*

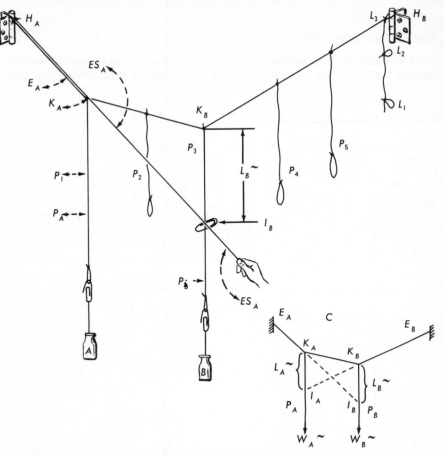

Fig. 5-3. This figure illustrates both techniques and concepts involved in the measurements of the three series. The small insert represents an idealized limiting case with the strings thought of as geometrical straight lines, the knots as points, etc. The symbols in the insert and in the more realistic diagram can be understood by noting the one-to-one correspondence between name-symbols, the quantity-symbol $L_B{}^\sim$, and features of the diagram and the corresponding words in the following description. Loop L_3 of the string *ECE* (see "making the *H*" under experimental technique hints for *ECE*) is attached to support H_B. If a hinge is not available to slip loop L_3 over, devise a hook with a coat hanger, or a loop of string you can fasten to L_3 with a pencil, or some other way to attach L_3 so that it can be easily taken off and put back. Objects *A* and *B* are hung from plumb lines P_1 and P_3. Extrapolation string ES_A is pulled straight and held parallel to E_A. Although ES_A is parallel to E_A, it is not an accurate extrapolation of E_A because it is pushed above E_A by the two knots at H_A getting in each other's way. To correct for this error in position of ES_A, imagine where the idealized perfect ES_A would go and put your real or conceptual I_B at the corrected place, i.e., the same distance below the real ES_A as knot K_A is below ES_A. Actual measurement of the length $L_B{}^\sim$ is only suggested on the diagram. The measurement string is actually held so that its knot is against K_B and is grasped so that a thumbnail marks the lower part of the string at I_B. Then the string is transferred to a table and held against a scale to measure $L_B{}^\sim$ in lul$^\sim$.

must find the best combinations by trial and error, or by analysis if you are so inclined. In some cases it may work out best to use adjacent strings.

Loop Used on E_B	Plumb-Line Used		NSU in lul		$L_B^A = L_A/L_B$
	for P_A	for P_B	L_A	L_B	
L_3	P_1	P_4	88.9	89.1	0.998
L_3	P_1	P_3	60.3	60.5	0.997
L_3	P_2	P_4	56.2	56.8	0.989

The values of L_B^A can be calculated by long division. However, when two numbers are nearly equal, the use of percentages as discussed in Sec. 5-4 can save a lot of work and reduce the probability of pencil and paper errors. Percentages are also the usual way of describing experimental accuracy. Section 5-4 will discuss accuracy and per cent accuracy as applied to the table of values for the *AB* measurements.

5-4   Result of AB Series, Accuracy, and Per Cent Accuracy

The three values of L_B^A obtained by measurements in the *AB* series are all different. Different measured values are inevitably found when accurate measurements are made. This feature is an important difference between measurement and counting. (See part 4 of *The Logical Structure of Weight Measurement* in Sec. 3-8, and discussions following QLF 3-1 and Eq. (3-27) with respect to counting and measuring.)

The basic problem in experimental accuracy is this: Something is measured which is thought to be an invariant attribute of nature. You expect to get the same value every time. But you do not. Your values scatter. They have a spread in values from lowest to highest. What can you conclude? The theories of probability and of mathematical statistics have been developed for the purpose of analyzing such a situation. These theories would require far too much space to explain here. We need, however, to cope with the reality that our measurements do scatter.

What we want from our measurement is a best guess of what we would have obtained and an estimate of how much we may have missed by. For our series of three measurements we shall use a very crude approximation.

Our best guess is the average of our three readings. This may be calculated in a hard way by averaging all of the numbers or by an easier way of finding how much bigger they are than 0.990 on the average and adding that to 0.990:

Hard way	Easy way (difference from 0.990)
0.998	8
0.997	7
0.989	− 1
3 ⟌ 2.984	3 ⟌ 14
.9947 or 0.995	4.7 or 5 and $0.990 + 0.005 = 0.995$

Accuracy: The largest of the measured values is 0.998 and the smallest is 0.989, giving a **spread** of $0.009 = 0.998 - 0.989$. This spread gives a crude description of the **accuracy** of the measurements. We can represent the whole range of values obtained by using the mathematical operation-symbol $\pm$. Consider 0.9935 ± 0.0045, where 0.0045 is half the spread; this expression means all values between $0.9935 + 0.0045$ and $0.9935 - 0.0045$, a range covering precisely the entire range of values. Because the average value is a more reasonable best guess for the real value, we represent the result of the series of three values by

$$L_B^A = 0.995 \pm 0.005 \quad \text{(in number size)}$$

in which we have rounded off the **half-spread** to a one significant figure-number by replacing 45 by 50 (the 0 does not count as a significant figure here). We shall for simplicity refer to 0.005 as the estimated experimental accuracy, or **accuracy** for short. From probability theory, we guess that the true value has about an even chance of lying between 1.000 and 0.990. However, we would not be very much surprised if we missed by twice the accuracy, or 0.010. But if we missed by, for example, five times the accuracy, or 0.025, and found 1.020, we should be worried and should search for possible reasons and do the experiment again.

Accuracy is most appropriately expressed in per cent. The 0.005 is 0.5% of 0.995 so that we can write

$$L_B^A = 0.995 \pm 0.005 = 0.995 \pm 0.5\% \quad \text{(in number size)}$$

Per cent is such a useful concept that we review it briefly below:

Per cent: Suppose that a \$100 dress or suit is reduced 10% at a sale. Then it costs \$90. Here is how the calculation goes. One per cent of any quantity or of any arithmetic number is one one-hundredth part of it. If you divide \$100 into one hundred parts, you get \$1. *You can always divide by 100 by moving the decimal point two places to the left.* If the dress had cost \$78.50, one per cent would be \$0.785. Suppose that the \$78.50 dress were reduced to \$70.00, a reduction of \$8.50. How many per cent reduction is this? This is the same as asking how many times bigger is \$8.50 than 1%, which is \$0.785. The ratio is a pure number:

$8.50 \div \$0.785 = 10.8$, or 11 rounded off to two significant figures

We can express this result and a number of other examples as follows:

> \$70 is 11% of \$78.50 less than \$78.50
> \$89 is 11% of \$100 less than \$100
> \$200 is 10% of \$200 more than \$180
> \$200 is 11% of \$180 more than \$180
> \$1000 is 50% of \$1000 more than \$500
> \$1000 is 100% of \$500 more than \$500
> 0.00604 is 1% of (either the 0.0604 or the 0.00610) less than 0.00610

What these examples show is that a 10% decrease from a big number to a smaller one is the same as a 11% increase from the smaller to the larger. For purposes of discussing scientific accuracy, you almost never care whether the accuracy is 10% or 11%. You would usually just call it 10%. You would take the same attitude about the dress. A 10% reduction is \$7.85 instead of \$8.50 for 11%. The 65¢ difference is not as important as the \$8.00 part which is about the same.

These considerations lead to a rule: *If two numbers, or quantities, are nearly equal (within 10%) find the per cent differences between them as follows: First, find 1% of either number by moving the decimal point over two places to the left. Second, find the difference between the two numbers. Third, divide the difference by the 1% value. The resulting quotient, a pure number, is the per cent difference.*

Percentage difference is very important because it has an invariant property. For example, suppose you had a car that is 12 ft long and a garage that is 11 ft long. The car is 9.9% of the garage longer than the garage. If you measure both in inches, you get 144 in. and 132 in. and the difference of 12 in. is again 9% of 132 in. What this example shows is that the car is 9% of the garage length longer than the garage **no matter** *what length unit is used for measuring both.* This is an example of

	QLF 5-3 The Invariance of Percentage Difference
WHAT	It is **always true** that the percentage difference between two quantities has the same value,
WHEN	**no matter** whether the quantities are prices of two items measured in dollars or the same two items measured in cents (which makes all the numbers 100 times bigger), or if they are two distances both expressed in NSU for feet one time and both NSU for inches another time,
WHEN NOT	**but not if** the per cent difference is so large that you make a mistake and calculate on the basis of 1% from the bigger number one time and the smaller one another time.

The invariance of percentage differences to the effects of changes of standard units in the NSU values is one of the reasons that percentage accuracy is the key attribute of accuracy to keep in focus when you evaluate your experiments.

Thinking in terms of percentages also helps in calculations. Specifically, the three sets of L_A and L_B values of the AB series can be treated by per cent as follows:

L_A	L_B	$L_A - L_B$	1% of L_A (or L_B)	% Difference of L_A from L_B	L_B^A
88.9	89.1	−0.2	0.9	−0.2	0.998
60.3	60.5	−0.2	0.6	−0.3	0.997
56.2	56.8	−0.6	0.6	−1.0	0.990

This shows that per cent calculations (using only one significant figure) accomplish exactly what long division did for this case where the two numbers are nearly equal.

5-5   A Prediction as a Theorem; Its Test by the AD Series of Measurements

The AC series of measurements resulted in the values given in the following table:

Loop Used on E_B	Plumb-Line Used		NSU in lul~		$L_C^A = L_A/L_C$
	for P_A	for P_C	L_A	L_C	
L_3	P_2	P_4	61.9	51.4	1.204
L_3	P_1	P_4	95.2	79.6	1.195
L_3	P_1	P_3	48.9	40.2	1.216

Since L_A and L_C differ by more than 10%, the short method of calculating L_C^A is not applicable and long division is used to obtain the L_C^A values. The spread of the L_C^A values is 0.021 and the average value is 1.205. Consequently we represent the best guess for L_C^A and its accuracy as

$$L_C^A = 1.205 \pm 0.011 = 1.205 \pm 0.9\%$$

This value for L_B^A can be combined with L_C^A to make a **prediction.**

The *prediction* we shall make is that if the new object D, which has never existed before and consists of B and C hanging together as a single unit, is put on a plumb line and then $L_A{}^\sim$ is measured, the as yet unmeasured $L_D{}^\sim$ will be found to be (within our limits of accuracy) as predicted by the qualified-equation:

$$L_D{}^\sim = \frac{L_A{}^\sim}{L_B^A + L_C^A} \quad \text{(in length)}$$

In this prediction we should use our best guess for the value of $L_B^A + L_C^A$; this best guess is

$$L_B^A + L_C^A = 0.995 + 1.205 = 2.200$$

In our actual experiment with A on P_1 and D on P_4, a value of 113.1 was obtained for L_A (in number of lul$^\sim$). Accordingly, the prediction for $L_D{}^\sim$ is

$$L_D = \frac{113.1}{2.200} = 51.3 \quad \text{(in number of lul}^\sim)$$

The actual measured value was 52.0, which differs by less than 1 lul$^\sim$ from the prediction or an error of 1 part in 52 or about 2%. This is satisfactory accuracy for the desk-sized home experiments. Now, on what logical relationship is the prediction based?

The prediction is a theorem derived on the basis of two postulates: Postulate 1 is the QLF 3-5 law of conservation of weight, and Postulate 2 is QLF 5-1, the reciprocity law of length and weight ratios. We reason as follows:

$W_A{}^\sim$ is the weight of bottle A—call it your standard unit of weight or the wub$^\sim$. (wua$^\sim$ with a to go with A might be confused with wua$^\sim$ of Sec. 3-6).

$W_B{}^\sim$ is the weight of bottle B (within a few per cent of 1.00 wub$^\sim$)

$W_C{}^\sim$ is the weight of object C (actually a *World Almanac* in the data above)

$W_D{}^\sim = W_{B+C}{}^\sim$ is the weight of objects B and C combined

From Postulate 1 we conclude that

$$W_D{}^\sim = W_B{}^\sim + W_C{}^\sim \quad \text{(in weight)}$$

From Postulate 2 and the definition of NSU values (in number of wub$^\sim$):

$$L_B^A = L_A/L_B = W_B{}^\sim/W_A{}^\sim = W_B \quad \text{(in number of wub}^\sim)$$
$$L_C^A = L_A/L_C = W_C{}^\sim/W_A{}^\sim = W_C \quad \text{(in number of wub}^\sim)$$
$$L_D^A = L_A/L_D = (W_B{}^\sim + W_C{}^\sim)/W_A{}^\sim = W_B + W_C \quad \text{(in number of wub}^\sim)$$

The last equation contains a prediction: Simply substitute equals for equals as follows: For W_B use L_B^A, and for W_C use L_C^A; then the equation becomes

$$L_D^A = L_B^A + L_C^A \quad \text{(in number size)}$$

This prediction leads to a predicted value $L_{D_p}^A$ (subscript p for predicted) of $0.995 = 1.205 = 2.200$ for the best guess and $\pm 0.005 \pm 0.011 = \pm 0.016$

for the accuracy, this last expression corresponding to the least accurate situation in which the errors add. These values lead to

$$L_{Dp}^A = 2.200 \pm 0.016 = 2.20 \pm 0.02 = 2.20 \pm 1\%$$

The last two expressions are obtained by rounding off so that the number of significant figures is in keeping with the accuracy.

On the basis of these comparisons between key attributes of our experimental situation, we are now in a position to give the reciprocity law a serious experimental test. The check of the first prediction of $L_D{}^\sim$ discussed above was encouraging; but perhaps some chance circumstance or a chance error produced the encouraging agreement. What we should do next is to take an extended series of measurements, the third series, and ascertain whether the series as a whole leads to a measured L_{Dm}^A value that does agree with the L_{Dp}^A prediction, taking into account what we know about the limited accuracy of our experiments.

Test of the prediction by the third series of measurements: Hang *B* and *C* together as a new object *D* from one plumb line and hang *A* from another. The series of measurements, shown below, includes the first pair of values discussed above in the prediction.

Loop Used on E_B	Plumb-Lines Used		NSU in wub$^\sim$		$L_D^A = L_A/L_D$
	for L_A	for L_D	L_A	L_D	
L_3	P_1	P_4	113.1	52.0	2.175
L_3	P_1	P_3	55.5	25.3	2.154
L_2	P_1	P_3	65.0	29.5	2.203

This table leads to a measured value L_{Dm}^A (subscript *m* for measured), consisting of an average value and an accuracy as follows:

$$L_{Dm}^A = 2.174 \pm 0.025 = 2.17 \pm 0.03 = 2.17 \pm 1.3\%$$

where the numbers have been rounded off in keeping with the accuracy. This measured value overlaps the prediction that $L_{Dp}^A = 2.20 \pm 0.02$. *In other words, 2.17 and 2.20 are equal within experimental accuracy. Consequently, we are justified in concluding that the prediction that $L_D^A = L_B^A + L_C^A$ is confirmed within experimental accuracy of approximately 2%.* (The 2% is an approximate combination of 1% and 1.3%.). *No laws of science can say more (except QLF 3-2). Other laws can, however, make such statements not with 2% accuracy, but with 0.000,000,002% accuracy, or even more precisely.*

The theory of errors is a branch of mathematics which has postulates and theorems useful for estimating whether or not failure of an experiment to agree perfectly with a prediction means that something is wrong with the theory of the prediction. (It explains how to combine the 1% and 1.3% to get about 1.7%.) This is a more advanced subject than is appropriate here.

What our three sets of experiments show is (1) that the three values, one each for L_B^A, L_C^B, and L_D^A, check the prediction

$$L_D^A = L_B^A + L_C^A$$

with an accuracy of about 2%, and (2) that the experimental values are also obtained with an accuracy of about 2%. To sum up, we have checked the prediction *within the limits of our experimental accuracy*, namely about 2%. Actually, our results are between 1% and 2%; *scientific caution calls for overestimating errors* rather than underestimating them. An accuracy of 2% should be adequate to convince you that QLF 5-1 is true to a very practical degree of accuracy. If you wished, you could replace your relatively thick string by steel piano wire and measure length on a meter stick and check QLF 5-1 to ½%. But 2% is a sensible place to stop in a course in physical science.

Experiments of your own invention: Now what we advise *you* to do is to try some new weights of *your own* choosing. Replace B by a book B' and C by a cantaloup C' or a cabbage or choose your own object and symbols and measure $(L_B^A)'$ and $(L_C^A)'$ for the new B' and C' and see if you find that once more

$$[L_{(B'+C')}^A]' = L_{B'}^A + L_{C'}^A$$

Still another experiment you can try is to ask a friend to take two paper bags, then in one of these put one to three bottles and put a different number also from one to three in the other. Then ask him to hang the two bags from two plumb lines. Don't look while he does this. Then you can find out how many bottles are in each bag without lifting or even touching either one. Just measure the two L's and compute the ratios. Here are all the possible cases:

No. of bottles in $A = 1$	1	2	2	3	3
No. of bottles in $B = 2$	3	1	3	1	2
$L_A/L_B = 2$	3	0.5	1.5	0.33	0.67

Compare your measured L_A/L_B ratio with these. It is **always true** that your measured ratio should come very close to one of these values, **no matter** which one your friend has selected, **but not if** he has cheated or the paper bags are very heavy. Remember, the larger number of bottles will be on the plumb line with the shorter L.

Now your logical position in regard to QLF 5-1 is like that of the man who knows that the second player always wins in take 1 or 4 in Sec. 2-3, or that you can't solve the two-king problem of Sec. 1-3, or that $M = P - 1$ in Sec. 2-6 of the tennis tournament puzzle. You are now faced with the question: What basic postulates underlie the law of reciprocity of length and weight ratios? Or is this law itself so fundamental that you need not try to "explain" it in terms of more basic ideas?

In this chapter we shall show that QLF 5-1 is a theorem from the more *basic law that the sum of the* **vector forces** *on a knot is zero when static equilibrium prevails.* But first we shall discuss what explanations in science mean in Sec. 5-6.

5-6   What Are Forces, Vectors, and Explanations?

What are vectors? "A quantity which is fully specified when and only when there are given its magnitude and an associated direction in space;

e.g., a velocity, a magnetic intensity."* "1. a line conceived as having both length and direction; 2. a quantity or magnitude capable of being represented by such a line as velocity or a force; . . ."†

One of the most effective ways of thinking about vectors is to represent them by arrows on a sheet of graph paper or any other paper with squares. So far as the conaddian aspects of vector forces are concerned, our desk-sized, string-bottle experiments will show you in this chapter that there are a set of one-to-one correspondences *between the way the arrows on paper can be added together and the way tension forces combine in the real world of strings and hanging weights.* Each arrow on the sheet of paper plays a role that has a one-to-one correspondence with the invisible tension forces in the string—conaddians that we can never see directly. We can, however, be sure that forces are really present in the strings because we can detect their presence and even measure them with tension gauges (Secs. 4-3 and 5-9). We shall refer to the arrows on paper that represent the forces (these are a form of diagrammatic symbol) as **proxies** because they play a role on paper, much as does the signed proxy of an absent stockholder at a corportation meeting. In both cases the proxy faithfully represents the absent reality for which it acts.

But what is a force? Dictionaries say that a force is "that which tends to produce motion, or a change of motion in a body." But in statics we have no motion. What we have shown in Chapter 4 is that up-forces are conaddians, in fact, $\pm$ or algebraic conaddians. We have been led by experiments to the concept of force as an invariant attribute of nature with conservative and additive properties. This concept combines with the action-reaction law to form logical structures that explain observable facts about the real world of our experiments. In the sense that the concept produces orderly explanations of observable facts in statics, we can say that force *is* a conaddian.

Two very general comments should be made about forces at this point. One has to do with their *prevalence*, the other with their *real nature*.

Static forces are all around us. Tension is present in guy wires that hold up telephone and power poles. The legs of chairs and tables have compression forces. Hanging lamps produce tensions in their wires. The cables of suspension bridges are under tension and curve upwards like the *ECE* lines of Figs. 6-1, 6-2, and 6-3 to hold up the load of the roadway that hangs below, as do weights A and B, or C, or C and D. Forces are indeed prevalent. But what are they really?

The explanation of this book that forces are conaddians may seem unsatisfactory. You may ask: "This is all very well; you have told us what forces do, how to calculate with them and to make predictions using them, but we still do not know *what* they *are. What are they, really?*" Science has no further answer to this question. It is true that the scientific theories, particularly those of modern physics, chemistry, electricity and magnetism,‡ let us understand how the forces we measure with elastically deformed springs or

---

* LeRoy D. Weld, *Glossary of Physics* (New York: McGraw-Hill Book Co., 1937).
† *The Winston Dictionary, College Edition* (New York: Holt, Rinehart and Winston, Inc., 1947).
‡ See other books in the Merrill Physical Science Series.

stretched rubber bands arise as a consequence of quantum-mechanical laws about electrons, protons, neutrons, and other strange nuclear particles. But this "explanation" only pushes the problem of what a force really is into a realm of more abstract mathematical symbolism. This abstract symbolism is worthy of great respect; it does have wonderful powers. Its predictions have created atom bombs, nuclear power plants, and transistors; all these since 1940. But is *this* any "explanation" of nature?

The power of science to permit the making of reliable predictions is one of its greatest contributions. It transcends the "explanations" demanded by mystics. When it can order a complex, chaotic, puzzling situation with a handful of concepts showing how conaddians fit into QLF's, it has produced the orderly relationships about nature that are its prime purpose. This purpose should be contrasted with the practice of science by scientists. This is another matter entirely. Scientists are people who are fascinated by science's challenges. They like to talk about it. They form large societies such as the American Physical Society which holds meetings all over the United States about ten times a year. For them the practice of science is a rewarding way of life.

But to return to the subject of explanations, in the preceding paragraphs we have been analyzing what we really mean when we think about explanations in science. This is an introspective process: we look at our own thinking procedures. *Introspective analysis,* as discussed later in Sec. 6-4, is one of the very powerful thinking tools. It helps to keep your mind on the track. In the case of forces, it should keep you from wasting time during a physical sciences course by looking for a fundamental explanation of what force is. Primitive man did look for what he felt were really fundamental explanations. Greek mythology had them. The god Thor pounding with his hammer was the explanation of thunder storms; this is a satisfyingly simple explanation, but it does not enable one to make any predictions about the noises in a radio set produced by the electrical currents (carried by electrons in the ionized atmosphere*) that discharge the electricity in a cloud.

To sum up: *Science brings orderly relationships into the observations of nature by setting up compact systems of concepts that have one-to-one correspondences with objective reality.* This is what it does to explain nature. Physical science is a great body of useful one-to-one correspondences.

In the above sense vectors explain forces. In the next section the authors of this book will explain vectors by setting up one-to-one correspondences between them and concepts already familiar to you of taking trips in Square City.

5-7   *Vectors, Vector Addition, and Resultant Vector*

A displacement vector, as used in physical science, it a quantitative invariant attribute of nature associated with *two points in space*, for example the corner of a room and the tip of a coat hanger hanging from a door knob, see $\vec{R}$ in Fig. 3-2(b).

Similarly, a mathematical vector is an invariant attribute of the relation-

---

* See Albert Miller, *Meteorology*, Merrill Physical Science Series.

ship of two points on a sheet of graph paper or in imaginary mathematical space (especially the three-dimensional space of Descartes in Fig. 3-2.

What this attribute is can be seen on a diagram more easily than it can be said in words. Figure 5-4(a) illustrates **displacement vectors,** or **vector lengths,** which are conaddians and are similar to quantity-symbols. Figure 5-4(b) shows mathematical vectors which are like number-symbols, being either vector pure numbers or vector NSU numbers.

The vector concept must be abstracted from many other attributes of the situation shown in Fig. 5-4. Part (a) shows Square City, which has blocks 1000 feet long. (This will be our SU of length, the block length or lub~.) The streets are schematically represented as lines. Six rides, which you should imagine that you take are represented by broad lines with arrows: solid lines for taxi rides, dashed lines for helicopter flights. The thin, solid lines are the vectors.

A vector is the invariant relationship between two points represented by a line having direction and length. All the $\vec{D}$~ symbols in part (a) are vector length symbols; they are one example of vector-quantity-symbols. The thin, straight line arrows on Fig. 5-4 are proxies on the paper map for real vector lengths in (imaginary) Square City.

When are two vectors equal? Answer: When they produce the same displacement. Examples of vector equalities are

$$\vec{D}_1\text{~} = \vec{D}_4\text{~} \quad \text{(in vector length)}$$

Vectors $\vec{D}_1$~ and $\vec{D}_4$~ are equal vectors because both produce the same motion; both transport you to an end point (at the arrowhead) that is two blocks east and one block north of where you start (at the dot on the vector). Similarly, if we let $\vec{D}_5$~ (not shown on the diagram) correspond to the H_5 trip, we can write

$$\vec{D}_5\text{~} = \vec{D}_6\text{~} = \vec{D}_4\text{~} = \vec{D}_1\text{~} \quad \text{(in vector length)}$$

What this series of equations means is that each of these vectors produces the same east displacement as the others and also the same north displacements. These east and north displacements are called the *east* **component** and *north* **component** of the vector.

To make this vector equality more vivid, consider what would happen if there were a straight steel I-beam for each vector, starting at the location of the dot and ending at the arrowhead. Then a derrick could pick up any one of the four I-beams and move it to any other I-beam and set it down and the two would fit perfectly on top of each other. Furthermore, the derrick driver could keep the I-beam pointing in exactly the same north-easterly direction all the time while he moved it. He would not have to turn or rotate the beam at all. Such a parallel motion of an object is called a **translation** to distinguish it from **rotation.** In vector symbolism, *two vectors are said to be equal in vector length if you can match them by translation.* This is what the equation-qualifier "(in vector length)" means in a qualified equation for vectors.

The concept of a **resultant vector,** or **vector sum,** is essential to using

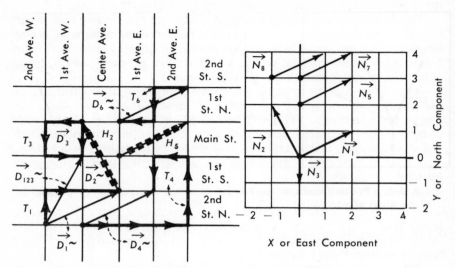

Fig. 5-4. **Vector displacements as the key attribute of taxi and helicopter rides.**

vectors in physical science. We shall illustrate it with journey J_{123} which is accomplished by taking trips T_1, H_2, and T_3 in that order. This journey starts at the intersection of 2nd Avenue W. and 2nd St. S. and consists of three successive rides: Taxi ride T_1 goes one block north and then two blocks east; next helicopter ride H_2 goes from Center Avenue and 1st St. S. on a straight line to 1st Avenue W. and 1st St. N.; finally T_3, the round-about taxi ride goes one block west, then one south, then one east. The journey ends at 1st Avenue W. and Main Street. As a journey, J_{123} is very inefficient because it travels six blocks by taxi and more than two by helicopter but it ends only a little more than two blocks from where it started. The total displacement produced by J_{123} is the arrow $\vec{D}_{123}$ from 2nd Avenue W. and 2nd Street S. to 1st Avenue W. and Main Street. This arrow corresponds to the vector length symbol $\vec{D}_{123}\text{\textasciitilde}$. This arrow in Fig. 5-4 on the paper page of the book is a **proxy** for a real displacement more than two blocks long in the (imaginary) Square City.

The *resultant vector* $\vec{D}_{123}\text{\textasciitilde}$ is the vector sum of $\vec{D}_1\text{\textasciitilde}$, $\vec{D}_2\text{\textasciitilde}$, and $\vec{D}_3\text{\textasciitilde}$ in accordance with the rules for **vector addition.** These rules, as we shall explain, correspond correctly to the net effect produced by J_{123}. The rule of operation for adding vectors as shown in Fig. 5-5 is as follows: Pick an **arbitrary zero** marked $\times$ as a starting point and "zero" the vector $\vec{D}_1\text{\textasciitilde}$ by putting its dot end on the starting point. Next put the dot end of $\vec{D}_2\text{\textasciitilde}$ on the arrowhead of $\vec{D}_1\text{\textasciitilde}$ (this adds the two displacements together); then put the

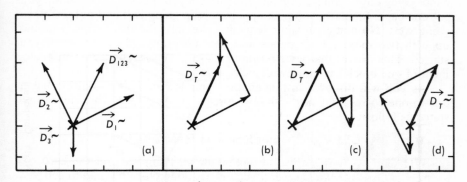

Fig. 5-5. The resultant sum, $\vec{D_T}\sim = \vec{D}_{123}\sim$, of three vectors is independent of the order of addition.

dot of $\vec{D_3}\sim$ on the arrowhead of $\vec{D_2}$. Part (a) shows the four vectors in zeroed positions. Part (b) shows the vector sum $\vec{D_1}\sim + \vec{D_2}\sim + \vec{D_3}\sim$. They add up to $\vec{D}_{123}\sim$. This is really not a surprise; it is a consequence of the definition of $\vec{D}_{123}\sim$ in terms of J_{123}. Now comes the useful part. **No matter** how you add $\vec{D_1}\sim, \vec{D_2}\sim$, and $\vec{D_3}\sim$, it is **always true** that you get the same total vector length. This is illustrated in part (c) for addition, not in the 123 order, but in the order 132, and again in part (d) for 321. In the form of an equation these results for the total vector or vector sum $\vec{D_T}$ can be expressed as follows:

$$\vec{D}_{123}\sim = \vec{D_1}\sim + \vec{D_2}\sim + \vec{D_3}\sim = \vec{D_2}\sim + \vec{D_1}\sim + \vec{D_3}\sim = \vec{D}_{213}, \text{ etc.}$$

(in vector length)

To grasp this principle, take action, use pencil and paper, try these simple cases of adding these three vectors in still other orders. Then you will acquire the necessary familiarity with the key attributes of vector addition to appreciate the simplicity of the reason why vectors add this way. If you don't have graph paper, but do have a pad of ruled paper, you can make adequately accurate graph paper by folding one sheet the long way and using the fold as a ruler both for measuring off the second set of lines and for drawing them.

As the above analysis shows, vectors satisfy the **commutative law** that says the value of the sum does not depend on the order of adding. Fundamentally, this result is a consequence of QLF 3-1, the law of conservation of objects. QLF 3-1 can be used as a postulate in a proof by carrying out a conceptual experiment as follows: Suppose that you make all the trips of J_{123} on foot walking the streets: replace H_2 by going two blocks north and then one block west. Suppose also that there is a pile of paperclips in the middle of each block on an east-west street and a pile of rubber bands in the middle of each block on a north-south avenue. You start with a few paperclips and rubber bands in your pocket. Every time you pass a pile of rubber bands going north, you pick up one and put it in your pocket; going south, you put one back. Similarly you pick up a paperclip going east and put one back going west. No matter in what sequence you take the three trips, you end up with two more rubber bands and one more paperclip than when you started. This proves that your *resultant* journey must amount to a displacement of one block east and two blocks north.

As you will discover in this chapter, this law of vector addition has a one-to-one correspondence with how forces act. As a QLF, this law can be stated as follows:

QLF 5-4   Vector Resultant Invariance Law

WHAT	It is **always true** that the resultant vector is the same when several vectors are added together end to end,
WHEN	**no matter** the order of addition or the kind of vectors, such as vector lengths or vector number sizes,
WHEN NOT	**but not if** general relativity effects are involved in real space* and not simply arrows on graph paper.

From the foregoing discussion, it is clear that vector displacements in Square City are conaddians. No matter how you divide up a journey into trips, if you add together all the trip vectors you get the journey vector. We have discussed only whole block journeys, but we could run alleys through the middle of the blocks or for that matter, change from Square City to the grid of a football field. Furthermore, vectors need not be restricted to a plane. We could equally well consider Cube Office Building in which we would go up and down stairs, elevators or escalators as well as north-south, and east-west.

Just as there are quantity-symbols and number-symbols, there are vector-quantity-symbols and vector-number-symbols. The NSU vectors (in numbers of lub~) or city block units are shown in part (b) of Fig. 5-4. They are related to the displacements of part (a) by having corresponding subscripts. The relationship may be clarified by checking the following observations:

$$\vec{H}_5 = \vec{N}_5 \sim \text{lub} \sim \quad \text{(in vector length)}$$

This equation relates two vectors that correspond perfectly when we associate the Main-Center intersection of (a) with the origin, or $x = 0$, $y = 0$ point, of (b). This is not a necessary condition for vector equality: The I-beam description of vector equality shows that the following eight vectors are equal.

$$\vec{D}_1 \sim = \vec{D}_4 \sim = \vec{D}_5 \sim = \vec{D}_6 \sim = \vec{N}_1 \, \text{lub} \sim$$

$$= \vec{N}_5 \, \text{lub} \sim = \vec{N}_7 \, \text{lub} \sim = \vec{N}_8 \, \text{lub} \sim \quad \text{(in vector length)}$$

There is clearly something special about the position of the three vectors $\vec{N}_1$, $\vec{N}_2$, and $\vec{N}_3$ in part (b). We call them *zeroed vectors*. They start at the

---

* See Isaac Maleh, *op. cit.*, Sec. 8-3.

zero point of *origin* in the graph paper. The other vectors $\vec{N}_5$, $\vec{N}_7$, and $\vec{N}_8$ are equal to $\vec{N}_1$ and can be zeroed by translating them like the steel I-beam also. Equality of vector-numbers have the equation-qualifier (in vector-number size).

In the next section we set up the one-to-one correspondence of vectors and forces and derive QLF 5-1, the reciprocity law of length and weight ratios, from the postulate QLF 5-5, force is a vector conaddian.

5-8   Force Is a Vector Conaddian

Here is the QLF which we take as a postulate. It fits all of our observations. We shall use it to derive QLF 5-1 on reciprocity of length and weight ratios as a theorem:

QLF 5-5 Force is a Vector Conaddian; Vector Force Concept	
WHAT	It is **always true** that the observable effects of forces are correctly predicted by setting up one-to-one correspondences between directions and magnitudes of forces and conceptual vectors acting as their substitutes or proxies on paper or in equations,
WHEN	**no matter** whether the forces are produced by the pull of gravity, tensions in strings or other contact forces, and no matter how many forces are involved or what directions they have,
WHEN NOT	**but not if** something is overlooked, such as radiation pressure due to light.

We shall also need the vector version of the QLF 4-2:

QLF 5-6   The Zero Vector Force Law of Statics

Since this law differs from QLF 4-2 only in replacing up-forces by vector forces in general, we shall not take space to state it completely here.

Let us now apply these vector force concepts to the *H* experiment of Figs. 5-1, 5-2, and 5-3. We assume that each string has a tension like the tension of Sec. 4-3. Now focus your attention on one of the least striking parts of the *ECE* string: knot K_A. This knot has three forces pulling on it. The symbols for these have adjective subscripts that identify the string: $\vec{F}_{EA}{}^\sim$, $\vec{F}_A{}^\sim$ and $\vec{F}_{AC}{}^\sim$. Each of these forces is represented according to QLF 5-5 by an arrow in Fig. 5-6. As remarked in Sec. 5-6, these arrows act on paper as proxies for the invisible tension forces in the string.

As for the trips that add to give $D_{123}{}^\sim$ shown in Fig. 5-5, we compute the total or resultant force by adding the vectors end to end from a "zero" starting point shown as an $\times$. There are actually six possible sequences for adding the three vectors of Fig. 5-6. All of them add to the same resultant vector. In keeping with the zero total force law of statics, this resultant vector must be zero. This is the situation shown in Fig. 5-6 with the six possible sequences indicated in the parentheses.

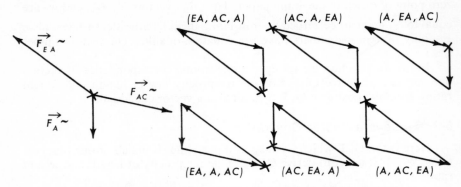

Fig. 5-6.   The zero total force law of statics applied to knot K_A.

Now what do we know about the size of any of the vectors in Fig. 5-6? If weight A is 1 wub~, as represented in Fig. 5-7, then the vertical down-force in Fig. 5-6 must correspond to a magnitude of 1 wub~. By the nature of vectors, all the corresponding lines in the six triangles are parallel and all the corresponding angles are equal. Consequently, if we take any one of the triangles on the graph paper that Fig. 5-6 represents, we can determine the magnitude of the other forces by comparing the lengths of the sides with the $\vec{F}_A$~ side which represents 1 wub~. One side corresponding to $\vec{F}_{AC}$~ represents the effect of the tension in C upon knot K_A. We shall use the reasoning of Sec. 4-3 to discuss this tension. In the symbolism* of Fig. 4-7 this force would be denoted $\vec{F}_{KA\,by\,C}$~. The action-reaction law QLF 4-1 and the invariant tension law QLF 4-3 can be applied to the forces at both ends of C to show that

$$\vec{F}_{AC}\text{~} \equiv \vec{F}_{KA\,by\,C}\text{~} \equiv -\vec{F}_{KB\,by\,C}\text{~} \equiv -\vec{F}_{BC}\text{~} \quad \text{(in vector force)}$$

where we have shown the relationship of the simpler adjective symbols to those like Sec. 4-3 by identity signs.

The objective of this section is to prove that QLF 5-1, the reciprocity law of length and weight ratios, is a theorem derivable from QLF 5-5, that force is a vector conaddian, and QLF 5-6, the zero vector force law of statics. The geometrical constructions needed for the proof are presented in Fig. 5-7. Here the *ECE* string and objects A and B are shown in (a). In this case we let object B consist of two bottles weighing 2 wub~. In accordance with the vector force concept and the zero force law, the sums of the three forces shown in parts (b) and (c) of the figure must both be zero. They must make closed triangles like Fig. 5-6. The triangles selected both start with the forces produced by the tension in C. As discussed above, $\vec{F}_{AC}$~ and $\vec{F}_{BC}$~ are equal and opposite. A consequence of this relationship is that if parts

---

* We deviate slightly and use the adjective-symbol KA instead of K_A for a practical reason: Subscripts to subscripts are inconveniently small to print and to read. This is an example of a **but not if** situation for the principle that symbols should have precise meanings. Another **but not if** is the mistake of C for bottle C and segment C.

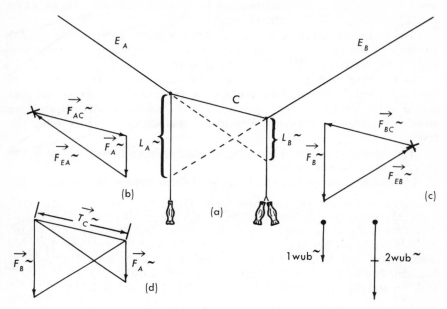

Fig. 5-7. The proof of the reciprocity law of length and weight ratios.

(b) and (c) were made of metal rods, both could be picked up and moved to part (d) and put down on top of each other without having to rotate, stretch, or bend; i.e., they can be superimposed by translation like that discussed for the imaginary I-beams in Square City in Sec. 5-7. Now for the theorem.

Part (d) of Fig. 5-7 contains the reciprocity theorem as a consequence. Compare it with the string segments $L_A{}^\sim$, C, and $L_B{}^\sim$ in part (a) of the figure. The two figures (a) and (d) are similar: all the corresponding triangles have equal angles. From the theorems of geometry we know that ratios of corresponding parts of similar triangles are the same for all corresponding pairs of parts. Consequently the ratios of the vector lengths for $\vec{F}_B{}^\sim$ and $\vec{F}_A{}^\sim$ (which are simply $W_B{}^\sim$ and $W_A{}^\sim$) have a ratio that is equal to the ratio of the corresponding lengths $L_A{}^\sim$ and $L_B{}^\sim$. In equation form, this says

$$\frac{L_A{}^\sim}{L_B{}^\sim} = \frac{W_B{}^\sim}{W_A{}^\sim} \quad \text{(in number size)}$$

This equation, which involves pure number ratios, is the WHAT part of QLF 5-1, the reciprocity law of length and weight ratios.

To sum up briefly what we have done: We applied the zero total force law (QLF 5-6) to the two knots K_A and K_B and expressed the zero force requirement in terms of arrows (or proxies for the forces) on graph paper in a one-to-one correspondence with the physical reality of strings and weights. We used the invariant tension principle (QLF 4-3) to carry out comparison operations between force triangles for knot K_A and for knot K_B and established the orderly relationship between the L_B^A ratio of lengths and the W_B^A ($= W_A{}^\sim / W_B{}^\sim$) ratio of weights.

The treatment just presented is one of the simplest of all possible demonstrations of the vector nature of forces. It uses very simple apparatus and elementary geometry. *But it does have a shortcoming.*

In the proof of Fig. 5-7, *unmeasured tensions are assumed to exist* in the E_A, C, and E_B strings. Furthermore, the value of these tensions are predicted by the lengths of their proxies in Fig. 5-7. What would happen if we could measure these tensions? Would our mathematical theory stand the test?

The answer is obtained by using the rubber-band tension-gauge in the experiment of the next section.

Incidentally, the planar law QLF 5-2 is also clearly established by the reasoning of this section. The three forces $\vec{F}_{AC}{}^\sim$, $\vec{F}_A{}^\sim$, and $\vec{F}_{EA}{}^\sim$ form a triangle; therefore, they lie in a plane. Since they are parallel to the three strings that meet at K_A, these strings also lie in a plane. This shows that our postulates correctly predict both the reciprocity law and the coplanar law. No other theory can be found that will explain the reciprocity law and the coplanar law as simply as do the three physical postulates QLF's 4-3, 5-5, and 5-6 and the mathematical theorem QLF 5-4 for vector addition.

5-9   The Parallelogram of Forces and the Rubber-Band Tension-Gauge

Rubber bands are cheap and readily available elastic links for a chain as discussed in Sec. 4-3. However, they show a phenomenon called **hysteresis.** *Hysteresis* means a situation in which the effect lags behind the cause. A big cause may have an influence that lasts after the cause is removed. Rubber bands show such effects but they can be substantially reduced by prestretching the rubber bands with a **conditioning operation.** After this has been done, a rubber-band tension-gauge can be made which permits measuring tension in strings with about ±10% accuracy. If you have steel springs available, such as are called for with Fig. 3-3(a), you may prefer to use these to eliminate the hysteresis problem.

Fig. 5-8 shows such a preparation of a tension-gauge. The gauge described employs three rubber bands of 3 in. length and ⅛ in. width. Take one of these and use your two thumbs to stretch it to about 9 in. Let it pull back, and then repeat. It will stretch more easily. Take it out to about 10 in. Repeat four or five times, working out to 15 in. (Some rubber bands may not take this much without breaking. If so, scale the stretch down.) After it is worked out to 15 in., repeat about 10 times. This is the conditioning operation.

Condition three rubber bands per gauge. Then prepare a double loop length of string with 15 in. from end of loop to end of loop (within ½ in.). To make one gauge, assemble three rubber bands, the string, and two paperclips as represented in Fig. 5-8.

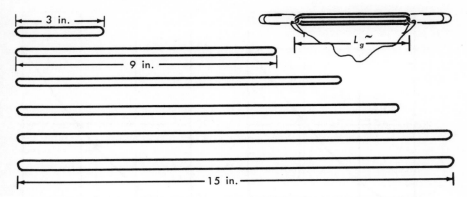

Fig. 5-8. Construction and conditioning of rubber-band tension-gauge. (Two rubber bands are represented on the paperclips; three are actually used.)

Make two of these tension-gauges, marking them No. 1 and No. 2 so they will not become mixed.

Next, calibrate the tension-gauge in terms of the $L_g{\sim}$values measured, as shown in Fig. 5-8, from end to end of the rubber bands, using known tensions in wub$\sim$: Fasten one end of the gauge high and hang one, two, and three (or more) bottles on it. Each time just before you read the length, pull the gauge out until the string is tight. This stretches the bands to 15 in. and reduces hysteresis effects. (If necessary to avoid breaking the rubber bands, shorten the string.)

Then load and unload the gauge, taking readings from end to end of the rubber band in lul$\sim$ or cm$\sim$ or in.$\sim$. Here is a typical set of data in cm for two gauges:

No. of wub$\sim$	0	1	2	3	2	1	0	3
L_{g1} cm	8.7	11.8	20.2	29.6	20.7	12.3	8.8	29.8
L_{g2} cm	8.6	11.2	18.8	29.2	19.6	12.1	8.5	30.0

The calibration data are shown plotted on Fig. 5-9; smooth curves are drawn by hand through the data. If your rubber bands are too weak or too strong or too short, put more or less together or replace single bands by chains as needed to produce a gauge that stretches about 10 in. for 3 lub$\sim$.

Next, using two supports, construct the Y configuration shown in Fig. 5-10. The string Y at the center may be made with the same knots as the *ECE* string and its plumb lines of Fig. 5-3. The string arms of the Y should be about 1 ft long so that only string is in front of the 8½ × 11 in. sheet of paper.

The experiment consists of adjusting the length of the strings and the weight of object A so that each gauge is pulled out about halfway. Before its L_g is read, each is pulled out to the end of its 15 in. string and allowed to relax while the weight object A remains on the Y. Then read and record each $L_g{\sim}$ value.

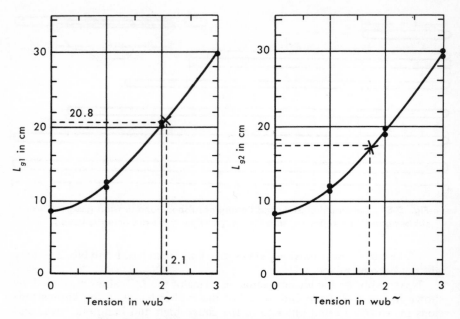

Fig. 5-9. **Calibration curves for two tension-gauges.**

Next mark the directions of the strings by putting six dashes for each string on a sheet of paper held to the Y by paperclips. These dashes are made in pairs, one dash on each side of the string as shown on Fig. 5-10(a).

Remove the paper, and draw a Y showing the force directions. This is done by putting three dots for the center of each string, i.e., one dot between each pair of dashes. Draw lines through the dots. Part (b) of the figure shows this process partly completed. (If, within experimental accuracy, the three dots of any string segment are not on a straight line, or if the three lines intersect as a triangle rather than meeting at a point, something has gone wrong. Repeat the experiment.)

Next construct a parallelogram of forces for $\vec{F_1}{}^{\sim}$ and $\vec{F_2}{}^{\sim}$ as shown in part (c). For this purpose select a convenient length, say 2 in., for 1 wub$^{\sim}$. Lay out the force vectors for $\vec{F_1}{}^{\sim}$ and $\vec{F_2}{}^{\sim}$ using the calibration curves to convert the stretched lengths L_{g1} and L_{g2} to forces. This process is represented in Fig. 5-9 for the L_{g1} value of part (b) of Fig. 5-10. Therefore $\vec{F_1}{}^{\sim}$ is 2.1 wub$^{\sim}$. Then make parallel lines by sliding two pieces of folded paper edge to edge like a straight edge and triangle or use parallel rulings on ruled paper to translate the force arrows parallel to themselves.

The parallelogram on Fig. 5-10 shows that the **resultant** $\vec{R}{}^{\sim}$ of $\vec{F_1}{}^{\sim}$ and $\vec{F_2}{}^{\sim}$ added together can be represented as the diagonal of the parallelo-

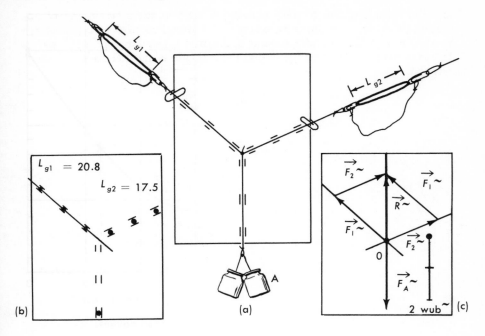

Fig. 5-10. Construction of parallelogram of forces using rubber-band tension-gauge.

gram, the sides being $\vec{F}_1{}^\sim$ and $\vec{F}_2{}^\sim$. This is the famous **parallelogram of forces.** Adding two sides of the parallelogram in the clockwise direction adds the forces in the order 1, 2; counterclockwise adds them as 2, 1. By QLF 5-4, both must lead to the same $\vec{R}$, an obvious result for a parallelogram.

From our postulates QLF 5-5 and 5-6, the sum of the three forces on the knot must be zero. This is exactly equivalent to requiring that the resultant $\vec{R}^\sim$ produced by $\vec{F}_1{}^\sim$ and $\vec{F}_2{}^\sim$ must be equal and opposite to the weight that produces $\vec{F}_A{}^\sim$. For the example of Fig. 5-10, the check is that $\vec{R}^\sim$ is a vertical up-vector of magnitude 2 wub~. If your experiment is carefully done, this will usually check to about 5 or 10 per cent. If good spring gauges were used instead of rubber bands, the results would be much closer.

What does all this exercise prove? What have you learned if your experiments worked well? You have found that a one-to-one correspondence between symbols and reality exists. With it you can predict unmeasured things. You have had an experience with exact physical science.

But perhaps you have also gained an esthetic appreciation as well. When you see a suspension bridge with its cables gracefully curving upwards you may find satisfiaction in understanding how this curve was known in advance by requiring the laws of Fig. 5-10 to apply to the massive suspension cable and the vertical cables to the roadway. When you see a steam shovel operating its cables or a tightrope walker on a stretched wire (see problems) you will have a deeper understanding of the orderly relationships that man has found in nature. It is the urge to find these relationships that drives scientists onward.

Chapter 6

Four Basic
Science-Thinking Tools

6-1 Introduction

At this point, our discussion of the physical science concepts essential to mechanics is interrupted for two pedagogical reasons: first, to summarize and organize some of the aspects of scientific thinking that have been used; second, to prepare the student to profit better from the presentation of the following chapters. In Chapters 1 through 5 the authors have repeatedly used a basic set of four science-thinking tools to create the orderly relationships expressed in qualified laws. The student should now have sufficient detailed *familiarity* with these tools so that he can appreciate their general features. At this point, therefore, we shall put these thinking tools themselves into an orderly relationship referred to as the **science-thinking diagram.**

Figure 6-1, which appears on the inside of the front cover, shows the orderly relationship of the four basic science-thinking tools. It is, in a real sense, the central theme of this book, and the phrases used in it appear many times in all the chapters. The emphasis placed on the particular attributes selected as the four basic science-thinking tools is an outcome of the research and teaching experience of the authors. However, the particular set chosen as *key attributes* for science-teaching methodology must be regarded as a *hunch* at the time of writing this book. The teaching of scientific thinking has not yet reached the state of theoretical development that permits formulating adequate QLF's about science-teaching pedagogy.

The four basic science-thinking tools are given numbers ① to ④ for ease of reference in this chapter. Elsewhere, they are referred to either by name or by abbreviation, but not by number. They fall into two main divisions: the creative search pattern (CSP), and the scientific logical structure.

We have defined tool ① in Fig. 6-1 as the creative search pattern *in toto*. It contains parts that are, in themselves, thinking tools. We discuss in Sec. 6-2 the CSP part of Fig. 6-1.

The three basic science-thinking tools of the scientific logical structure are the acor ② , which is a logical structure that leads to the qualified law form ③ , which contains a qualified-equation ④ . The acor is discussed more fully in Secs. 6-2 and 6-3. The qualified law form, as used for me-

121

chanics and the other exact sciences, involves orderly relationships that are frequently best expressed as qualified-equations, ④ in Fig. 6-1.

All four tools have been used extensively in the preceding chapters, and are equally important in the following chapters. We insert this chapter in order to review the tools and to prepare you better for the following chapters, which have been written so as to give you opportunities to use these tools to develop, for yourself, parts of the concepts of center of gravity, moments, potential energy, and buoyant forces. In fact the familiar **you can't do it, no matter what** experience may actually lead you to a payoff hunch about the law of conservation of energy.

6-2   *The Creative Search Pattern, CSP*

The **creative search pattern** starts with a **question** or a **chaos** consisting of some sort of disorderly relationship that provokes the human mind to try to make sense out of it. If possible, a question should be clearly formulated; however, Fig. 6-1 does not follow the conventional dictum of the so-called scientific method by telling you to "define the problem" as your starting point. The authors disagree with this dictum because it is not always possible to define the true problem usefully at the start. For example, the real questions in the tennis tournament puzzle of Chapter 2 and the two-king problem of Sec. 1-3 were not initially apparent. The important problem in the tennis tournament appeared only after the hunch about the law $M = P - 1$ had occurred. The two-king problem presented a similar situation. The problem turned out to be not "what should A do to lose" but instead, "can A lose—and if not, why not?" In place of "define the problem" as a starting point, we suggest that the most valuable course to follow with a confusing new problem is to apply the first creative search-thinking tool: **action.**

It is impossible to overemphasize the importance of *action* in creative search. Any action will help: even reading the problem at hand aloud several times or copying it word for word with a pencil or trying to put it into different words. Effective forms of action involve your voice, eyes, ears, fingers, arms, imagination in conceptual experiments, and many other forms. Use of your muscles and mind in these forms of action forces you to become familiar with details of the problem. The word **familiarity** in Fig. 6-1 as we define it for the CSP means detailed, specific knowledge about the problem at hand.

Further use of the creative search-thinking tools produces **hunches** in addition to familiarity. The authors propose that these hunches occur when your associative memory recognizes correspondences or analogies between parts of your problem and parts of previously learned examples of somewhat similar, orderly relationships. This recognition may occur even though the orderly relationships of the new problem are hidden by complexities that obscure the key attributes. (The scheduling of the byes in the tennis tournament problem is an example of an obscuring complexity.)

All of the search-thinking tools when put into action increase the likelihood that your mind will recognize the new orderly relationship in your problem. The search-thinking tools do this, we conjecture in Fig. 6-1, by helping Action pump acor patterns out of your memory reservoir so that you can compare them with familiar features of the problem being studied. When your **associative memory** recognizes a good analogy between key features of a known acor and key features with which you have familiarity in your new problem, then you have the **payoff hunch** that lets you **transfer** and extend your old experience to fit the new situation. The important **result** is an acor pattern that produces an orderly relationship among the key attributes of your problem.

The associations that you intuit as hunches are, it is certain, psychologically mysterious things. Two similar experiences may help to explain the nature of hunches. Almost everyone remembers having had the strange feeling that he was experiencing something that had happened before. Another common experience occurs while trying to remember something about a particular person—usually his name of where he comes from. You may have a definite feeling that the name has two syllables, or that perhaps it begins with B or D. But the name itself may take minutes to come back, if it does at all. A *hunch* must be something like these partial memories.

One dashed line going from question directly to hunch is shown in Fig. 6-1. This situation usually occurs when the problem is, or seems to be, so similar to a known problem that the answer seems at once obvious. Sometimes it does turn out this way; but more often this hunch is wrong, and testing it serves chiefly to add familiarity.

It is important to realize that a hunch that fails can be very useful. Testing out a wrong hunch increases familiarity and improves the chances of having the payoff hunch. The student should be aware that creative research in science usually involves far more failures than successes. The creative workers are very careful to avoid dangerous and expensive mistakes. But they worry little about other mistakes; they use them as stepping stones on a path to new and better hunches.

The puzzles and other examples in this book have been selected so as to supply you with a reservoir of acor patterns with logical structures like those of the conservation laws in science. They may enable you to have *hunches* and to take intellectual leaps that actually took the human race centuries to accomplish. It is, however, less important that you actually succeed in making these leaps on your own than that you get a feeling for what the process of having a payoff hunch is really like. This understanding will give you an important insight into the nature of science and the thinking processes of scientists.

An analogy is to compare the creative search pattern of scientific thinking with the simpler problem of putting together a jigsaw puzzle. If you look at the pieces with straight edges, which probably are the outer boundary, you observe certain *key attributes,* such as all light blue or all dark green colors. This detailed *familiarity* with the jigsaw puzzle at hand and your past experience with similar jigsaw puzzle structures leads naturally to the hunch that the light blue is sky and the dark green is a foreground of grass. Your associative memory has recognized one-to-one correspondences between key attributes of the piece in your hand and those of similar pieces you have encountered in other problems. Usually this recognition is a payoff hunch that helps to produce the orderly relationship of an assembled puzzle. This is a very rudimentary acor pattern.

This association of an old *logical structure pattern* with one hidden in a new problem is called **transfer** by the educational psychologists. Transfer is a famous feature of many branches of science and engineering. The so-called *analogue* computer "transfers" electrical voltages and currents to represent motions in mechanical systems. The science-teaching approach of this book, in which the logical structures of games and puzzles are used as a basis for understanding the orderly relationships of scientific laws, is based on the concept of transfer.

Transfer of the frustrating experience of having the inevitable, wrong hunches of the creative search pattern is another important goal of this book. To sum up: Don't worry about the mistakes; take action in your thinking, learn from your mistakes, and keep going.

6-3 The Acor Pattern, QLF and QE

The word **acor,** like conaddian, is a new word used in this book to focus attention on a certain aspect of scientific thinking. As shown in Fig. 6-1, it is made up of letters in the phrases used to describe the logic of measurement in Sec. 3-8. The logic of measurement of any conaddian is an acor pattern in which the conaddian property is the orderly relationship.

The action-reaction law QLF 4-1 is the orderly relationship part of an acor pattern. The key attributes were the changes in readings of the scales supporting students A and B. The comparison operation consisted of comparing changes in the two scales when the students pushed on each other. The orderly relationship of equal and opposite changes for the two scales was interpreted as QLF 4-1.

The vector resultant invariance law QLF 5-4 is an example of an acor depending wholly on theory and definition. In this case, the acor is also a PPT, or postulate-proof-theorem, structure. Each vector has two key attributes: its east-west displacement, and its north-south displacement. (These two parts are called *components*.) The proof, which was only outlined in Sec. 5-7, was that the east-west parts of all the vectors add like $\pm$ lengths on a line, and so do the north-south parts. The orderly relationship was QLF 5-4.

An example of the development of an acor described in the terminology of this section is given in Sec. 5-8. This is presented in the summarizing paragraph following the equation that proves QLF 5-1 as a theorem.

The classification of any particular logical structure into the three parts of the acor is not absolutely fixed. It depends to some degree on the experience of the user of the acor. In particular, the beginning student of vectors may regard QLF 5-4 as a difficult acor. The experienced student, on the other hand, will take QLF 5-4 as a key attribute of some situation and use it as a postulate in finding a new acor. This was what we did in arriving at the vector force concept QLF 5-5.

A well-stocked memory reservoir of acor patterns is probably the most valuable possession a science student may have. He should try to see how the development or logical structure of new scientific laws that he encounters fit into his scheme so that he can be best prepared to transfer his knowledge to new situations.

The remaining two basic science-thinking tools, 3 and 4 of Fig. 6-1, are the qualified law form QLF, and the qualified-equation, QE. Both were thoroughly discussed when introduced in Secs. 1-2 for QLF and Secs. 2-7 and 3-3 for QE.

6-4 Conclusion

This chapter is an analysis of how thinking about science is done, especially the processes by which new scientific thought structures are developed. It is related to the scientific aspects of epistemology, which is the study of the nature and grounds of knowledge. This aspect of this chapter may appropriately be described as **introspective analysis.** This phrase emphasizes the fact that the intent is to make the student more aware of how his own mental processes work on difficult problems. If the student can classify his attacks on problems in terms of the features of Fig. 6-1, he will probably find out what works best for him, and may develop personal viewpoints that differ somewhat from those presented in this chapter.

If the suggestions of this chapter do contribute to the student's becoming aware of his own processes of thinking, this introspective analysis may well prove more valuable to him than any of the specific tools we have discussed.

Chapter 7

Moments and Center of Gravity

7-1 Introduction

The entire investigation reported in Chapters 7 and 8 involves only two fundamental measurements: weight and length. All of the apparatus used for experimentation (with the exception of the balanced rotated lever) can be easily duplicated. You are encouraged to perform all the experiments personally and to study carefully the logical and mathematical reasoning.

These chapters are especially designed to give you a first-hand experience of theoretical science. Our purpose is to involve you in a *creative search* for laws of statics of rigid bodies, again conducted in the way of the physicist, and to give you opportunities to use *search-thinking tools* to achieve some important *results* arranged in a logical structure. Your understanding of the significant attributes of weight, length, moments, center of gravity, potential energy, and buoyant forces will enable you (1) to predict when things will remain at rest and when they will fall, whether in air or in water; (2) to know how the weight of one object or a collection of objects can be represented as a single geometric point; and (3) to discover and prove the special law of conservation of potential energy, from which the existence of two other forms of energy will be deduced in Chapter 9. Most important of all, we hope you will have the opportunity to *reflect* about this creative search pattern in scientific thinking, and to recall the questions, hunches, and results that gave you new familiarity and objective knowledge about what previously was chaotic and difficult to understand.

7-2 An Observed Invariant Relationship About a Dot

Look at the dot marked on a piece of cardboard set in a wire cage in Fig. 7-1. The cage suspends freely from a bent paperclip hook attached to the end of a string. There is some "magic" about the dot in the wire cage. By magic, we mean that the dot contradicts our ordinary experiences about dots. Here is the magic. No matter where the cage is suspended from the

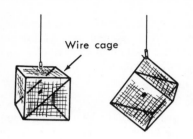

Wire cage

Fig. 7-1. The dot always exists directly below the point of suspension, no matter the suspension point on the cage.

hook, the dot always exists directly below the point of suspension!

Hook the cage from a corner point and then sight down the vertical string: the dot is directly below the corner point of suspension. Suspend the cage from a point on its side or edge, and the dot will not go anywhere except directly below the point of suspension.

We must conclude from these observations that this is a very unusual dot. **You can't** change the invariant relationship between the position of the dot and its point of suspension, **no matter what.** We must wonder about this observed invariant relationship of the dot in the cage. How extensive is the dot, what does it represent, when does it occur, and how is it related to other attributes of nature? These are some of the questions we will answer in this creative search pattern.

7-3 How to Locate the CG (Name-Symbol for the Dot)

Let us make sure that we can reproduce this newly observed phenomenon. If the dot were erased, could we find it again? Yes!

1. Suspend the wire cage. (See Fig. 7-2.) Tie one end of a string at the

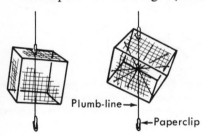

Plumb-line→

←Paperclip

Fig. 7-2. The CG is located at the intersection of vertical plumb-lines from different points of suspension on the object.

point of suspension on the cage. Drop the other end of the string (which has a paperclip attached to it) in a vertical downward direction from the point of suspension through the cage. (This string, which uses the weight at its bottom end to locate a vertical line, is called a *plumb-line.*) Tie the loose end of the string to the other side of the cage. We know the dot is somewhere along the vertical line represented by this string.

2. Suspend the cage from another point. Again, use the plumb-line to locate a vertical line from the point of suspension; do this by tying one end of the string to the point of suspension and dropping the end with the weight vertically downward to the other side of the cage. You will find it **always true** that this second string intersects the first string. The dot, in fact, is at the point where the two strings intersect!

3. If the cage is suspended from still another point, a third vertical string will intersect the first two strings. This further confirms the intersection point

of the dot, as will other vertical strings of plumb-lines tied from different points of suspension.

This unique dot, operationally defined by the above steps, has a scientific name. We shall give the dot through which all real and/or imaginary vertical strings pass, the abbreviation and name-symbol *CG*, signifying that the intersection of the strings is the **center of gravity** of the object.

7-4 Is There a CG for All Objects?

Now what is this fascinating center of gravity point? As a simple research question, we ask: Is *CG* a physical property of just the cage, or is there *always* a *CG* attribute directly below *any* point of suspension for any object freely suspended?

We can begin by trying some simplest cases. Where is the *CG* of a square piece of cardboard (about 12″ × 12″), a fish-shaped piece of cardboard (about 14″ long), a circular piece of cardboard (about 10″ diameter), and a wire clothes hanger? Try to locate and name the *CG* of these different objects, two of which are shown in Fig. 7-3. (We urge you to obtain the simple pieces of materials described in this section. It will be a worthwhile scientific experience for you to perform these and other experiments that will be described later.)

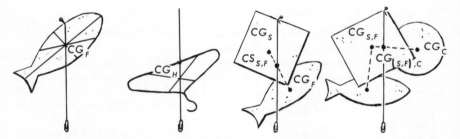

Fig. 7-3. The CG of a freely suspended object always lies directly below the point of suspension.

Fig. 7-4. The CG of more than one object always lies directly below the point of suspension on a straight line connecting two CG's.

1. Pin the square cardboard to a wall or edge of a table, making sure that the cardboard is free to swing about the pin. Use the string plumb-line with the attached paperclip weight to draw a vertical line on the cardboard. Suspend the cardboard from another point, and draw a second vertical line. The intersection of the two lines is the center of gravity point. Mark it and give it the name-symbol CG_S, the S standing for the square.

We observe that CG_S always exists directly below the point of suspension, **no matter** how many times the object is suspended and vertical lines are drawn. The same results are obtained with CG_F for the cardboard fish and with CG_C for the cardboard circle. (Obviously the adjective symbols are F for fish and C for circle.)

2. Suspend the wire clothes hanger from a point on the hanger. Tie one end of the string of the plumb-line to the point, and tie or tape the string

across the wires to represent the downward vertical line from the point of suspension, as shown in Fig. 7-3. Suspend the hanger from a different point, and repeat the procedures for locating the vertical line from the point of suspension. The intersection of the two strings, or CG_H (H is for hanger), **is always** below the point of suspension, **no matter** the point of suspension or whether CG is on the object or in space about the object.

3. What happens to the CG when two or three objects are rigidly held together? Use tape or a rubber band to fasten rigidly together the cardboard square and the cardboard fish. Then locate and mark the $CG_{S,F}$ of the combined square and fish. (Fig. 7-4). The new $CG_{S,F}$ (read "sea gee sub ess eff" meaning "combined center of gravity of the square and the fish") is again directly below the point of suspension. Furthermore, it is **always true** that $CG_{S,F}$ lies on a straight line that connects CG_S and CG_F!

4. What happens to the CG when the cardboard circle is added by being rigidly fastened to the square and the fish combination? The new combined $CG_{(S,F)C}$ again is directly below the point of suspension *and* also on a straight line that connects $CG_{S,F}$ and CG_C! Although now we wonder more than ever about these dots, we still don't have any explanations—yet.

Are these observed CG relationships true when the suspended objects are not rigidly held together? Connect the cardboard square, fish, and circle by lengths of rubber bands in a non-rigid arrangement. We conclude that there is a combined $CG_{(S,F)C}$ directly below the point of suspension for each arrangement of the objects. (Simply imagine the three objects rigidly held together so that you could re-suspend them to find the intersection of two vertical strings.) We also conclude, however, that there is no single $CG_{(S,F)C}$ for all positions. The $CG_{(S,F)C}$ may change, because the objects are redistributed when re-suspended, and the individual CG's do not remain in a fixed arrangement with respect to each other.*

The discovery of CG and its invariant location with respect to the point of suspension can be summarized in a qualified law form, as follows.

QLF 7-1 Location of CG	
WHAT	It is **always true** that, for every object or rigid assembly of objects suspended to rotate freely about a point, there exists a unique CG point related to the object, which is directly below the point of suspension,
WHEN	**no matter** the material, size, or shape of the objects, the points at which the object or objects are suspended, whether CG is located in an object or in empty space, whether the object or objects are rigidly or non-rigidly connected together,
WHEN NOT	**but not if** the assembly of objects is swinging, moved by wind, or pulled by magnets.

---

* If you wish, experiment further by varying the sequence of combining the CG's. For example, combine CG_F and CG_C; then add CG_S to locate $CG_{(F,C)S}$. We predict that the combined $CG_{(F,C)S}$ will be located at the same point as $CG_{(S,F)C}$.

In addition, we can summarize two other orderly relationships about the location of *CG*, also based upon the solution of a few simplest cases.

1. The combined *CG* of two objects exists directly below the point of suspension on a straight line that connects the two individual *CG*'s.

2. Since we can combine 2 and then 3 *CG*'s into a single *CG* (as we did with the square, fish, and circle), we can formulate the hunch that *any* number of *CG*'s can be combined into a combined *CG* located directly below the point of suspension.

Question: How can such hunch-laws about the location of the *CG* of 1, 2, and 3 objects be further checked experimentally, or proved with greater certainty for any number of objects? We now turn our search to explore these and other new relationships about *CG*, as we investigate one of the oldest and most famous problems in theoretical science.

7-5   The Balanced Lever Problem

Archimedes (287-212 B.C.) was the first theoretical scientist to experiment with the balanced lever to study the question "What are the laws concerning things that balance?" His famous treatise endeavored to explain the more complicated cases of the lever by postulates of self-evident, idealized simplest cases.

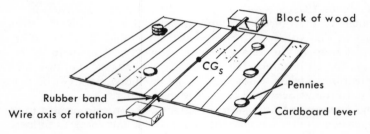

Fig. 7-5.   This experimental model can be easily constructed to investigate balanced levers. Why does this lever balance?

Our search to understand the balanced lever problem will be facilitated if we construct and manipulate an *experimental model* of a balanced lever. Figure 7-5 illustrates a model, described below, which we can construct to investigate the balanced lever problem.

1. Use the 12″ × 12″ square piece of cardboard to represent the *lever*.

2. Use tape and a rubber band to fasten a straight 15″ wire (cut from a wire clothes hanger) above the *CG* of the square cardboard; place the wire between two smooth, supporting objects of equal height (such as two thin sardine cans or blocks of wood) so that the cardboard can rotate freely; then carefully adjust the position of the wire (or add tape to one side of the cardboard) until the cardboard exactly balances in the horizontal position. The bottom edge of the wire is the *axis of rotation* of the, now, initially balanced lever.

3. Represent different persons or things on the initially balanced lever by placing stacks of *pennies* on the square cardboard lever.

Thus we have selected three physical things about the balanced lever problem upon which to concentrate our research attention. Indeed, of all the possible attributes to explore, we have chosen to research the attributes and relationships of the *lever, axis of rotation,* and *pennies.* How would you now efficiently use this physical model to investigate the question, "When do objects balance on a lever?"

7-6 Solutions of Simplest Cases of Balanced Lever

Try to solve simplest cases. After each experiment, try to explain the results. Some results are discussed below and shown in Fig. 7-6.

Case of Zero Penny. The cardboard lever can be balanced in a horizontal position when its *CG* is directly *below* the axis of rotation (wire), **no matter**

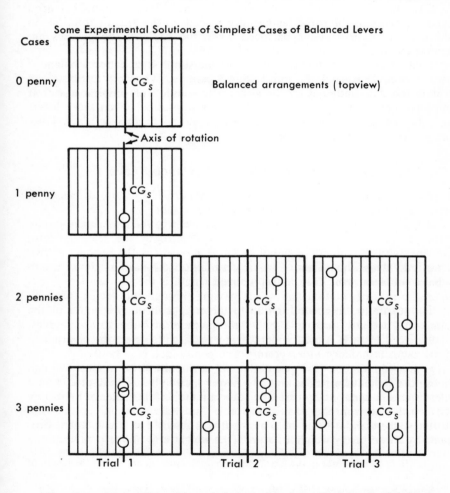

Fig. 7-6. The cardboard lever is balanced horizontally in each of these simplest cases. Why?

how the wire is rotated about the *CG* of the lever. Like the hanging wire cage, the lever is in equilibrium whenever its *CG* is *below* the axis of rotation.

On the other hand, when the cardboard lever is *above* the wire so that its *CG* is directly *above* the axis of rotation, **you can't** get the lever to be stable (it tips over easily), **no matter** how you try.

Case of 1 Penny. When the *CG* of the penny is directly on the axis of rotation, the lever is balanced. The farther the *CG* of the penny is moved away from the axis of rotation, the more the lever tends to become unbalanced.

Case of 2 Pennies. Again, the cardboard lever remains balanced when its own *CG* and the *CG*'s of the two pennies are on the axis of rotation. The lever also is balanced when the distances from the *CG*'s of the pennies to the axis of rotation are equal.

Case of 3 Pennies. Again, an initially balanced lever remains balanced when the *CG*'s of the three pennies are placed on the axis of rotation. In addition, the lever remains balanced when the *CG*'s of the pennies are arranged as shown in trials 2 and 3 of Fig. 7-6.

Look at the experimental solutions of the simplest cases for a balanced lever, especially trials 1, 2, and 3 with 3 pennies. What key attribute can explain the data gathered by the systematic solution of simplest cases? If you have not yet found a numerical relationship about when these levers are balanced, stop at this stage of the search and *try to discover the law* before going on to the next section.

7-7   *Discovery of an Acor Pattern for Balanced Levers*

What we are looking for is a new acor pattern (like those discussed in Secs. 3-2 for counting and 3-8 for measuring weight).

Attribute. The key discovery that brings order to the experimental data is the recognition of a new attribute. It is defined by the scientific term **moment,** with the quantity-symbol of *M*. A *moment* is the product of two measured values: the weight of the object multiplied by an imaginary length called a **moment arm**. This conceptualized length is the shortest length between the axis of rotation and a line passing through the vector force. In our investigations, this force is due to the weight through the *CG* of the pennies!* Carefully study in Fig. 7-7 the moment arm due to the pennies.

Standard Unit. It is convenient for our research to select the *penny-inch* to represent 1 *standard moment unit*. The penny-inch is to be thought of as a real unit of moment, just as a dollar bill is a real unit of money. We can choose the standard moment unit of a penny-inch to be a penny placed on a ruler extended horizontally from the edge of a table. The center of the penny (*CG*) is 1 inch from the edge of the table (axis of rotation).

Thus, the standard unit of a moment was selected as the moment produced by a one-penny weight or **wup~** (the **w**eight **u**nit of one **p**enny) at one

---

* It will become clearer in the next section that the moment arm is *not* the length of the arm of the physical lever. Like the creation of "shaded" and "plain squares" in the checkerboard puzzle, a "moment arm" is also a conception. It is a measurable length between an axis of rotation and a line representing the direction of a force.

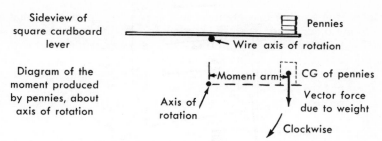

Fig. 7-7.   A diagram of a moment includes the vector force and its moment arm.

inch~ from the axis of rotation, so that the unit of moment is the penny-inch, or **mupi**~ (the **m**oment **u**nit of one **p**enny-**i**nch).

Comparison Operation. We can describe operations for comparing the value of an unknown moment to the standard moment unit. Let us measure, for example, the moment of an elephant suspended from the end of a diving board (Fig. 7-8). To do this, first count the number of pennies that we must place 1 inch from the axis of rotation of an imaginary, straight rigid lever in order for these penny-inch moments to equal the elephant moment. If it requires 60,000,000 pennies placed 1 inch from the axis of rotation, then we can say that the elephant moment is 60,000,000 times greater than the 1 standard penny-inch, or that it is 60,000,000 penny-inches. (We could also measure the elephant moment by moving 1 penny 60,000,000 inches away from the axis of rotation.)

The logic of this comparison operation for measuring an unknown quantity of moment can be more precisely described in symbolic terms. Consider another unknown quantity of moment M~ produced by a stack of N pennies that weigh N wup~, and whose CG is located L inches~ from the axis of rotation. In comparison to the standard moment unit of one penny-inch or 1 mupi~, the stack produces a moment $N \times L$ times larger than 1 mupi~. Hence, M~ $= N$ wup~ $\times L$ inches~ $= N \times L$ wup~ in.~ $= N \times L$ mupi~ (in moment). This quantity-equation (in keeping with QLF 3-2) reduces to the NSU equation $M = +NL$ (in number of mupi~), when the $+$ sign corresponds to the algebraic convention that CW moments are plus.

Orderly Relationship. One of the first observed numerical relationship, or scientific law, is that *objects will always balance when the sum of the individual moments in a counterclockwise (CCW) direction about the axis of rotation equals the sum of the individual moments in a clockwise (CW) direction.*

Note how this law of moments for balanced levers can explain the balanced arrangements of pennies observed experimentally and tabulated in Fig. 7-6. Calculate the numerical value of the moments, for example, of trial 2 of the case of 3 pennies. The CCW moments (in penny-inches) equals the CW moments: $1 \times 4 = 1 \times 2 + 1 \times 2$. Again, as for all of the simplest cases investigated, the CCW and CW moments in penny-inches of trial 3

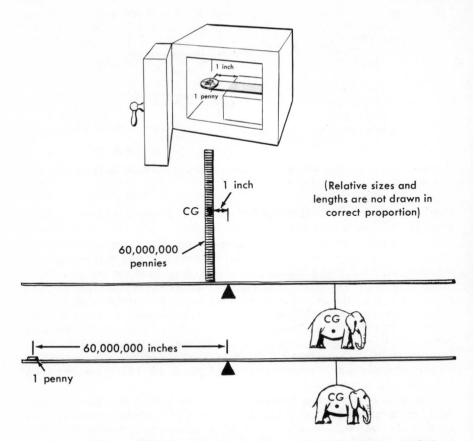

Fig. 7-8. **One penny-inch abritrarily selected and preserved in a vault is used as a standard unit of comparison for measuring the number of standard moment units contained in elephant moment.**

also are equal: $1 \times 5 = 1 \times 2 + 1 \times 3$. Now try the case in Fig. 7-5. Do you calculate that NSU values in penny-inches of the *CW* and *CCW* moments are each equal to 12?

We can more compactly state this law of moments that predicts when objects will balance. Since we assign a negative ($-$) value to a *CCW* moment and a positive value to *CW* moments, and since the NSU values of the *CCW* and *CW* moments are equal, *the algebraic sum of the individual moments always equals zero for a balanced lever.* This necessary condition for equilibrium can be compactly stated in symbolic terms as

$$\Sigma M = 0 \quad \text{(in mupi}^{\sim}\text{)}$$

The capital Greek letter Σ (sigma) signifies "algebraic sum of the individual parts", so the equation is usually read as "Sigma *M* equals zero", or "The algebraic sum of the individual moments equals zero (in the moment unit of one penny-inch)".

When the law of moments for a balanced lever is stated as $\Sigma M = 0$, we sum up the individual moments in penny-inches of trial 2 of the case of 3 pennies (Fig. 7-6) as follows: $(1)(-4) + (1)(2) + (1)(2) = 0$. In each of the experimental trials where CG's are on the axis of rotation, again the levers are balanced because the sum of the individual moments equals zero about the axis of rotation. To illustrate, the numerical values of the individual moments of trial 1 of the case of 3 pennies can be summed up as follows: $(1)(0) + (1)(0) + (1)(0) = 0$. In these two examples illustrating $\Sigma M = 0$, we have not included the moment due to the lever itself, because it is zero in these trials.

Thus we have discovered another attribute of nature which displays the amazing property of *additivity*. As we do for the measured values of individual weights, lengths, and volumes, we can add and subtract NSU values of moments according to the rules of arithmetic. The discovered invariant relationship, it seems, is that when the sum of the individual moments equals zero, the arrangement of lever and weights always will balance about the axis of rotation.

7-8 *Testing the Law of Moments for Balanced Levers*

At this stage of our research, the law $\Sigma M = 0$ is based on the experimental solution of a few simplest cases. When is the law true and when is it not true? Here are some specific investigations to further familiarize ourselves with the applicability of this newly discovered relationship. (The results are summarized in Fig. 7-9.)

1. What happens to the moments if we use another object, say, the cardboard fish, as the balanced lever? Fasten the straight wire as the axis of rotation across the CG of the cardboard fish so that the lever balances. Then place pennies as shown in Fig. 7-9. The sum of the individual moments about the axis of rotation equals zero, **no matter** the material, size, shape, or weight of the initially balanced lever.

2. What happens to the moments if the weights are suspended below the lever? Use a pin to freely suspend the cardboard fish lever so that the lever is initially balanced (Fig. 7-9). Hang different weights (such as paperclips) from strings attached to one side of the fish lever, and then rebalance the lever to its original position by suspending weights on the other side. *The sum of the moments about the axis of rotation equals zero if the measured lengths of the moment arms are the perpendicular distances from the axis of rotation to the vertical vector force (weight) acting through both the point of suspension and the CG of the hanging weight.*

3. What happens to the moments if a balanced lever bends? Tape two pennies on a cardboard lever so that the lever is balanced in a horizontal position. Then bend one side of the lever downward (Fig. 7-9).

The lever will not remain balanced, because bending decreases the moment arm of the weight of the penny on the bent side of the axis of rotation. In fact, a limiting case would occur if the bending made the side vertical so that the moment arm, and consequently the value of the moment, became zero.

You actually can feel this difference in the moments caused by changes in

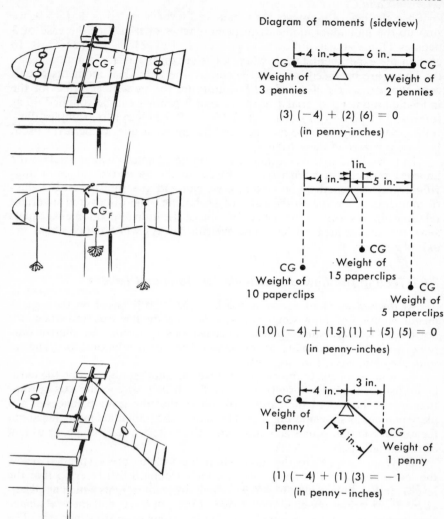

Diagram of moments (sideview)

|← 4 in. →|← 6 in. →|

CG• Weight of 3 pennies   △   CG Weight of 2 pennies

$$(3)(-4) + (2)(6) = 0$$
(in penny-inches)

1 in.

|← 4 in. →|← 5 in. →|

△

CG Weight of 15 paperclips

CG• Weight of 10 paperclips

CG Weight of 5 paperclips

$$(10)(-4) + (15)(1) + (5)(5) = 0$$
(in penny-inches)

|← 4 in. →| 3 in.

CG• Weight of 1 penny   △   4 in.   CG Weight of 1 penny

$$(1)(-4) + (1)(3) = -1$$
(in penny-inches)

Fig. 7-9. How is the law $\Sigma M = 0$ for balanced levers affected when (1) levers are different size, shape, and weight, (2) objects are suspended below the lever, and (3) the balanced lever becomes bent?

the moment arm. Holding a heavy book in your hand, extend your arm horizontally; then hold the arm in a vertical position so the book is above the elbow (axis of rotation). The moment is maximum when the arm and the book are held in the horizontal position.

4. What happens to the moments if the cardboard lever is balanced when the axis of rotation is *not* on the *CG* of the lever? Fasten the wire (axis of rotation) so that the cardboard-fish lever cannot be initially balanced; for example, displace its *CG* two inches from the axis of rotation. (Fig. 7-10). Now

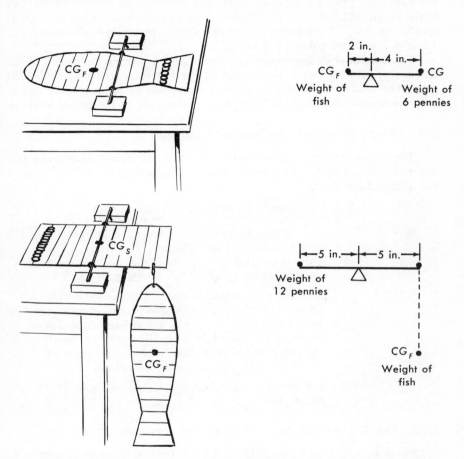

Fig. 7-10. How is the law $\Sigma M = 0$ for balanced levers affected when the CG of the lever is not on the axis of rotation?

balance the lever by placing pennies on the other side of the axis. Will the sum of the moments on the two sides of the axis of rotation be equal?

Yes, the law of moments is true for the case shown in Fig. 7-10, *if we postulate that the total weight of the fish acts at its center of gravity* CG_F, causing a *CCW* moment about the axis of rotation. Then, when we apply our discovered law of moments to this example, we can write:

Weight of fish~ $\times$ moment arm~ = weight of pennies~ $\times$ moment arm~

Weight of fish~ $\times$ 2 inches~ = 6 pennies~ $\times$ 4 inches~

Weight of fish~ = 12 pennies~

Does the weight of the fish equal the weight of 12 pennies, as predicted by these calculations based upon the law of moments and the postulate that all the weight of the fish is concentrated at its *CG*? Suspend the fish from the balanced, square-cardboard lever, and compare the weight of the fish to the weight of 12 pennies (Fig. 7-10). You will find that, within the experimental accuracy of this measurement operation, the weight of the fish equals 12 wup~, or the weight of 12 pennies.

Thus, we have demonstrated experimentally that when the weight of the fish acting at CG_F equals the weight of the fish measured on a balanced scale, the sum of the moments of the pennies and of the fish lever equals zero, **no matter** whether the CG of the lever is or is not on the axis of rotation.

7-9   Law of Moments for Balanced Levers

These experiments suggest situations when the newly discovered law will and will not apply. The results can be summarized in one sentence in the qualified law form.

QLF 7-2 Law of Moments of Balanced Levers	
WHAT	It is **always true** that for a balanced lever the sum of the individual moments on the two sides of the axis of rotation are equal, or the algebraic sum of the individual moments is zero ($\Sigma M = 0$),
WHEN	**no matter** the material, shape, size, or weight of the lever or of the balanced objects, the number and measured values of the weights, the standard unit of moment used for measuring the moments, whether the objects hang below the lever, or whether the CG of the lever is or is not on the axis of rotation,
WHEN NOT	**but not if** . . . . (None observed in these experiments.)*

7-10   The CG-Weight Point: Stable and Unstable Equilibrium

Recall that in order to weigh the fish (Sec. 7-8) by calculating moments, we postulated that the total weight of the fish was concentrated at the CG point. We now can prove that the moment produced by an object is equal to the moment that the total weight would produce if located at the CG point.

In Fig. 7-11, for the balanced object suspended from a pin, the sum of the moments about the axis of rotation R is zero. There are two forces acting on the object, the upward thrust force $\vec{T}^{\sim}$ due to the action by the pin and the downward weight force $\vec{W}^{\sim}$ caused by the gravitational attraction to the earth. The individual moment due to $\vec{T}^{\sim}$ equals zero, because $\vec{T}^{\sim}$ passes through the axis of rotation R. Since $\Sigma M = 0$, the moment due to $\vec{W}^{\sim}$ must also be zero.

Since $\vec{W}^{\sim}$ is not zero, its moment arm must be zero. If we assume that

---

* A **but not if** can occur if the lever is spun so that other forces are exerted on the objects.

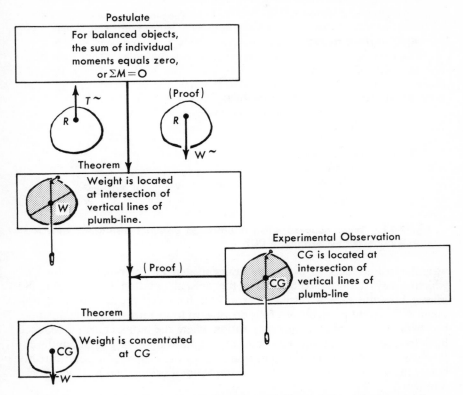

Postulate

For balanced objects,
the sum of individual
moments equals zero,
or $\Sigma M = O$

(Proof)

Theorem

Weight is located
at intersection of
vertical lines of
plumb-line.

Experimental Observation

CG is located at
intersection of
vertical lines of
plumb-line

(Proof)

Theorem

Weight is concentrated
at CG

Fig. 7-11. **Can you prove that the total weight of an object is concentrated at its CG?**

all the weight can be considered to be concentrated at a point, a zero moment arm means that the weight attribute must be on the vertical line through the point of rotation R as indicated by the plumb-line. When the cage is suspended from another point, by the same reasoning, the total weight must be on the second vertical line indicated by the plumb-line. Since these two vertical lines (and any other vertical lines) always intersect at the same point, we conclude that the attribute we call the "weight of the object" for calculating moments is located at the intersection of the straight lines.

But the attribute "*CG* of the object" also is located at the same intersection. Hence, we conclude that the weight of the object is located at the *CG* point.

Let us now use this new **CG-weight** concept, where the total weight can be concentrated as a "point" weight, to analyze further some of the simplest cases of moments already observed—those that involve one object and an axis of rotation.

1. The dot in the hanging wire cage was our first experience of a balanced object producing zero moment. The example illustrates how the

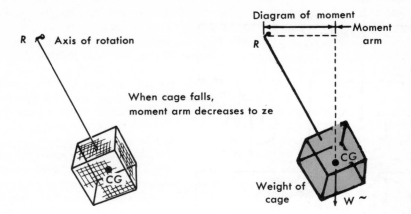

Fig. 7-12. **What happens when a balanced object is displaced? How is stability affected by location of CG?**

weight attribute acts as if it were concentrated at a geometric point *CG*, which always hangs directly *below* the axis of rotation (Fig. 7-12). **No matter** how the cage is displaced from this balanced position of zero moment, *CG*-weight point always falls downward to its lowest possible position, i.e., back to its original, balanced position where the moment arm is reduced back to zero. The next time you hang a lamp, flower pot, or picture, and want it to stay at rest at a certain spot, think about the *CG*-weight point directly below the axis of rotation, hanging in **stable equilibrium**, and producing zero moment.

2. Recall what happened when we tried to balance the *CG* of the cardboard lever *above* the straight wire, or the axis of rotation. The cardboard was in **unstable equilibrium**, because it was difficult to balance above the wire, **no matter** how we tried. The instability can now be easily explained. As soon as the total weight at the *CG* of the cardboard is displaced from its position above the axis of rotation, a moment is produced by the "point" weight at *CG*. The unbalanced moment causes a downward rotation of the lever until the *CG*-weight point regains its equilibrium position at the lowest point to which it can fall, which is directly below the point of suspension.

Such objects as books, boats, and tight-rope walkers can tip over when there are unbalanced moments produced by the *CG*-weight point's being displaced from above the axis of rotation. To give you a personal experience with this simplest case, place your toes so they touch a wall. If you try to stand on your toes, you will always fall backwards. Another version of this stunt is to place your heels against the wall and try to bend over to touch your toes. You will always fall forward.

This analysis of the *CG*-weight point's falling down when displaced from above the axis of rotation suggests a second method for finding the *CG* of an object. Place the cardboard fish on an edge of a table, or on any other edge of a sharp object. Extend the fish over the edge little by little. When the fish just begins to fall over the edge, we conclude that the *CG*-

weight point of the fish is above the edge, which is the axis of rotation. Draw a line that corresponds to the edge on the cardboard fish. Extend another part of the fish over the edge so that when it falls again, we can locate the *CG* above a second axis of rotation. Draw the second line on the fish, again to correspond to the edge. The intersection of the two lines locates the *CG*-weight point of the cardboard fish.

3. A propeller, fan blade, automobile tire, or any object that is rotated, is usually designed to be balanced in every rotated position. This condition of **neutral equilibrium** is achieved when the *CG*-weight point is placed *on* the axis of rotation. Accordingly, there are no moment arms, and hence, no moments at any rotated position of the object to retard its motion.

This fact suggests a third way to locate the *CG* of the cardboard fish. Try to balance the fish on a vertical axis of rotation, such as on the tip of your finger. When the object is balanced on the finger, the *CG*-weight point always will be on this axis of rotation, where the object produces zero moment at any rotated position.

We have postulated, experimented, and proved that for calculations of moments, the weight of an object can be considered to be located at the *CG* of the object. These results can be combined with the previous law about the location of *CG* (Sec. 7-4) and summarized in the qualified law form.

	QLF 7-3 The *CG*-Weight Law
WHAT	It is **always true** that for calculating moments, the weight of an object or collection of objects can be considered to be concentrated at the *CG*,
WHEN	**no matter** the material, size, shape, or weight of the objects, the points at which the objects are suspended, whether *CG* is located in an object or in empty space, or whether the objects are rigidly or non-rigidly connected together,
WHEN NOT	**but not if** . . . . (None observed in these experiments.) *

7-11   Location of CG-Weight Point for Two and Three Weights

Recall that when the cardboard square and fish were balanced together in a hanging position (Fig. 7-4), the $CG_{S,F}$ for the combined weights of the square and the fish was located on a line connecting CG_S and CG_F; but *where* on the line is $CG_{S,F}$ located? *Question:* When two and three weights are added together, and combined into a single weight, where is their *CG*-weight point?

Some experimental results are described below and tabulated in Figs. 7-13 and 7-14.

Trial 1. Note what happens to the moments when the two individual pennies are replaced by a combined stack of 2 pennies, with their *CG* located at the *balance point* of the line connecting the two individual *CG*'s. In penny-

---

* Again, a **but not if** can occur when an object is subjected to other forces when spun on an axis.

inches, the single moment produced by the single *CG*-weight point equals the sum of the two moments produced by the two individual weights!

Trials 2 and 3. Whenever 1 and 2 pennies are replaced by a single stack of 3 pennies with their *CG* again located at the *balance point,* the one moment produced by the single *CG*-weight point equals the sum of the two moments produced by the two individual weights.

The **balance point** is our new discovery. It is the *CG*-weight point for two

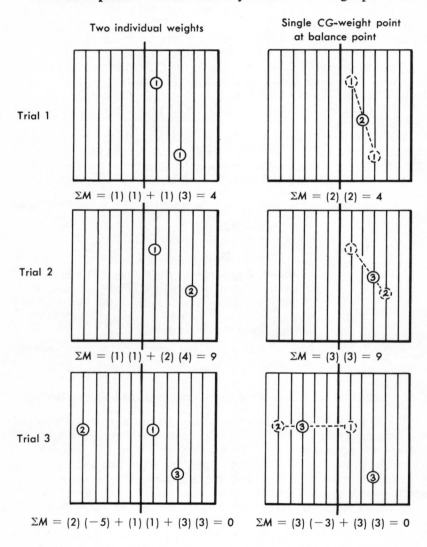

Fig. 7-13. Locate the CG of the two individual weights at their balance point. Then the moment of the single combined weight at CG equals the sum of the moments of the two individual weights.

individual weights. It is located by imagining that the two individual weights are balanced about it, as if the two weights were on an imaginary lever, and the distances from the individual CG's to the balance point are the imagined moment arms!

Trial 4. Is the $CG_{S,F}$ (as recorded in Fig. 7-4) located at the balance point between CG_S and CG_F, even though these two objects are hanging in space? If so, we can make a simple prediction and an experimental check.

The observed ratio of the distances from the individual CG's to the balance point is about 1 : 2. Hence, using the law of moments, we can predict that the cardboard square will be twice as heavy as the fish. Weigh the square and the fish on a balanced scale, and you will find their weights as predicted, within the range of the accuracy of the experiment.

Trial 5. Three separate stacks of 1, 2, and 3 pennies are balanced on the cardboard lever shown in Fig. 7-14. When any two weights of pennies are replaced at the balance point by a single weight equal to the addition of the two individual weights, the lever remains balanced, and the total moment remains zero. Then, by the same procedures, add the third weight to the two combined weights, so that now there is only one weight on the lever. By the successive finding of balance points, the single CG-weight point is located.

From this trial we conclude that the CG-weight point located by the "method of successive balance points" produces the same measureable moment as the three moments produced by the three individual weights, **no matter** the sequence of adding the weights or whether the number of weights combined is 2 or 3.*

The location of the CG's for the preceding simplest cases of 2 and 3 weights suggests the following hunch-law stated in the qualified law form.

QLF 7-4	The Single Moment Produced by the CG-Weight Point
WHAT	It is **always true** that about any axis of rotation the sum of the moments of individual weights is equal to the single moment that would be produced by one CG-weight point, where the combined weight equals the sum of the individual weights and acts at the CG located by the "method of successive balance points",
WHEN	**no matter** the number or magnitude of the weights, the positions of the weights in space, the sequence of combining the weights, or whether or not CG is on the axis of rotation,
WHEN NOT	**but not if** . . . . (None observed in these experiments.)†

---

* Actually, you should, on your own, locate the CG of the simplest cases of 4 and 5 weights using the "method of successive balance points." This stage of our research is like solving for the simplest cases of 2, 3, 4 and 5 players in the tennis tournament.

† Two **but not if**'s may occur; one when the weights change at different positions due to a non-uniform gravitational field of force, and another when new forces are exerted on the objects due to an acceleration of the objects.

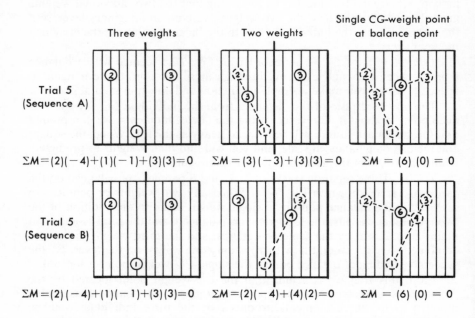

Fig. 7-14. Locate the CG of three individual weights by combining the weights in any sequence using the *method of successive balance points*. The moment of the single combined weight equals the sum of the three individual moments. For balanced weights, CG is on the axis of rotation.

7-12   Location of CG-Weight Point by Mathematical Analysis

Question: Is it **always true** that the *CG*-weight point can be located by the method of successive balance points, **no matter** the sequence of combining the individual weights, the number of weights added together, or the position of the weights?*

To answer this research question, we now search for a more general proof of the qualified hunch-law, which was based on the experimental results of a few simplest cases. The task is a difficult one. However, the solution will be made possible by some of the most powerful search-thinking tools used in theoretical science: symbols and diagrams, and the postulate-proof-theorem form of reasoning using the logical theorems of mathematics.

We shall try to locate by mathematical analysis the *CG*-weight point for any three weights located in one dimension (on a straight line). A more rigorous analysis requires consideration of the more general cases of *any* number of weights in one dimension, in two dimensions (plane), and in three dimensions (space). However, the simplest case that we have selected to research by mathematical analysis will serve our purposes. Its solution will

---

* This is like "It is **always true** that $M = P - 1$, **no matter** the sequence of byes, the number of byes, or the number of players" in the tennis tournament puzzle. As in the tennis tournament puzzle, this research question calls for a proof to achieve knowledge of greater generality and certainty.

suggest the more general solutions, with minimum mathematical complexities. More important, the research procedures will expose, in an elementary way, some of the basic scientific thinking used in theoretical science.

First, try to solve an example involving 3 specific weights distributed on a straight line as shown in Fig. 7-15. The weights are 12 lb, 8 lb, and 20 lb.

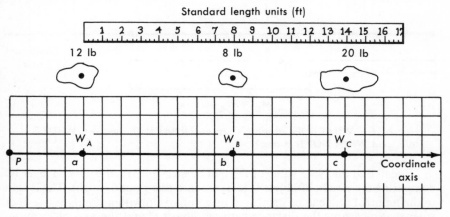

Fig. 7-15. Where is the CG for the three weights of 12, 8, and 20 lb distributed so that their CG's are on the straight line? Where is the CG for any three objects of weights W_A, W_B, W_C distributed at any distances *a, b,* and *c,* from *P* on a straight line?

Where is the *CG*-weight point? Is it on the left or the right of the 8-lb weight? What if there were 137 weights (like 137 players in a tennis tournament)? Must we apply the method of successive balance points 136 times to locate the *CG?* And once the *CG* is located, how can we be sure that the sequence of combining the weights does not change the location of *CG?*

We can analyze these questions about this "three-weight" problem by using the marvelous powers of algebra. Consider any three weights with their individual *CG*'s distributed in a straight line. (Fig. 7-15). The NSU symbols (in lb) for the individual weights are W_A, W_B, and W_C, and the NSU symbols (in ft) for the displacement of their *CG*'s are *a, b,* and *c,* the distances from an arbitrary origin point *P* of a coordinate axis. *Question:* By mathematical analysis, formulate a quantitative relationship that will predict the location of the *CG*-weight point.

7-13   Algebraic Representation of a Moment

The task seems formidable, but let's begin with the simplest case of just *one* moment. How can we represent a moment by algebraic symbols?

Consider a simplest case of object *C* located on the right side of the axis of rotation *X,* causing a clockwise moment about *X.* The correspondence of this moment to symbols and diagram is shown in Fig. 7-16. The NSU value of the *CG*-weight of object *C* (in lb) is W_C, and its displacement from the origin point *P* of the coordinate axis (in ft) is *c.* The distance of the axis of rotation *X* from *P* (in ft) is *x.*

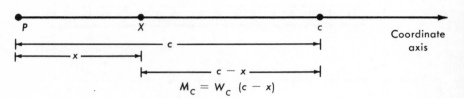

$$M_c = W_c (c - x)$$

Fig. 7-16. WHAT is the algebraic representation for a moment, WHEN is it true, and WHEN NOT is it true?

Recall that the NSU value of W_C can be measured on a balanced lever by comparing the weight of object C to a standard one-pound weight. The length of the moment arm can be measured by comparison with a standard one-foot ruler that measures the distance between object C and the axis of rotation, (which is equivalent to measuring the distance c and then subtracting from this number the distance x). The product of these two numbers (W_C) $(c - x)$ equals the moment of object C (in ft-lb).

These numerical values and arithmetic operations can be summarized in the following compact algebraic statement. (This algebraic representation of a moment is also diagrammed in Fig. 7-16)

DEFINITIONS OF SIGNIFICANT ATTRIBUTES

NSU Symbols	Quantity Compared to Standard Unit
M_C	Moment of object C due to its position (compared to a ft-lb~)
W_C	Weight of object C (compared to a lb~)
c	Any displacement of object C from origin point P of coordinate axis (compared to a ft~)
x	Unknown displacement of axis of rotation X from the origin point P (compared to a ft~)
$c - x$	Length of the moment arm of object C (compared to a ft~)

$$M_C = W_C (c - x)$$

We shall attempt to reason from our more established knowledge about moments and center of gravity, using as postulates two basic relationships: QLF 7-2, the $\Sigma M = 0$ law for balanced levers, and QLF 7-3, the *CG*-weight law with the concept of the *CG*-weight point for calculating moments. The method of analysis will be, first, to use algebraic symbols to represent the significant attributes of the postulate statements, second, to manipulate logically these algebraic symbols by utilizing the powers of algebraic theorems until new testable relationships are deduced.

To what extent does this algebraic formula represent the measured value of a moment; that is, when is $M_C = W_C (c - x)$ true, and when is it not true?

1. Is $c - x$ a correct representation of the length of the moment arm, **no matter** where the origin point P is located on the coordinate axis? As a specific example, let the object C be located at point Q which is 4 ft to the right of the axis of rotation so that its moment arm is 4 ft. Then calculate what happens to the value of the moment arm, stated algebraically as $c - x$, when the origin point P is: to the left of X; at X; between X and Q; at Q; and to the right of Q.

The solutions of these numerical examples are tabulated in Fig. 7-17. Note that the calculated value of $c - x$ always produces a moment arm that has a numerical value of 4. We conclude, therefore, that it is **always true** that the algebraic symbols $c - x$ represent the correct numerical value of the moment arm, **no matter** where the origin point P is located on the coordinate axis from which c and x are measured.

2. What if the weight is on the left or the right side of the axis of rotation? Is the algebraic formula $M_C = W_C (c - x)$ still true? Again consider a specific example, such as the object C having a weight of 5 lb and being located either to the left of the axis of rotation X or to the right of X (Fig. 7-17).

The solution of these two cases, when the moment arm is 3 ft, is reported in the figure. Note that the algebraic formula $M_C = W_C (c - x)$ yields the correct numerical value for the moment, when algebraic signs are made negative for a *CCW* moment about X and positive for a *CW* moment, **no matter** the position of object C on the coordinate axis, or whether c is larger or smaller than x.

3. What if a force were directed upwards instead of downwards about the axis of rotation, such as that exerted by a toy balloon capable of lifting 5 pounds? Represent the numerical value of the upward force W_C as a negative number, signifying that the upward force (causing a *CCW* moment about X) is opposite in direction to a downward weight (causing a *CW* moment). Check for yourself that $M_C = W_C (c - x)$ is **always true, no matter** whether the direction of the force is up or down or in any direction about X, the axis of rotation.

We can summarize our investigations about the algebraic representation of a moment as follows.

QLF 7-5	Algebraic Representation of a Moment
WHAT	It is **always true** that $M_C = W_C(c - x)$,
WHEN	**no matter** the location of origin point P on the co-ordinate axis, whether the object C is located on either side of the axis of rotation, or whether the force W_C is directed upwards, downwards, or in any direction about the axis of rotation,
WHEN NOT	**but not if** the positions of P, axis of rotation, and the CG of object C are not on a straight line.

This is a significant algebraic discovery! It means that it is **always true** we can describe any moment in the *same* algebraic form of $M_C = W_C(c - x)$, **no matter** the measured values of W_C, c, and x!

Location of origin point P	Standard length units (ft)  1 2 3 4 5 6 7 8	Measured value from P (in ft)		Calculated value (in ft)
		c	x	(c − x)
To left of X	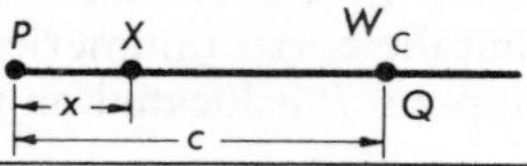 P X W$_C$ Q	6	2	$6 - 2 = 4$
At X	 P W$_C$ X Q	4	0	$4 - 0 = 4$
Between X and Q	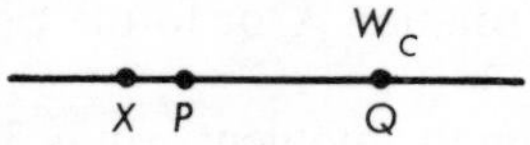 W$_C$ X P Q	3	−1	$3 - (-1) = 4$
At Q	 W$_C$ X Q P	0	−4	$0 - (-4) = 4$
To right of Q	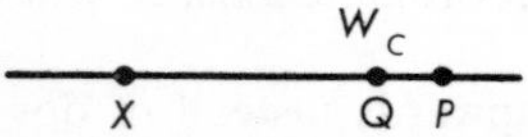 W$_C$ X Q P	−1	−5	$-1 - (-5) = 4$

Location of object C of W$_C$	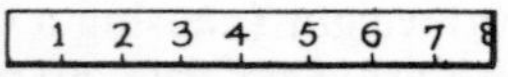 1 2 3 4 5 6 7 8	Measured value			Calculated value (in ft -lb)
		W$_C$lb	c (ft)	x (ft)	$M_C = W_C(c-x)$
To right of X	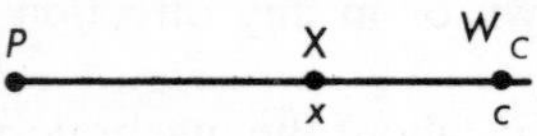 P X W$_C$ x c	5	8	5	$M_C = 5(8 - 5) = 15$
To left of X	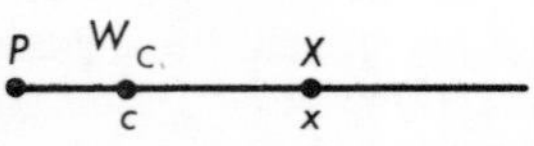 P W$_C$ X c x	5	2	5	$M_C = 5(2 - 5) = -15$

Fig. 7-17. The algebraic symbols $M_C = W_C(c - x)$ have a one-to-one correspondence with real moments.

7-14 *Algebraic Proofs about* CG *and Moments*

Now that we have discovered a correct and invariant form for a moment which corresponds to all real cases,* we can use this algebraic thinking tool to solve for the location of *CG*. We return to the "three-weight" problem (Fig. 7-15) in which the weights are placed so their *CG*'s are on a straight line and balanced about an unknown point of rotation, *X*.

Since each moment can be described by the same algebraic form discovered earlier, $M_C = W_C(c - x)$, **no matter** the location of *X*, we can let *x*, the unknown displacement (in ft), be the coordinate number for any point on the coordinate axis. Thus, we write the fundamental postulate about balanced levers $\Sigma M = 0$ in the following algebraic form:

$$W_A(a - x) + W_B(b - x) + W_C(c - x) = 0 \text{ (in number of ft-lb)}$$

A problem of balanced objects has been reduced to one of elementary algebra! The mathematical statement written as an NSU equation involves six numbers that can be measured (W_A, W_B, W_C, *a*, *b*, and *c*) and one unknown number *x*. Here the NSU symbol *x* represents the distance that the axis of rotation is from *P*, which for the balanced lever is also the location of *CG*. Hence, when we algebraically solve for the unknown value of *x*, the number will represent the location of *CG*! To emphasize this fact, we will write *x* as x_{CG} to signify that *CG is located at x*.

Follow now the mathematical operations that lead to the solution of x_{CG}. These elementary algebraic steps are illustrated, step by step, in the postulate-proof-theorem structure in Fig. 7-18.

Note the results achieved by the algebraic solution of this simplest case of three balanced weights. The newly deduced Theorem 2 predicts that the numerical value of x_{CG} equals the ratio of two quantities; i.e., x_{CG} *equals the algebraic sum of the individual moments about any arbitrarily chosen point of origin P divided by the sum of the individual weights!*

The new theorem now enables us easily to locate the *CG* of the three-weight problem previously left unanswered in Fig. 7-15. The problem has now been reduced to a calculation in arithmetic. To illustrate, we can conveniently choose *P* to be located where the 12-lb weight is located (where length *a* is zero), and when we substitute the numerical values of W_A, W_B, W_C, *a*, *b*, and *c*, the prediction is that *CG* is 8.6 ft from *P*.

$$x_{CG} = \frac{W_A a + W_B b + W_C c}{W_A + W_B + W_C} \text{ (in number of ft)}$$

$$x_{CG} = \frac{(12)(0) + (8)(8) + (20)(14)}{12 + 8 + 20} = 8.6$$

To test your understanding, calculate the location of *CG* when *P* is located at any position on the coordinate axis *X*. Also locate *CG* by the method of successive balance points. In each case, we predict that your answer will be the same as the above calculated value. The *CG* of the three individual weights lies 0.6 ft to the right of the 8-lb weight.

---

* This discovery is like finding the key relationship $E = M$ in the tennis tournament puzzle.

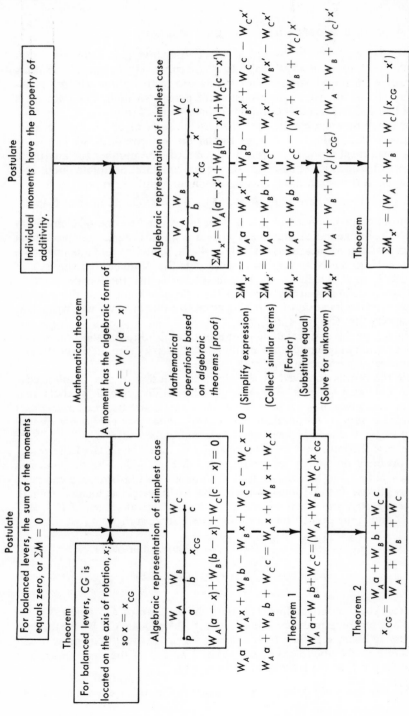

Fig. 7-18. Can you derive an algebraic formula for locating CG, reasoning from laws of moments for balanced levers?

Fig. 7-19. Can you prove that any number of moments can be combined to one moment produced by sum of weights at CG, reasoning from the postulate that moments are additive?

We can now generalize for the case of 137 or any number of weights on the coordinate axis. The algebraic proof would be similar to that just achieved for the three-weight problem. For four weights, for example,

$$x_{GG} = \frac{W_A a + W_B b + W_C c + W_D d.}{W_A + W_B + W_C + W_D}$$

Thus, we can write a more general formula for the location of *CG* for any number of weights on the coordinate axis.

DEFINITIONS OF SIGNIFICANT ATTRIBUTES

NSU Symbols	*Quantity Compared to Standard Unit*
x_{CG}	Displacement of *CG* from any arbitrary origin point *P* on coordinate axis (compared to a ft$^\sim$)
ΣM_i	Sum of the individual moments about P, $W_A a + W_B b + W_C c + \dots$ (compared to a ft-lb$^\sim$)
ΣW_i	Sum of the individual weights, $W_A + W_B + W_C + \dots$ (compared to a lb$^\sim$)

$$x_{CG} = \frac{\Sigma M_i}{\Sigma W_i}$$

Similar algebraic formulas can be derived for the more general cases when the weights are distributed on a two-dimensional plane (e.g., the square cardboard lever) and in three-dimensional space (e.g., the wire cage). We shall not treat these more general cases here; instead, we will search for orderly relationships in the situations when the three weights are *not* balanced and x_{CG} is *not* on the axis of rotation. What happens then?

Consider the simplest case of any three unbalanced weights on the coordinate axis when the moments do not equal zero about an axis of rotation at displacement x' from *P*. (See Fig. 7-19.) For this case of unbalanced moments, the sum of the moments equals the addition of the individual moments, and $M_C = W_C (a - x')$ is the algebraic form for any moment about the axis of rotation at displacement x'. (See QLF 7-5.) Accordingly, we now can easily write the algebraic sum of the individual moments:

$$\Sigma M_{x'} = W_A (a - x') + W_B (b - x') + W_C (c - x')$$

As shown step by step in Fig. 7-19, we can, using elementary algebraic theorems, search these symbols for new relationships between *CG* and moments. A discovery occurs when we notice that the quantity $W_A a + W_B b + W_C c$ is related to x_{CG}, as noted in Theorem 1 of the preceding proof in Fig. 7-18. When equal values are substituted into the postulate-proof-theorem structure diagrammed in Fig. 7-19, a new algebraic theorem is deduced.

Note that the new theorem $\Sigma M_{x'} = (W_A + W_B + W_C)(x_{CG} - x')$ is in the same algebraic form as $M_C = W_C (a - x')$, where $W_A + W_B + W_C$ act like a single combined weight with a moment arm equal to $x_{CG} - x'$! Thus the theorem predicts with great certainty what we previously observed experimentally in a few simplest cases in Secs. 7-10 and 7-11. By reasoning from the fundamental postulate that moments have the property of additivity, we have achieved a mathematical proof that *the individual moments can be reduced to a single moment when the weights are combined to a single weight at the CG!*

A general mathematical expression can be stated for any number of weights about any point of rotation x'. Again the algebraic proof would be similar to the proof just achieved for the three-weight problem. Thus, a more general relationship for the sum of the individual moments is as follows:

DEFINITIONS OF SIGNIFICANT ATTRIBUTES

NSU Symbols	Quantity Compared to Standard Unit
$\Sigma M_{x'}$	Sum of the individual moments about axis of rotation X of displacement x' (compared to a ft-lb~)
ΣW_i	Sum of the individual weights (compared to a lb~)
x_{CG}	Displacement of *CG* from arbitrary origin point P on coordinate axis (compared to a ft~)
x'	Displacement of axis of rotation X from P (compared to a ft~)

$$\Sigma M_{x'} = (\Sigma W_i)(x_{CG} - x')$$

Note that for the special case of balanced levers, x_{CG} is on the point of rotation, so that $x_{CG} = x'$. Consequently, the moment arm of ΣW_i equals zero ($x_{CG} - x' = 0$). The right side of the equation above goes to zero so that $\Sigma M_{x'} = 0$, which is what we first experimentally discovered for balanced levers.

As a quick check of this new theorem, use it to calculate the moment produced by the weights in the three-weight problem of Fig. 7-15 about a point of rotation 2.6 ft to the right of the 20-lb weight. The theorem predicts (again when P is located at the *CG* of the 12-lb weight) that

$$\Sigma M_{x'} = (\Sigma W_i)(x_{CG} - x')$$
$$\Sigma M_{x'} = (12 + 8 + 20)(8.6 - 16.6) = -320 \quad \text{(in number of ft-lb)}$$

When the sum of the individual moments about the axis of rotation is calculated, the value in ft-lb also is a *CCW* moment of -320.

$$\Sigma M_{x'} = M_A + M_B + M_C$$
$$\Sigma M_{x'} = (12)(-16.6) + (8)(-8.6) + (20)(-2.6) = -320$$

We can summarize the results of our investigation by the methods of mathematical analysis of this simplest case of the three-weight problem in the following qualified law form.

QLF 7-6	Algebraic Representation of the Single Moment Produced by the *CG*-Weight Point
WHAT	It is **always true** that on a coordinate axis about any axis of rotation *X*, the sum of the moments equals the single moment that would be produced by the *CG*-weight point, or $\Sigma M_{x'} = (\Sigma W_i)(x_{CG} - x')$,
WHEN	**no matter** the origin point *P* from which the positions are measured, the number or measured value of the weights, the location of the axis of rotation or the weights on the coordinate axis, or whether the moments are *CW* or *CCW*,
WHEN NOT	**but not if** the *CG*'s of the weights are not on a straight line.

Chapter 8

Potential Energy and Buoyant Force

8-1 Balanced Lever at Any Rotated Position

Place a pin through the exact center-of-gravity point of the cardboard fish (Fig. 8-1). The fish remains balanced, **no matter** to what position the object is rotated, because the moment arm of the weight concentrated at *CG* is always zero, and consequently the sum of the moments about the pin is always zero.

Now freely suspend two weights, say, 20 and 10 paperclips, from a straight line passing through the *CG*, so that they balance each other, and the cardboard fish lever rests exactly in the horizontal position. Then rotate the lever to any other position, but before you let go of the lever, make a prediction. Will the weights oscillate back to their original position, continue to move downward, or remain stationary?

If you try this, you will see that the balanced lever remains at rest, **no matter** the angular position of the balanced lever!

Will the balanced lever remain at rest in any angular position if the friction at the axis of rotation is greatly reduced? We can design and build a low-friction, balanced lever, using a meter stick as the lever. Drill a hole exactly at its *CG*, and insert a hollow cylindrical ball bearing to hold a cylindrical rod about which the lever will rotate. Drill four more holes, and insert ball bearings at the 10-, 30-, 70-, and 90-cm marks, making sure that the centers of the ball bearings are on a straight line. Through each of these ball bearings, hang bent hooks of equal weights. When different weights are suspended from the hooks (because of the ball bearings), the weights hang in a vertical direction, **no matter** the rotated position.

For the simplest case, balance a 100-gram and a 200-gram weight on the precision lever. Once the balanced lever is set into slow rotation by a small force, it continues to turn for a long time because of the nearly negligible friction forces acting to retard the motion. When the balanced lever is stopped in any rotated position, it remains at rest at its new angular position.*

What is the law? Why does this complex, balanced lever, rotated at its

---

* How well this precision balanced lever remains at rest in any rotated position depends on several factors: whether the hooks always hang in a vertical direction, how much the lever bends when in the horizontal position, whether the ball bearings are on a straight line, etc.

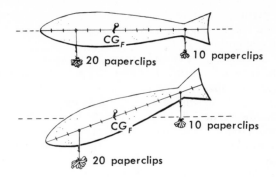

Fig. 8-1. Will this fish lever balance in any rotated position? Why?

CG, remains at rest even though the positions of the objects change with re-spect to the axis of rotation?

To search for a logical explanation, we again will use the methods of mathematical analysis and the reasoning style of Euclidean geometry (pos-tulate-proof-theorem structure). We will use our search-thinking tools of idealized limiting cases and symbols and diagrams to try to solve the simplest case for any two weights.

The complex, balanced lever designed to rotate at its *CG* can be idealized and represented as a geometrical diagram in Fig. 8-2 as follows:

1. *If the lever is always balanced,* the total moment is always zero. Since the moment is not affected by the weight of the lever, we can imagine that the lever is weightless and can be diagrammed as a geometric line.

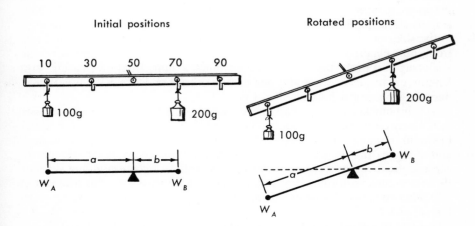

Fig. 8-2. Diagram of the idealized limiting case of the balanced rotated lever.

2. *If the centers of all the bearings lie on a straight line, and the lever is rigid,* these points of suspension from which the objects hang in any rotated position can be idealized as existing on a straight-line lever and at a fixed distance from each other.

3. *If the objects A and B hang from frictionless bearings, the CG's of* the objects always will hang directly below the points of suspension no matter the rotated position. Since we can move the *CG*'s on the vertical line passing through the points of suspension without affecting the value of the moments, we can assume the vertical distances from the *CG*'s to the points of suspension to be zero. Hence, the *CG*'s, and therefore the weights of *A* and of *B*, W_A and W_B, can be considered to be on the straight-line lever at any rotated position.

4. *If the bearings that support the lever are frictionless,* the lever rotates at constant speed forever when given the slightest push.

Follow now the proof that this *idealized limiting case of the balanced lever,* outlined in Fig. 8-3, will remain at rest at any angular position.

Scientific Law $\Sigma M = 0$ as Postulate. $\Sigma M = 0$ for the horizontal, balanced lever being investigated. Thus for any two weights, W_A and W_B, at distances a and b on opposite sides from the axis of rotation, we can state: $W_A a = W_B b$. Will the law $\Sigma M = 0$ be true when the balanced lever is rotated from the horizontal to any other position?

Notice that in the rotated position, the moment arms are shorter, and they decrease to zero when the lever is rotated to a vertical position. The moment arms of W_A and W_B in the rotated positions are shown dotted in the diagram and are symbolized as a' and b'. Hence the moment at the rotated position on the left side is $W_A a'$ and on the right, the moment is $W_B b'$. Can we *prove* that these two moments are exactly equal: $W_A a' = W_B b'$, **no matter** the rotated position?

Geometrical Correspondence of Moment Arms. The discovery of another key attribute in this search for a proof occurs when we notice that the moment arms a and b are related to the moment arms a' and b'. The lengths of the moment arms are related to each other because they correspond to the sides of two similar geometrical triangles! This hunch has come to us from our experience with geometry and the concepts of similarity for analyzing past problems. Of course, the hunch assumes that the bearings and lengths on the lever have the one-to-one correspondence with points and lines in geometry as tabulated in Fig. 8-2.

Using our knowledge of geometry, we see that the two shaded triangles in the figure can be proved to be similar in shape by the use of geometrical theorems dealing with equal corresponding angles (the angle between a and a' equals that between b and b'; two other angles are $90°$). Hence we can use the theorem from geometry that the ratios of corresponding sides of the two triangles are equal. For the geometric example shown, this means that side a is two times as long as side b, i.e., $a/b = 2$, and side a' is two times as long as side b', i.e., $a'/b' = 2$; thus $2 = 2$ or, in symbolic form, $a/b = a'/b'$. (This last relationship will hold, of course, for any other ratio of a/b.)

Algebraic Analysis. We now have two true statements: $W_A a = W_B b$ is a logical consequence of the scientific law $\Sigma M = 0$, and $a/b = a'/b'$ is a

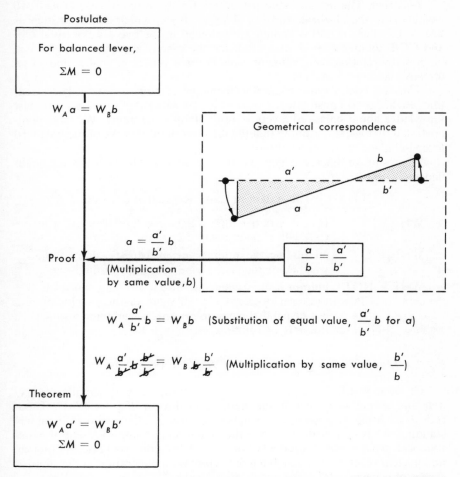

Fig. 8-3. Can you prove that the idealized limiting case of the balanced lever will balance at any rotated position?

relationship about lever arms derived from proved mathematical theorems about similar triangles. From these two symbolic equations, can we logically deduce that $W_A a' = W_B b'$?

Once again, logical reasoning about the relationships of the complex array of symbols representing many values (W_A, W_B, a, b, a', b') is greatly facilitated by an algebraic analysis, as outlined in Fig. 8-3. Note that the analysis involves the application of two basic mathematical theorems to achieve the desired proof: (1) An equation remains true when the value on each side of the equation is multiplied by a same value; (2) An equation remains true when a symbol in the equation is replaced by a symbol of equal value.

Theorem. The newly deduced theorem for the simplest case of any two weights is in the algebraic form of $W_A a' = W_B b'$, which can be written as $\Sigma M = 0$, when $+$ and $-$ values are assigned to the two always equal *CW* and *CCW* moments. A similar proof for the case of any three weights can be done by relating their moment arms in three similar triangles, and so on for any number of weights.

Thus we have examined another example of how an established scientific law $\Sigma M = 0$ (postulate), analyzed by mathematics (proof), led to new knowledge about balanced levers $W_A a' = W_B b'$ (theorem). We have demonstrated by logical reasoning that the idealized limiting case of the balanced lever is balanced in any position.

The results of this investigation can be summarized in the following qualified law form:

QLF 8-1 The Balanced Lever Rotated at *CG* Law	
WHAT	It is **always true** that a balanced lever rotated at its *CG* will remain balanced in any position,
WHEN	**no matter** the number or measured value of the weights, or the size, shape or weight of the lever,
WHEN NOT	**but not if** the weights do not always hang vertically, the lever does not remain rigid, or the weights are not suspended from points on a straight line through the axis of rotation.

8-2   A Machine Designed from the $W_A a' = W_B b'$ Law

Of what worth is the new scientific knowledge experimentally observable and logically capsuled in the mathematical form $W_A a' = W_B b'$? Theoretical scientific knowledge is valuable because it offers increased understanding. It also offers the basis for the invention and improvement of many practical technological products, such as television, rockets, antibiotics, and nuclear reactors, to name but a few. Here is an illustration of this applied aspect of science.

Suppose that the hypothetical Giant Lever Engineering Company (just organized for the purpose of this creative search pattern) designs and builds gigantic lever machines. The company decides that the prototype experimental model (Fig. 8-2) and the special scientific law $W_A a' = W_B b'$ derived from the idealized limiting case of the balanced lever (Fig. 8-3) can be used as the theoretical basis for inventing a gigantic steel lever machine (shown in Fig. 8-4) to lift tons of railroad cars to various levels in a multistoried train switchyard. The engineers propose that the lever be designed to approach the *idealized limiting case*, in which the mechanical lever behaves as a straight, rigid, weightless, and frictionless lever. The following conceptual experiment illustrates how this specially designed machine could lift a 2-ton and a 1-ton car.

First, push the cars (which move on low friction wheels on railroad tracks) to a position where the cars can be hooked to long cables from the

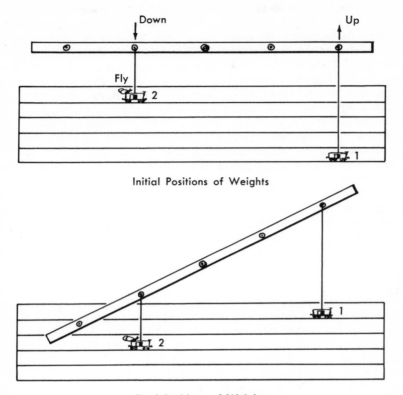

Initial Positions of Weights

Final Positions of Weights

Fig. 8-4. This theoretical giant lever machine based on the idealized limit-ing case of the balanced rotated lever is designed to move tons of weight with the aid of a trained fly.

lever. Next, suspend from the lever the two cars whose weights are in the ratio of 1 : 2, so their moment arms are in the ratio of 1 : 2. This obedience to the $\Sigma M = 0$ law of moments keeps the lever balanced, so it can be rotated by the application of a small force. Now move away the tracks.

What is the minimum force required to move the tons of weight? We can reduce the value of the retarding *friction forces* by the use of better ball bearings in the balanced lever, and we can also reduce the value of the *inertial forces** of the railroad cars by moving the weights slower. In fact, we can imagine these friction and inertial forces to be reduced to smaller and smaller values, until the limit is reached at which the total force needed to move the lever approaches a zero value. In other words, we can use the search-thinking tool of the *idealized limiting case* of the balanced lever to conduct *conceptual experiments* independent of the heat and motion effects.

---

* These friction forces which cause heat and inertial forces that oppose the change in motion of the objects are important concepts developed in Chapter 9.

To dramatize this idealized limit, that the force required to move the 2-ton and 1-ton weights can be made to approach a zero value, imagine that we train a fly to operate the Giant Lever Machine. The fly could sit on one of the weights on the *down* side of the lever and this minute force will cause the weights of the idealized limiting case of the balanced lever to slowly rotate. As the weights approach the desired levels, the fly moves to a weight moving upwards and slows the rotation to a stop. Conceptually, a 2-ton and a 1-ton weight can be moved several stories by a trained fly! To further idealize this lever system, we can imagine that the supporting cables are unstretchable and weightless and that the different tracks are horizontal levels on which weights can be placed and moved by a zero force.

In short, we have conceived of an idealized limiting case of a balanced lever that can move a system of many weights to many new levels by negligible influence (a fly). Yet this conceptual fantasy is based upon a prototype experimental model and rests upon the firmly established scientific law of moments. As you shall see, such idealized limits are effective search-thinking tools in scientific analysis.

8-3   Conceptual Experiments with Idealized Limiting Case of Balanced Lever

What are the theoretical limitations to what the lever machine can do? Can we design a giant lever and train a fly to move any number of weights to any horizontal level? More specifically, suppose that the job required the seven weights shown in Fig. 8-5 to be moved up and down a multistoried building from their initial to final positions. Can you, as an engineer of the Giant Lever Company, invent a lever machine of *any* design that will do the job with the aid of a trained fly? The weights can be moved along their horizontal levels with zero force. Any number of weights can be attached to the lever and moved at one time, and they can be moved in any sequence. Try to solve this problem before reading the next paragraphs.

We can try to solve the simplest relevant cases by performing conceptual experiments. Four trials and their solutions are discussed below and tabulated in Fig. 8-6, using symbols and diagrams.

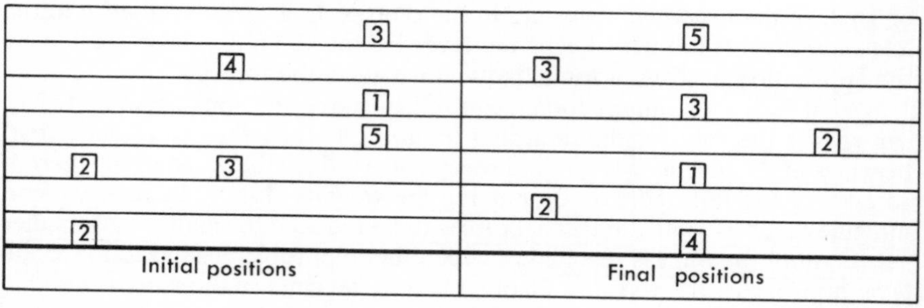

Initial positions		Final positions	
	[3]		[5]
[4]		[3]	
	[1]		[3]
	[5]		[2]
[2]	[3]	[1]	
		[2]	
[2]			[4]
Initial positions		Final positions	

Fig. 8-5. Can you move all seven weights (in lb) from their initial to final positions (distances in ft) with the idealized balanced lever and a trained fly? In this idealized limiting system, the weights can be moved horizontally with zero force.

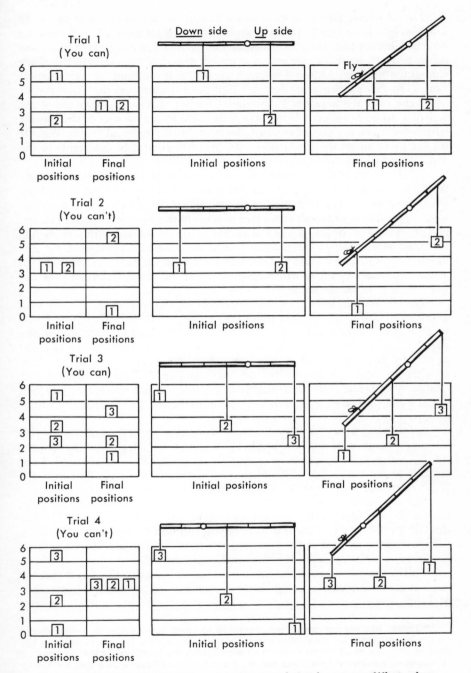

Fig. 8-6. Results of conceptual experiments of simplest cases. What scientific law can account for why you can solve trials 1 and 3 and why you can't solve trials 2 and 4?

Trial 1. What kind of a lever machine can we design that will move the 2-ton weight from the 2nd floor and the 1-ton weight from the 5th floor, so both weights are placed on the 3rd floor? Since the 1-ton weight is to be moved down 2 levels, hook a cable to it and the other end of the cable to the *down* side of the horizontal lever 2 length units on the lever from the axis of rotation. (On this particular design, 1 length unit marked on the lever is 1½ times the distance between 2 horizontal levels). Likewise, since the 2-ton weight is to be lifted up 1 level, attach its cable to the *up* side of the lever 1 length unit from the axis of rotation. Swing aside the railroad tracks. Whistle for the fly to sit on the *down* side until the lever rotates both weights to the 3rd horizontal level.

Trial 2. Can this lever machine and the trained fly move both weights from the 3rd floor, so the 1-ton weight is moved to the "ground" or 0 floor while the 2-ton weight is moved to the 5th floor? Try to solve this problem. You will find that **you can't** move two weights to this new arrangement on the lever balanced according to the law of $\Sigma M = 0$ and rotated with a negligible force, **no matter** where the lever is placed, how long it is designed, or how much it is rotated. We must wonder why. Is it possible that we *cannot* design a machine that can move with negligible force the seven weights to the desired arrangements shown in Fig. 8-5?

Trial 3. We can balance all three weights for trial 3 on a sufficiently long giant lever at the appropriate point on the *up* and *down* side of the lever, according to the law $\Sigma M = 0$, and then rotate the balanced weights to the desired final positions with the aid of the fly. Another method would be to move any two weights at a time, **no matter** the sequence, until all three weights are located in the desired final arrangement.* Thus the Giant Lever Company can state, with some degree of confidence, that several designs and operational procedures are available for moving the three weights to their new positions.

Trial 4. Let us try to move the three weights to their final positions with one single rotation of the idealized balanced lever. Attach each of the weights on the appropriate *up* or *down* side of the lever, so they are suspended according to the law of $\Sigma M = 0$. However, neither you nor the fly can move the three weights to the desired arrangement, **no matter** what.

But can you move the weights two at a time, in some manner, using the balanced lever and the fly, so that all weights eventually are moved to the desired levels? You can try and try, but **you can't** do it, even with a hundred different trials, **no matter** the length of the lever, how many times the lever is moved, or in what sequence the weights are moved.

This is the second case that we cannot solve. We ask again: Is it that we are not clever enough in using the lever machine to move the weights two at a time, but if we search long enough the desired weight configuration can

---

* This is like placing successive paperclips to cover two squares at a time in the checkerboard puzzle or combining two weights at a time on a cardboard lever by the method of successive balance points. In the present investigation what law will predict the kinds of possible weight arrangements moved by the idealized balanced lever with negligible force?

be achieved with the idealized balanced lever? Or could it be that a funda-mental law yet to be discovered places theoretical limitations on what weight configurations can exist in nature; and, like man's historical quest for the perpetual motion machine, any search for ways to move all the weights to certain configurations is certain to fail?*

Study the tabulated results in Fig. 8-6 of our conceptual experiments dealing with the 4 trials of simplest cases. Search the data. *Search the numerical relationships until you can predict and check by conceptual experiments the more general problem of Fig. 8-5 of whether all seven weights can be moved by the balanced lever and the fly.* As you may suspect, an im-portant discovery of a significant numerical attribute of nature can occur at this time that can bring order to the data without the necessity of referring to the concepts of "moment" or "balanced lever"!

8-4   *Discovery of an Acor Pattern for Potential Energy*

Perhaps you were "lucky". Because of your detailed familiarity with the experimental results, and your ability to recall similar scientific patterns previously experienced, you may have "discovered" one of the most impor-tant acor patterns in science.

Attribute. You may have focused attention upon a very significant attribute of nature. Its scientific name is *potential energy* and its abbreviation symbol is *PE*, often used as both a quantity- and a number-symbol. Its cal-culated value in our experiments is equal to the product of two numerical quantities: *the measured value of a force due to weight multiplied by the measured value of the height of the weight measured from any arbitrary horizontal level.*

If you focus upon this attribute, you can bring order to the data compiled by the conceptual experiments, because the measured values of individual potential energies can be related into a *conservation law* that predicts why certain weight configurations are not possible, **no matter** what.

Let us display a quantity of potential energy, then, and describe opera-tions for measuring it. If you have not yet found this *law of conservation of potential energy,* the discovery may occur as you now gain more familiar-ity with the numerical aspects of this significant attribute.

Standard Unit. Suspend a weight of 1 pound at a height of 1 foot above a horizontal table top. We can define this as *1 foot-pound of potential energy* (abbreviated as 1 ft-lb~), relative to the table top, which is chosen as the arbitrary reference level. In terms of our NSU conventions, we can write this *1 standard potential energy unit* of 1 ft-lb~ as **pufl**~ for **p**otential energy **u**nit in **ft-lb**. We shall preserve it with our other physical standard reference units of length, weight, and moment in the vault at our hypothetical Bureau of Standards and Measurement.

Comparison Operation. How shall we measure an unknown quantity of

* If you have mastered the concepts of invariance and conservation taught in Chapters 1 to 5, you may have already intuitively hunched that these operations can't be done because of a *conservation law.*

potential energy, or *PE?* As an example, consider a 2-lb chipmunk on a lower branch of a tree. Let us calculate the quantity of *PE* due to its *CG*-weight, relative to the "ground" and also to the "upper branch" levels.

If the *CG* of the chipmunk is 3 ft *above* the ground, the numerical value of the height relative to the ground can be defined as a *positive* value. Hence, the potential energy due to the chipmunk's weight above the "ground" horizontal level also is a *positive* value equal to 3 ft~ × 2 lb~ = 6 ft-lb~. A quantity of 6 ft-lb~ of potential energy has the same potential energy value as 6 of the 1 pufl~ standards displayed in the Bureau of Standards and Measurements. This is equivalent to 6 one-pound objects located one foot above the horizontal level, or a single one-pound object located 6 feet above the horizontal level, or any values of weight and height whose product equals 6 ft-lb~. Now, if the chipmunk is 2 ft *below* the upper tree branch, its height relative to the upper tree branch will then be designated by a *negative* value, such as —2 ft. Calculations lead to a *negative* value of potential energy measured relative to the "upper branch" horizontal level of —2 ft~ × 2 lb~ = —4 ft-lb~. A quantity of —4 ft lb~ amounts to 4 times the *PE* contained in 1 pufl~, and the minus sign signifies that the weight is below the arbitrary horizontal reference level, so the direction of the vector force due to the weight is away rather than towards the horizontal level.

The example of the chipmunk is a particular numerical illustration of a quantity of potential energy. How can we represent by algebraic symbols the measured value of *any* quantity of potential energy (as we accomplished in Sec. 7-13 for a moment)? Consider any object *A* with its *CG* at any position with respect to an arbitrarily chosen horizontal reference line. The quantity of *PE* due to the position of object *A* can be stated algebraically as a *quantity*-equation as:

DEFINITIONS OF SIGNIFICANT ATTRIBUTES

NSU Symbols	Quantity Compared to Standard Unit
$(PE)_A$	Potential energy of object *A* due to its position (compared to a ft-lb~)
W_A	Weight of object *A* (compared to a lb~)
h_A	Height of *CG* of object *A* with respect to any horizontal reference level (compared to a ft~)
$W_A h_A$	Weight of object *A* multiplied by height of *CG* of object *A* (compared to a ft-lb~)

$(PE)_A{}^{\sim} = W_A{}^{\sim} h_A{}^{\sim}$
(in potential energy)

or as an *NSU* equation

$(PE)_A = W_A h_A$
(in number of pufl~)

As illustrated by the chipmunk example, W_A is a positive number; thus $(PE)_A$ may be either a positive or negative number, depending on whether object *A* is located above or below the horizontal reference level.

Thus, the measurement of *PE* is seen to include three parts of the logic of measurement discussed in Sections 3-2 and 3-8. The key attribute is *PE*. A standard unit is the ft-lb. The comparison operation is: (a) compare weight with the lb (i.e., find NSU in lb); (b) find height above reference level in ft (i.e., find NSU in ft); and (c) multiply the two NSU values to get the NSU value of *PE* in ft-lb. These are the **aco** of an **acor** pattern which is completed in the next section when the orderly relationship discovered is that *PE* is a conaddian.

8-5 Discovery and Algebraic Representation of the Law of Conservation of Potential Energy

Let us now go back to the idealized limiting case of the balanced rotated lever and the tabulated results of the conceptual experiments. What was your hunch? Did you notice a fundamental numerical relationship about the calculated values of the individual potential energies in trials 1 and 3? By some insightful inductive leap, did you see that *the sum of the individual potential energies in the initial positions equals the sum of individual potential energies in the final positions?*

In trial 3 of Fig. 8-6, for example, with respect to the 0 horizontal level, perhaps you observed the following numerical relationships about the potential energy units: For the initial positions, in number of ft-lb, the sum of the three potential energies equals $(1)(5) + (2)(3) + (3)(2) = 17$; and for the final positions, the sum of the NSU potential energies equals $(3)(4) + (2)(2) + (1)(1) = 17$.

The total potential energy is conserved! The NSU values of potential energy are *conservative* and *additive* in the solvable problems of trials 1 and 3. The sum of the individual potential energies for the idealized rotated lever does not change when the weights change from their initial to final positions, **no matter** the number or magnitude of the weights moved, the sequence or number of times the weights are moved, the changes in height of the weights, or the size of the circular arcs that the weights are moved through by the different lengths of the lever. On the other hand, note that the total potential energy is *not* conserved in trials 2 and 4. Can it be that *no* machine can ever be built (based on the idealized limiting case of the balanced rotated lever and the fly) that is capable of moving weights to arrangements that violate this law of conservation of potential energy?

Does the law predict whether the more general case of 7 weights can be solved? Let us try it. Select *any* arbitrary horizontal level as zero reference level from which to measure the heights.* The arithmetic calculations show for the example in Fig. 8-5 that the NSU value of *PE* (in ft-lb) is 67 for the initial and final arrangements of weights, when the lowest weight is considered at zero reference level. Since the total potential energy is conserved, we can

---

* Check for yourself, trying simplest cases, that the law of conservation of potential energy is **always true, no matter** the horizontal reference level from which the heights are measured. This is like testing that the choice of origin point *P* does not affect the algebraic representation for a moment.

predict that the 7 weights *can* be moved to the final arrangement with the idealized balanced lever and the trained fly.

To test this prediction, conceptually balance the 7 weights on the idealized balanced rotated lever, as your experiences with moments and trained flies have taught you to do. As predicted, the 7 weights can be moved to the final positions with one rotation of the lever.

Thus a main discovery for the idealized balanced rotated lever is that *the sum of the individual potential energies is always conserved* (a constant value). This law can be simply written as an NSU equation, as follows:

$$\Sigma PE = \text{constant} \quad (\text{in number of ft-lb}^\sim)$$

We have called this relationship of a **con**servative, **add**itive, **inv**ariant attribute of **n**ature the *law of conservation of potential energy* for the idealized balanced lever.

If the total potential energy is always constant or conserved, then, obviously, there can never be any change in the total quantity of potential energy. Thus, another way of stating the law of conservation of potential energy is that *the total change in the potential energy is always zero*, which we can write in symbols as an NSU equation.

$$(\Delta PE)_{\text{total}} = 0 \quad (\text{ in number of ft-lb}^\sim)$$

Here $(\Delta PE)_{\text{total}}$ represents the sum of the individual changes in potential energies in ft-lb; or $(\Delta PE)_{\text{total}} - (\Delta PE)_A + (\Delta PE)_B + (\Delta PE)_C + \ldots$. (When object A moves *up*, $(\Delta PE)_A$ is a $+$ number signifying that there has been an increase or gain in *PE*. If object A moves *down*, $(\Delta PE)_A$ is given a $-$ value to indicate a decrease or loss of *PE*.)

You may already have found this second way of viewing the conservation law. In the solvable trials 1 and 3, where potential energy is conserved, you will find the same invariant relationship, $(\Delta PE)_{\text{total}} = 0$. The *increase* in potential energy always equals the *decrease* in potential energy. The total change in NSU of potential energy in ft-lb for each of the 4 trials has been calculated and tabulated in Fig. 8-7.

8-6 Proof of the Law of Conservation of Potential Energy

Can you demonstrate a *proof* that the law of conservation of potential energy for the idealized balanced lever, $(\Delta PE)_{\text{total}} = 0$, can be derived as a theorem by mathematical reasoning from the postulate $\Sigma M = 0$? Examine again the detailed proof for the balanced lever at any rotated position presented in Fig. 8-3, but this time focus your attention upon the two *vertical sides* of the similar triangles! If you had noted previously that the two vertical sides correspond to the *change in heights* of the two rotated weights, you could have discovered then, by mathematical analysis, the law of conservation of potential energy! As a test of your understanding, now try to prove that $(\Delta PE)_{\text{total}} = 0$ is true for any number of weights rotated on the idealized balanced rotated lever, before you read the next paragraph.

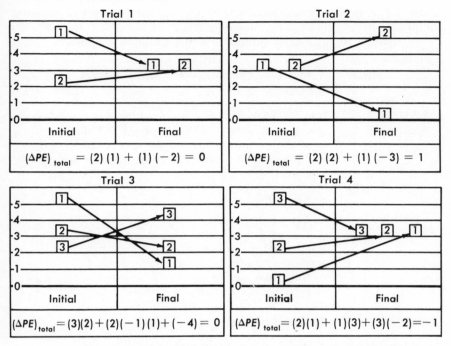

Fig. 8-7. Solutions of simplest cases in terms of conservation law.

The proof is almost identical to the one presented in Fig. 8-3. The postulate statement is $\Sigma M = 0$, or $W_A a = W_B b$. Another true statement is $\frac{a}{b} = \frac{\Delta h_A}{\Delta h_B}$, derived from the geometrical correspondence of the two shaded similar triangles between the *moment arms* (a and b) and the *change in heights* (Δh_A and Δh_B) of objects A and B. When these two true statements are combined algebraically, the theorem $W_A \Delta h_A = W_B \Delta h_B$ is derived, which equals $(\Delta PE)_{total} = 0$ when increases and decreases in heights are accounted for as $+$ and $-$ values. A similar proof for any number of weights can be achieved by these procedures used for the simplest case of any two weights.

$$\boxed{\frac{\Sigma M = 0}{W_A a = W_B b}}$$

$$\frac{a}{b} = \frac{\Delta h_A}{\Delta h_B}$$

$$W_A \Delta h_A = W_B \Delta h_B$$

$$\boxed{(\Delta PE)_{total} = 0}$$

8-7 Qualified Law of Conservation of Potential Energy for a Balanced Rotated Lever

The conceptual experiments dealt with the slow rotation of the idealized limiting case of the balanced meter stick mounted on ball bearings at its center of gravity. The fundamental new insight was the discovery of potential energy and its conaddian properties. The results of our search to this point about potential energy can be summarized in a qualified law form.

QLF 8-2	Law of Conservation of Potential Energy for Idealized Balanced Rotated Lever
WHAT	It is **always true** when a balanced lever system is set into motion with a negligible force and slowly rotates at constant speed, that the sum of the individual potential energies of the suspended weights remains constant, or ΣPE = constant, and therefore the total change in the potential energy equals zero, $(\Delta PE)_{total} = 0,$
WHEN	**no matter** the number, shape, and measured value of the weights, whether the weights are rotated in small or large circular arcs to different horizontal positions, how the potential energy of the individual weights increases or decreases, or what horizontal reference level is chosen to measure the potential energies,
WHEN NOT	**but not if** the lever bends, or there are measurable amounts of motion and heat that reduce the total potential energy of the lever system, or the potential energies change by a measurable amount due to some external disturbance on the weights (e.g., the weights swing back and forth while being rotated, or the change in height alters the values of the weights).

This is a very restricted law of conservation of energy, but it is a big step from the static balanced lever. At present, the law is a hunch based upon conceptual experiments of an idealized limiting case, but the law of conservation of potential energy for levers does work. The law does apply to a whole class of related situations. We shall show in the next section how the law predicts experimental facts about submerged objects in water. Finally, we shall prove that this hunch for a very particular idealized situation is the simplest case of conservation of energy. In Chapter 9, we shall show how the law can lead to the general law of conservation of energy, including kinetic energy and heat energy.

8-8   Discovery of Buoyant Force and Archimedes' Principle from $(\Delta PE)_{total} = 0$

What scientific law explains why it is easier to lift a person when he is floating in water than when he is out of water? How can you measure the weight of a battleship? What causes a helium-filled balloon to rise? These are some of the questions you will be able to answer when you correctly apply this newly deduced law of conservation of potential energy to a new situation to answer the question, "What causes an object to weigh less in water than it does in air?"

As usual, we begin with a specific example and some typical measurements. First, measure the weight of an object C (C is a name-symbol for an unopened can of soup) when it is suspended in *air* from one end of a lever, as shown in Fig. 8-8. Say a typical measured value of the "weight of can when suspended in air" equals 400 grams.* Use the symbol W_{CA} for the NSU weight (in grams) of the can in air. Next, measure the weight of the can when it is suspended in *water*. A typical measured value of the "weight of the object when suspended in water" is 80 grams. Use the symbol W_{CW} for the NSU weight (in grams) of the can in water.

Is it surprising that the number of standard gram weights required to balance the object in *water* is *less* than when it was suspended in *air*? In this illustrated example, why does the can of soup weigh 320 grams less in water than in air: $W_{CA} - W_{CW} = 400 - 80$ (in number of grams)?

Question: Does the law of conservation of potential energy apply for weights raised and lowered in water as well as in air? If so, can we again imagine our idealized balanced rotated lever moving objects up and down that are suspended in water and in air? The problem is to account for the loss of 320 grams.

If we consider the soup can immersed in water and hanging from a string (Fig. 8-8), then the tension (see Sec. 4-3) in the string is found to be always 80 grams, **no matter** how high or low we hold the can. So far as the lever is concerned, it is as if 80 grams of weight were hanging from it. Accordingly, for a balanced lever with equal lever arms, C hangs from one

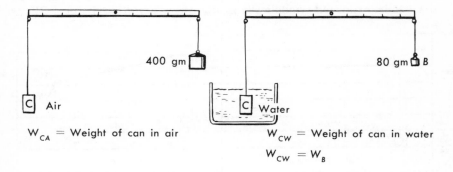

W_{CA} = Weight of can in air W_{CW} = Weight of can in water

$$W_{CW} = W_B$$

Fig. 8-8. Experimental measurements of weight of object C in air and in water.

---

* Another arbitrary standard unit of weight often used in scientific work is the gram~. It can be written as a wug~ (weight unit of a gram).

side and is balanced by a weight B so adjusted that $W_{CW} = W_B$ (in number of grams).

Imagine now that the idealized balanced lever is slowly rotated (see Fig. 8-9), so that the object C in the water is raised 10 cm, while the weight B in the air is lowered 10 cm. Represent these changes of equal heights of B and C more generally as Δh (in number of cm). For low velocities of motion in water there is little resistance, so again the idealized limiting case is approached for conducting conceptual experiments and extending the law of conservation of potential energy.

It requires a "bright" hunch to notice that it is a significant fact that volumes of water and air are also moved by the idealized lever at the same time that the two suspended objects B and C are moved. It is not obvious that as the lever rotates, and as the object C in the water moves up, a volume of water is displaced to slowly fill the space left empty by the object in the water. Neither is it obvious to imagine that the water is displaced from the space finally occupied by the object, so that the *volume of the displaced water moves downward and equals the volume of the object C.*

Similarly, when the weight B suspended in the air at the other end of the lever rotates downward, a *volume of air equal to the volume of weight B is displaced upward.* These volumes of water and air displaced by the objects B and C are represented by dotted lines in Fig. 8-9. The NSU weight in grams of the water displaced by C is symbolized as W_W and the weight of the air displaced by B as W_A.

Now we are ready to apply the law of conservation of potential energy to the conceptualized situation, including the lifting and lowering of the displaced weights of air and water. Hence, *the increase in PE* (due to object C of weight W_{CA} and the volume of displaced air of weight W_A each moving up Δh) *equals the decrease in PE* (due to object B of weight W_B and the volume of displaced water of weight W_W each moving down Δh). This equation can be expressed symbolically as $W_{CA}\Delta h + W_A\Delta h = W_B\Delta h + W_W\Delta h$

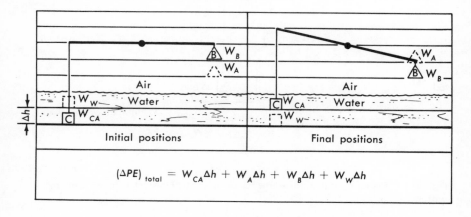

$$(\Delta PE)_{total} = W_{CA}\Delta h + W_A\Delta h + W_B\Delta h + W_W\Delta h$$

Fig. 8-9. **Law of conservation of potential energy applied to a conceptual experiment leading to Archimedes' principle.**

(in number of gm-cm~). Since $W_{CW} = W_B$, and Δh's are identical numbers, we can write the following NSU equation.

$$W_{CA} + W_A = W_{CW} + W_W \quad \text{(in number of gm~)}$$

Reasoning from the law of conservation of potential energy for levers, we have deduced from new conceptual experiments a new scientific theorem, which relates the weights of quantities of air, water, and any other object (such as a can of soup)!

If we consider that the weight of the displaced air W_A is negligible compared to the other three weights, we can further simplify the numerical relationship by omitting W_A. We then can state, as a special case of the derived theorem, that $W_{CA} = W_{CW} + W_W$; or, to state the consequence in another form, we can write:

$$W_W = W_{CA} - W_{CW} \quad \text{(in number of gm~)}$$

This special scientific law was discovered by Archimedes. It is known in science as *Archimedes' principle* dealing with objects at rest in water (hydrostatics). It states that *the weight of the displaced water equals the loss of the weight of the object when measured in air and water!*

To explain why this happens, we can conceptualize the existence of a new attribute of nature: *buoyant force*. It is the force that always acts upward to cause the apparent loss of weight by an amount equal to the weight of water displaced!

Thus, Archimedes' principle predicts that the loss of 320 gm of weight will equal the weight of the water displaced by can C. When we measure the weight of a volume of water equal to the volume of the can, within the experimental accuracy of the measurements, this displaced volume of water weighs the predicted 320 grams. We have achieved our first experimental verification of the law of conservation of potential energy of levers.

In summary, a logical consequence of the application of the law of conservation of potential energy to objects raised and lowered in water was the deduction, and later experimental verification, of a significant new attribute of nature, buoyant force, and a new relationship, called Archimedes' principle. These results are stated in the following qualified law form.

QLF 8-3 Archimedes' Principle	
WHAT	It is **always true** that a buoyant force is exerted upward on any object in a fluid, so that the weight of the object in the fluid is reduced by an amount equal to the weight of the fluid displaced,
WHEN	**no matter** the size, shape, or weight of the object, whether the fluid is water or air, or whether the object is partly in water and partly in air.
WHEN NOT	**but not if** . . . . (None observed in these experiments.)

8-9   Argument that Idealized Balanced Rotated Lever
Is Simplest Case of Conservation of Energy

Our investigation has concentrated on the idealized limiting case of the balanced lever. The lever rotates at a constant, very slow speed, and the changes in potential energy of the two weights are exactly equal and opposite —thus, the total energy is constant. We now make an assertion. The simplest meaningful example of conservation of energy is the idealized limiting case of the balanced lever with two weights in ratio of 2 : 1 at distances from the frictionless bearing in the ratio of 1 : 2. The assertion is argued by the following criteria and reasoning.

1. The simplest example should involve two energies. This follows from the fact that conservation means that as several quantities change, their sums remain constant. The simplest case of this is clearly one involving only two quantities, so that when one increases by a certain amount, the other decreases by an equal amount. The 2 : 1 ideal balanced lever does just this.

2. The two energies in the simplest example should both be of the same kind. This is because it is obviously easier to think about two examples of one sort of thing rather than one example each of two sorts of thing. The 2 : 1 ideal balanced lever satisfies this because the two energies are of the same kind. Both are gravitational potential energies of weights in a room.

3. The one kind of energy in the simplest example should be the simplest kind of energy. Gravitational potential energy of weights in a room is the simplest kind to show and to measure. Measurement involves the combination of three operations, all of which have been learned in elementary grades: first, height is measured, which is simply a length measurement upwards (or at least vertically); next, weight is measured which requires a balance or a lever; finally, the measured values from these two operations are multiplied together. No other energy is as simple to measure. For example, kinetic energy also involves time and velocity measurements, and heat energy involves temperature measurements and a complex of experiments related to heat capacity. The ideal 2 : 1 balanced lever satisfies the requirement of using only this simplest of energies.

4. The fact that one of the two energies increases by the same amount that the other decreases should clearly represent some basic law and not be some sort of accident. This is why the 2 : 1 ratio is used. If there were two equal weights at equal lever arms, equal changes could be a result of symmetry. But for a 2 : 1 ratio, the equality of these changes is seen to result not from symmetry alone, but from the law of levers and from the basic nature of space (as analyzed by the theorems in geometry for similar triangles). Thus, a 2 : 1 ratio is much more meaningful than a 1 : 1 ratio would be. Furthermore, 2 : 1 is the simplest ratio next to 1 : 1. From this, it follows that the simplest example should have precisely the ratio 2 : 1 that we have given it.

From these four points we conclude that the *simplest example of con-*

servation of energy must involve the gravitational potential energy of two weights, one twice as heavy as the other, with the potential energy change of one being equal and opposite to that of the other. The very slowly rotating idealized limiting case of the balanced lever with 2 : 1 ratio achieves exactly these results. Thus we conclude that a very strong (probably irrefutable) argument has been made that the idealized limiting case of the 2 : 1 lever is truly the simplest example of conservation of energy.

Chapter 9

Newton's Laws, Mass and Energy Concepts, and History

9-1 Introduction to Mass and Time

In this chapter we shall discuss a number of the most important, remaining invariance principles and acor patterns in mechanics. Much of this material will be presented as a survey, although suggestions and outlines of logical reasoning like that used for weight, vector forces, moments, and potential energy are presented sometimes in small type or as problems.

To make the link with conventional textbooks clearer, QLF forms are presented in the body of the text, the wording being only a little altered from conventional writing to fit the QLF form. For the same purpose we do not use the tilde consistently. Where the formulas are common ones found in many books, we sometimes omit the tilde and the equation-qualifiers so that the equations take their conventional forms.

Two particularly important quantities that are used for the first time in this chapter are time and mass. Time is so familiar a conaddian that we shall not discuss it except to remark that in relativity it loses its conaddian properties.* The concepts of velocity, speed and acceleration depend on time. The relationship of mass to the more familiar, everyday simpler concept of weight of Chapter 3 is discussed in Sec. 9-3.

The chapter ends with a historical review of creative search patterns that led to the logical structures of mechanics.

9-2 Speed, Velocity, and Acceleration, $S = \frac{1}{2}gt^2$

Speed is what you read on the speedometer of your car. The idealized limiting case of speedometer would read instantaneous speed: a moment after you had accelerated so that the car was going faster, the speedometer would indicate how many miles you would go in one hour if you kept exactly at the speed you had at that instant.

Velocity means vector speed exactly as displacement in Fig. 5-4 means vector length. A proxy arrow for vector speed or velocity can be drawn on paper next to a map showing the actual path much as the zeroed number vectors in Fig. 5-4 were drawn next to Square City. We shall use the symbol $s^{\sim}$ for speed as a quantity and s for its NSU value and v or $\vec{v}$ for velocity.

---

* See Isaac Maleh, *op. cit.*, Chap. 7.

The magnitude of v is s, just as the magnitude of a force in Fig. 5-7 is a tension in a string.

The expression v^2 (or $\vec{v} \cdot \vec{v}$ in advanced vector symbolism) simply means s^2 or speed squared. Kinetic energy of a body depends on speed through v^2 and since

$$s^2 = v^2 \quad \text{(in number of speed squared units)}$$

it does not matter which is used. Speed-squared units are $(\mathrm{lu/sec})^2$ or $\mathrm{lu}^2/\mathrm{sec}^2$, in general, and $\mathrm{m}^2/\mathrm{sec}^2$ in a system that uses the 1 meter for 1 lu.

Acceleration is the instantaneous speed of the needle of an ideal speed-ometer. If this needle started at 0 mph (miles~/hr~) and moved up steadily so that it passed one 10 mph division every second, this would represent an acceleration of 10 mph per second or 10 miles~/hour~ $\times$ sec~, the example discussed in Sec. 3-3.

Acceleration is what you feel during takeoff of a jet transport. You are pushed back into your seat and you feel a little heavier. This effect is readily understandable on the basis of Newton's $\vec{F} = m\vec{a}$ law discussed in Sec. 9-8.

Acceleration is not what gives you a funny feeling when an elevator starts down or stops after a fast trip up; what you feel then is a *change* in acceleration. You can feel this also if you bring your car to a stop with steady pressure on the brake pedal. Just as the car comes to a dead stop, the front end bobs up, and you feel a jar and push deeper into your seat. This jar occurs at the instant that the deceleration, or negative acceleration, produced by braking drops to zero. You can make a smooth stop by easing off the brakes so that the acceleration drops slowly to zero.

Newton recognized the importance of acceleration when he formulated his second law of motion: $\vec{F} = m\vec{a}$, where $\vec{F}$ is force, m is mass, and $\vec{a}$ is acceleration. This law, expressed as a qualified-equation, and the general form of conservation of energy are two of the most important concepts of this chapter. To understand $\vec{F} = m\vec{a}$, one must understand acceleration, in its vector form, as well as velocity. As discussed in the introduction, the balance of emphasis selected for this book permits only an outline to be presented in this chapter.

The concepts required by $\vec{F} = m\vec{a}$ are comparable in complexity to those involving displacement and forces, and can be put into orderly rela-tionships using the same thinking tools. We shall limit our discussion to a few simple examples, treating in this section the case of constant accelera-tion that leads to the famous formula for falling bodies.

The general conclusions stated in following sections about conservation of energy will be presented in a form that is not dependent on working through the following logical structures printed in small type.

The famous falling body formula of Galileo, discussed historically in Sec. 9-10, is the qualified-equation

$$S = \tfrac{1}{2} g t^2 \quad \text{(in number of ft)}$$

where $g = 32.2$ ft/sec^2 is the acceleration of gravity, t is the number of sec of fall, and S is the number of ft of fall. This is an NSU qualified-equation and has the same form in any units for length and time measurements.

The t^2 term can be understood by transferring knowledge relevant to the sum of a series of odd integers:

$n =$ number of the odd integer	1	2	3	4	5	6
number size of the odd integer	1	3	5	7	9	11
sum of odd integers up to the nth one	1	4	9	16	25	36

The general result is that the sum of n odd integers starting with 1 always adds up to n^2.

Next consider the relationship of these sums to the length obtained in the conceptual experiment of adding n sticks of wood end to end: the first stick is one ft; the second, 3 ft; the third, five ft, etc. After you have put down 1, 2, 3, . . . n sticks, you have a row 1, 4, 9, . . . n^2 ft long.

Now suppose a toy jet-propelled car (a slow one, at that) starts when a stop watch reads zero and reaches the end of the first stick when the stop watch reads 1 sec$^\sim$, i.e., when $t = 1$ (in number of sec$^\sim$); the end of stick 2 at $t = 2$, etc.

The toy car goes 1 ft in the first second, 3 ft in the second second, 5 ft in the third second. This means its average speed for the first second is 1 ft/sec; for the second, 3 ft/sec; for the third, 5 ft/sec, etc. Its average speed increases 2 ft/sec every sec so that its average acceleration is 2 ft/sec per sec or 2 ft/sec^2.

This analysis correctly suggests the following conclusions that precise mathematical analysis (best done using the mathematical thinking tools of **calculus** that Newton invented for such purposes) confirms: a constant acceleration $a = 2$ ft/sec^2 produces a distance of t^2 ft in t sec and an instantaneous velocity of $2t$ ft/sec, which is exactly equal at the mid-second instants to the average velocity for each one-second interval.

If every stick were made twice as long, while the time of one sec$^\sim$ per stick were kept the same, then all the distances and velocities and, consequently, the acceleration also would be twice as great so that $a = 4$ ft/sec^2. For these two cases, with sticks 1, 3, 5, and 2, 6, 10 ft long, the distances travelled are correctly given by the same formula $S = \frac{1}{2}at^2$ with $a = 2$ in the first case and $a = 4$ in the second case. The instantaneous speed is $s = at$ so that $t = s/a$ and $S = \frac{1}{2}s^2/a$ in both cases. These two formulas for S for constant acceleration are very useful in understanding kinetic energy.

If each stick were exactly 16.1 ft long the distances would be 16.1 t^2 and the acceleration would be 32.2 ft/sec^2 and the velocity would be 32.2 t (in number of ft$^\sim$/sec$^\sim$). These last values are in agreement with experimental observations on falling bodies. They give $S = \frac{1}{2}gt^2$ where g is the **acceleration of gravity**:

$$g = 32.2 \quad \text{(in number of acufts}^\sim\text{)}$$

where acufts$^\sim$ is used to stress that acceleration is a conaddian having its own standard unit with "fts" meaning the ft and sec system. In the meter-second system g is 9.80 m/sec^2 where m is the meter. In general $g^\sim = 32.2$ ft$^\sim$/(sec$^\sim$)$^2 = 9.80$ m$^\sim$/(sec$^\sim$)^2(in acceleration).

A falling body has a vector velocity which changes only in the vertical direction, the vector direction of $g^\sim$. A consequence is that when a bomb leaves an airplane it starts down initially so that from the airplane it looks as if it were dropped from a platform at rest.(How Galileo's creative search discovered $g^\sim$ is discussed in Sec. 9-10.)

To illustrate the conaddian property of speed, imagine a freight train of flat cars going 30 miles per hour; a trainman walks from car to car at 2 miles per hour. He starts forward from the caboose just as the caboose crosses Zero Grade Crossing. Six minutes later (0.1 hour), he has walked 0.2 miles ahead of the caboose which itself has moved 3 miles. He has moved 3.2 miles down the track from Zero Grade Crossing in 0.1 hour, so that his speed is $10 \times 3.2 = 32$ miles per hour. The fact that $32 = 30 + 2$ illustrates that speeds are additive.* Similarly, velocity is a vector conaddian.

---

* This additivity has WHEN NOT situations in relativity. See Isaac Maleh, *loc. cit.*

9-3   Mass, Momentum, and Conservation of Momentums

Mass is a conaddian attribute of matter closely related to weight. A set of experiments, like those for measuring weight, can be carried out to establish the conaddian properties of mass. All these experiments depend upon effects involving velocity and acceleration. A brief outline of one possible method will suffice here.

Mass is a measure of an amount of matter. We select bottle B_1 of Fig. 3-7, or alternatively the standard kilgram, as our SU of matter or mass. Two bodies can be compared for mass as follows: Make an experiment like a head-on collision on a highway. The two masses slide on frictionless tracks and are equipped so that they clamp together automatically when they collide. Just after collision the combined mass can either stop dead or move in either direction, depending on the relative sizes and speeds of the masses. It is found that the balance condition of stopping dead involves an invariant ratio for the two masses. If B_1 moves at one speed $s_1{}^\sim$ and the unknown at a speed $s_2{}^\sim$, then when the balance condition occurs $s_1{}^\sim/s_2{}^\sim$ **always** has the same ratio, **no matter** what the speeds are, **but not if** the speeds are large enough to involve relativistic effects. The ratio of $s_1{}^\sim/s_2{}^\sim$ is the mass m_2 of the unknown in NSU, with B_1 as the SU of mass.

These experiments, like those with moments in Chapter 7, show that there are two new conaddians involved. The lever experiments accepted as a postulate that lever arm lengths are conaddians. Then from the experiments themselves it follows that moments and weights are both conaddians.

The collision experiments assume to begin with that speeds are conaddian and then establish that masses are conaddians and so also is the vector quantity **momentum.** The proxy on paper for momentum is an arrow proportional to m, the NSU value for mass, and to s, the NSU value for speed; the arrow has the direction of the actual motion.

The mass comparison experiment depends on a law closely resembling the law of levers. If two masses m_1 and m_2 in NSU move with vector velocities $\vec{v_1}$ and $\vec{v_2}$, when they interact, the head-on collision corresponds to taking speed along the x-axis so that v_1 becomes s_{1x} and v_2 becomes s_{2x}; and if $s_{1x}/s_{2x} = -m_2/m_1$, then $m_1 s_1 + m_2 s_2 = 0$, both before and after collision. This two-body example is a simplest case of the law of **conservation of momentum.**

$$\Sigma m_i \vec{v_i} = M\vec{V} = \text{const} \quad (\text{in vector momentum})$$

where $M = \Sigma m_i$ and V is the velocity of the center of mass, or CG.

The most basic experimental fact that is disclosed by these experiments is this: take an unknown body A; then take another body B as SU for both weight and mass. Measure the unknown against the SU. This produces two NSU values—one for weight, call it $W_B^A = W_A{}^\sim/W_B{}^\sim$, and another for mass, call it $M_B^A = M_A{}^\sim/M_B{}^\sim$; then QLF 9-1 says that it is **always true** that $W_B^A = M_B^A$. This QLF is one of the most fundamental facts of nature.

The invariant attribute of weight of QLF 3-4 is thus seen to concern a more fundamental invariant attribute of nature than weight. The postulates that best lead to orderly relationships that explain these observations are Einstein's postulates of relativity. Newton's gravitational theories put the facts in order, also, but more as observed laws than as theorems from more basic postulates.

For our purposes, QLF 9-1 means that we can equally well call our weight values mass values when the same body is used as a reference standard. Accordingly, we can equally well use M or m or W for NSU symbols for amounts of matter. Mass is a far more invariant property of a body than is weight. The mass measurement collision experiment will work equally well when done by astronauts in a MOL (manned orbiting laboratory) as it will on earth, and will give the same NSU values even though the bodies have lost all their weight in orbital flight.

9-4   From the Pendulum to the General Law of Conservation of Energy

Concepts of velocity and speed are essential in extending the famous law of conservation of energy from the very restricted case of the idealized balanced lever to conservation of mechanical energy. This extension can be based on relatively straightforward observations of one or more pendulums. A vitally important simple case was studied and interpreted by Galileo (See Sec. 9-10). His experiment consisted of releasing a pendulum bob B to let it swing down from a height $H^{\sim}$ above the horizontal floor F on a string from an initial point I to a position S where the string hits a nail N. The bob then swings up on an arc of a smaller circle to a reversal point R, where it stops and then retraces the path backwards. As Fig. 9-1 shows, Galileo observed that the CG of B rose nearly to the same height $H^{\sim}$ at R as it started from initially at I.

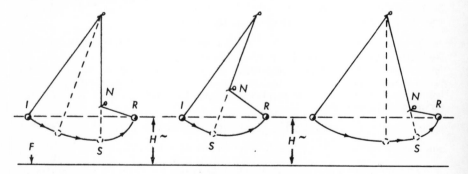

Fig. 9-1.   **One demonstration of conservation of energy by Galileo.**

Fig. 9-1 illustrates the experiment for the idealized case of a bob taken to have all its weight at a point. The results can be summed up by saying that (this is QLF 9-2) it is **always true** that the potential energy lost as the bob swings down and gains speed is recovered as the bob slows down during its upswing, **no matter** where the nail is placed, **but not if** our observations are precise enough to detect losses due to friction.

A direct consequence of this observation, together with additional observations on pendulums described for Fig. 9-2, is that the conaddian *PE~* is converted to another conaddian form of energy of motion, called **kinetic energy** or *KE~*. The amount of energy that a body has by virtue of its motion can be calculated from its velocity or speed. One very important result obtained in Sec. 9-5 is that doubling the speed increases the energy fourfold. This strong dependence of energy on speed emphasizes the importance of the speed concept in mechanics.

When *KE~* is calculated and added to *PE~* for the pendulum bob, the sum of the two, namely the total energy *TE~*, is found to remain constant throughout the swing. The reasoning presented in Sec. 9-5 leads to an acor pattern for expressing the *KE~* of a weight *W* moving with a velocity *v* so that the amount of *PE~* the weight contains can be expressed in the same SU of energy as its *PE~*.

The reasoning required to reach the conclusion about the *KE* formula is like that followed for weight, vector forces, moments, potential energy, and buoyancy. Sec. 9-5 presents a condensed version as deductions reached from the observations of Figs. 9-1 and 9-2.

The resulting law of conservation of energy obtained in Sec. 9-5 can be stated as follows: (QLF 9-3) It is **always true** that a set of pendulum bobs hanging on strings and interacting by pulling on each other by additional strings has a constant total energy *TE~* calculated by adding at any instant the NSU values TE_1, TE_2, TE_3, etc. for all the bobs:

$$\Sigma TE = \text{constant} \quad \text{(in number of energy units)}$$

where the sum is over all the bobs. This sum *remains constant,* **no matter** how many bobs or strings are involved or how they move, **but not if** there are appreciable losses of energy due to friction and heat or to stretching of the strings.

The logic of QLF 9-3 can be compared to the Take 1 or 4 game of Sec. 2-3. Conservation of *PE* in QLF 8-2 is like conservation of remainder for QLF 2-2 *when the only permitted play is "take away 1"*. QLF 9-3, which adds *KE* to *PE,* is like adding the play "take away 4". What, we may ask, is similar in energy consideration to QLF 2-3 that says that the remainder is conserved by all plays of the form "take 1 plus a multiple of 3"? The next laws deeper than conservation of energy in physics are the postulates of quantum mechanics. These show (QLF 9-4) that in all individual processes **no matter** what interactions between electrons, protons, neutrons, etc. occur or how much energy goes into radiation (light, etc.), it is **always true** that the total energy is conserved. This QLF includes heat energy, electric energy, and chemical energy, the energies discussed in Sec. 9-6, since all of these result from energy of elementary particles and radiation. No really satisfying, simpler postulate system for conservation of energy has been found than quantum mechanics. Many physicists hope that one will be discovered that will add an elegant and compact new acor for energy.

In the next sections we shall consider CSP's that show how mechanics contributes acor structures relevant to conservation of energy. (The survey parts are set in this size type, and condensed acor patterns are set in small type.)

9-5   Analysis of Kinetic Energy and the Pendulum; $KE = \frac{1}{2}mv^2$

The idealized pendulum has for its bob B_a in Fig. 9-2(a) a heavy weight conceptually compressed to a point at its center of gravity. The bob hangs from a fixed point on an inextensible, weightless string. An actual pendulum made of an 8 oz lead fish weight is a good approximation. When left undisturbed the bob hangs straight down with its CG at the lowest point, QLF 7-1.

The SU we shall use in this section will be called the lu~ for length, the sec~ (or ordinary second for time) and the mu~ for mass and the wu~ for weight. Both the wu~ and the mu~ are invariant attributes of nature associated with the same standard unit of matter which might be any of those in Fig 3-7. The SU for speed and acceleration are the su~ $= 1$ lu~$/1$ sec~ and the accu~ $= 1$ su~$/$sec~ $= 1$ lu~$/($sec~$)^2$. The unit of PE is the wu~ $\times$ lu~ or pu~.

Bobs B_a, B_b, B_c, and B_g all have m mu~ of mass and also m wu~ of weight. B_g weighs 2 w~. All the strings are L lu~ long, except for (g), which is $4L$ lu~ long. Next, suppose that B_a is held to one side so that it is A lu~ in straight-line distance from its lowest point or minimum PE position. For a small pull, A the straight line cord differs by a negligible percentage from the arc length that B_a has actually moved. At distance A lu~, B_a is h above the minimum where $h = A^2/2L$ as can be established by similar triangle reasoning represented in part (e): The triangle with hypotenuse A lu and short side h lu is similar to the two big triangles each with hypotenuse L lu and short side $(A/2)$ lu; consequently

$$h = A^2/2L.$$

We shall next demonstrate how the $h = A^2/2L$ theorem from geometry can be used as a key attribute postulate in an acor pattern which shows that **kinetic energy** KE must be proportional to (mass or weight) times (speed)^2. The other postulates needed for the proof are the observations reported in Fig. 9-2.

What is kinetic energy? Suppose that at $t = 0$ sec~, B_a is released from a stationary start at a distance A_a lu and a height h_a lu above its minimum so that its initial PE~ is PE_a~ $= mh_a$ pu~ $= mA_a^2/2L_4$ pu~. After 1 sec it has lost its initial PE_a~ as it moves through the minimum position. As Galileo observed, this PE_a pu cannot really be lost because after 1 sec~ more, the pendulum regains its full initial PE_a pu~. In fact (for the ideal no-friction case) it regains its PE_a pu~ every 2 sec. This is **intermittent conservation.**

The lost PE_a is evidently not lost, but is stored in the motion at the minimum point. Evidently, motion contains something that can be converted to PE; it is called KE. Observation (5) of Fig. 9-2 shows that doubling the weight of bob B_d compared to B_a doubles the PE loss, but leaves the motion the same. Hence, the KE in a moving bob must double if the weight of the bob doubles.

If the bob B_b is pulled out half as far as B_a, then its $PE_b = \frac{1}{4}PE_a$ and by observation (2) its speed at the bottom is half as fast. Hence, reducing the speed by a factor of two reduces the KE by a factor of four.

How fast does B_a move at the minimum? How do we determine its speed? The concept of speed for bob B_c in (c) is easy because (c) swings in a circle at a constant speed of one full circle or $2\pi A_a$ lu~ in exactly 4 sec~ so that its speed is $s_c = (\pi A_a/2)$ (in number of su).

Bob B_a does not have constant speed. It has zero speed at the ends of its swing. At the bottom its instantaneous speed is exactly equal to S_c su by observation (4). B_a gets this speed of $s_c = A_a/2$ (in number of su~) by losing a height $h_a = A_a^2/2L_4$.

What orderly relationship exists between h_a and the speed s_c which it produces, or which in turn will raise it to h_a again? Substitute $A_a = 2$ s_c/π into $h_a = A_a^2/2L_4$ and find $h_a = 2s_c^2/\pi^2L_4 = s_c^2/(\pi^2L_4/2)$

This expression is in accord with observation (8): Suppose that (a) and (g) have

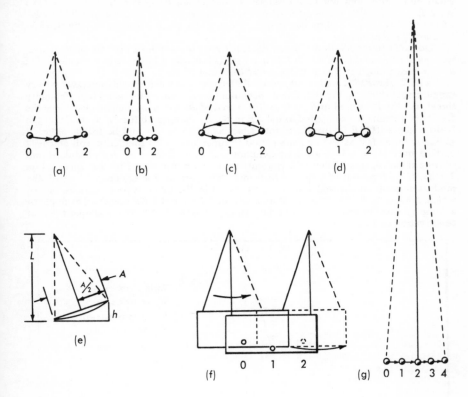

Fig. 9-2. Ten observations about pendulums. (1) The 4-sec~ pendulum (a) is L_4~ $= 3.99$ m long (13 ft) and has a period of 4 sec: If its bob, name-symbol B_a, starts at time 0 sec, it will reach its minimum position in 1 sec, the far side at 2 sec, the bottom again at 3 sec, and return to original position at the end of 4 sec. For the idealized limiting case, it repeats with a period of 4 sec~. (2) If a second identical pendulum (b) is pulled out half as far and started simultaneously with (a), it will keep in step. (3) If a third identical pendulum (c) is started simultaneously with (a) and (b) with a side push so that it swings in a circle, it keeps in perfect step with (a) and (b). (4) If the radius of (c)'s circle is equal to the amplitude of (a)'s swing and you observe (c) directly behind (a), then the bob of (a) will continue to hide that of (c) except for a nearly imperceptible up and down motion for (a). (5) A pendulum like (a) but with a bob twice as heavy stays perfectly in step with (a). (6) A point pendulum of lenght L when pulled out until its straight line distance to its minimum point is A rises a height $h = A^2/2L$ (proof by similar triangles). (7) Every point of a door, including the doorknob (the black dot), hung on two lines L_4~ long swings through an arc like (a) and is synchronized with (a). (8) A pendulum (g) of length L_8~ $= 4L_4$~ has an 8-second period exactly twice as long as that of (a). (9) In general, two pendulums of length L and L' have periods T and T' where $(T'/T)^2 = L'/L$. (10) Synchronism begins to fail by 1% only if A/L is more than 0.3; for $A/L = 0.1$, accuracy is better than 0.1%.

equal bobs. Pull both out to a distance A_a lu~. Then $PE_g = mA_a^2/2L_8 = m$ (¼) $A_a^2/2\ L_4 = $ (¼) PE_a (in number of pu~). Consequently (g) has one-fourth the PE~ of (a) so that it goes half as fast at the bottom. Consequently it takes exactly twice as long as (8) demands.

Door (f) in observation (7) has PE and KE as if every little element of its matter were an ideal pendulum of length L lu like (a). This is why it has exactly the same period as (a) even though its CG is much lower than that of B_a.

Is KE~ plus PE~ equals total energy TE~ conserved when weights interact? A very simple case is shown in Fig. 9-3. The B_a pendulum is identical with Fig. 9-1(a). Geometry shows that the PE stored in B_b is three times that of B_a for equal weights. But since the KE in B_b is negligible compared to the KE in B_a, B_a acquires all the PE as its KE at the bottom. Since its KE is, therefore, four times as much as it would be for B_a alone, it moves twice as fast as (a) and the period is cut in half. This prediction can be easily verified by making a Fig. 9-2(a) pendulum and a matching Fig. 9-3 pendulum and starting them together. They will vibrate with two vibrations of Fig. 9-3, one of Fig. 9-2(a). If they get out of step and then into step again at, for example, 21 to 10, the prediction has been checked with 5% accuracy. Fig. 9-3 involves four energies, one of which, KE_b, is negligible. It is therefore a case of 2 PE's and 1 KE and is an example of a "simplest case" of conservation of total energy just as the 2 : 1 lever is a simplest case of conservation of PE.

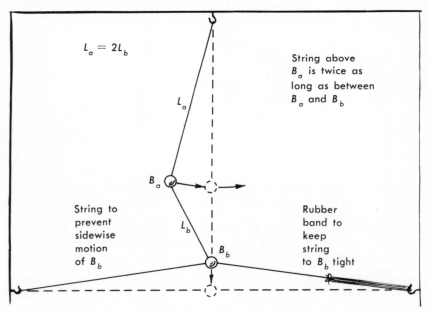

Fig. 9-3. **Example of conservation of energy with interaction between two equal pendulum bobs.**

Pythagoras' theorem can be applied to a comparison of the motions of (a) and (c) to establish that at all points of B_a's swing its PE and its KE add up to a constant, namely $mha = mA_a^2/2\ L_4$ pu~ $= PE_a$.

Scientific purposes require a unit of energy that can be used even in a space capsule, where weight is lost. The appropriate unit is one of kinetic energy, call it the ku~, that corresponds to a mass of 2 mu moving at 1 su. A mass of m mu moving at s su will have $(m/2)$ times as much energy due to its mass ratio and $s^2 = v^2$ times as much due to its speed ratio, where the equality $s^2 = v^2$ comes from Sec. 9-2. (We use v^2 to fit the usual formula for KE.) In ku~ the energy takes the form

$$KE_{m,s} = \tfrac{1}{2} mv^2 \text{ ku}$$

The ratio of the ku~ to the pu~ depends on whether the comparison is made on earth or on the moon or in a space capsule. In a space capsule, the pu~ would represent no energy at all; on the moon, the force of gravity is six times less than on earth. In general, from the falling body equation, we know that an energy of mh pu~ becomes equal to $\tfrac{1}{2}\,mv^2$ ku~ when $h = v^2/2\ g$. This relationship and conservation of energy lead to

$$\tfrac{1}{2}\,mv^2 \text{ ku}^{\sim} = mh \text{ pu}^{\sim} = mv^2/2\ g \text{ pu}^{\sim}$$

from which it follows that

$$\text{pu}^{\sim} = g \text{ ku}^{\sim} \text{ or } \text{pu}^{\sim}/\text{ku}^{\sim} = g$$

This is an equation of **dimensional analysis.** The ratio of these two energies depends on the system of units as well as the field of gravity. This simple ratio of g rather than $2\ g$ occurs because $\tfrac{1}{2}\,mv^2$ is chosen as the kinetic energy formula. The reason for this choice depends on the SU of force used to simplify in Newton's second law so as to obtain $F = ma$ and not $F = \tfrac{1}{2}\ ma$.

The equation $h_a = s_c^2/(\pi L_4/2)$ can be used to measure g since $h_a = s_c^2/2\ g$ by conservation of energy which applies equally well whether s_c^2 is produced by free fall or by swinging on a string. Consequently $g = \pi^2 L_4/4 = 980$ cm/sec^2 for $L_4 = 399$ cm. This result is one of the many successes of theoretical mechanics.

9-6 Heat, Power, and Work

Two other forms of energy are essential to understanding mechanics: heat and elastic energy.

The recognition that heat was a form of energy and not a substance came in the eighteenth century. Benjamin Thompson (Count Rumford), 1753-1814, established this result by studying heat generated while cannon barrels were being bored. A logical structure of heat energy measurement, like that for weight in Sec. 3-8, was made possible by James Prescott Joule, 1818-89, who determined the **mechanical equivalent of heat** [see 1 gram-cal $= 4.185$ joule (in energy) in table below]. When heat energy $HE^{\sim}$ is expressed in NSU for number of pu~ or ku~, it is found that

$$PE + KE + HE = \text{constant}$$

for any system that does not exchange energy with its surroundings.

Elastic energy is what is stored in a spring when, for example, you wind up your watch or your clock or a wind-up toy or when you stretch the rubber in a sling shot. Elastic energies are calculable on the basis of **Hooke's law.** Robert Hooke, 1635-1703, not only discovered and stated his law but used it in the invention of the spiral spring for clocks. Hooke's law is the earliest and classical example of **linear laws** for small disturbances. This law states that within the limit of elasticity (for example, how far you can bend the radio antenna on your car before it stays a little bent) the force (or stress) on a body (such as a spring) is proportional to the strain (how much it is bent or stretched in respect to the shape it would have if left alone). From Hooke's law it can be proved that the elastic potential energy PE_E stored in a spring varies as displacement squared, just as it does for the $h = A^2/2\,L$ formula for the displacement A of a pendulum.

An example of all four energies acting together will illustrate conservation of energy in a more general situation. Imagine object A of Chapter 5, a 1 wub~ weight hanging from one of the tension-gauges of Fig. 5-10. Pull it down with your hand. This stretches the rubber bands. Release it, the rubber bands pull object A upward giving it both KE~ and PE~. It rises to the top of its motion and stops. At this reversal point all the energy furnished by the rubber bands has been converted to PE.

Then A falls again and oscillates up and down a few times and stops. At this point all the originally stored energy in the rubber bands during the down-pull has been converted into heat. If we denote the elastic potential energy in the rubber band as PE_E, then what we would find in a precise study is that $PE + PE_E + KE + HE =$ constant   (in energy) during the oscillation. Each cycle is smaller than the previous one because each time some of the mechanical energy of $PE + PE_E + KE$ has gone into HE.

You can easily sense the relationship between mechanical energy and heat. When you drive downhill using your brakes, mechanical energy goes into heat in the brake drums. They generate smoke and odors and even fail to work if they become too hot. If you rub your hands together hard, your palms become hot. Mechanical energy is turned to heat there. (If you stretch a rubber band while it touches your lips you feel it become warm; but this phenomenon is actually more complex than simple frictional heat.)

The concepts of **work** and **power** are important mechanical concepts. We shall introduce them here since they are particularly convenient in describing the generation of heat. We shall discuss them, using a table of standard units of energy. There are many energy units in use, and here are some relationships, the value of E_B^A being the pure number ratio of the two SU quantities:

Table of E_B^A Values

A〳 B	joule	ft-lb	kg-cal	BTU	kw-hr
joule = newt-m	1	0.738	2.389×10^{-4}	9.48×10^{-4}	2.778×10^{-4}
ft-lb	1.356	1	3.24×10^{-4}	1.286×10^{-3}	3.767×10^{-4}
kg-cal	4,185	3,087	1	3.968	1.162
BTU	1055	777.9	0.252	1	0.2930
kw-hr	3600	2654	0.8599	3.412	1

Definitions:

    ft-lb = energy needed to lift 1 pound-weight 1 foot
    joule = energy of 2 kg of matter moving at speed of 1 meter
             per sec $= 10^7$ erg

erg   = energy of 2 gm of matter moving 1 cm/sec

BTU   = energy necessary to warm one lb of water 1°F (Fahrenheit) = British Thermal Unit

kg-cal = energy necessary to warm 1 kg of water 1°C = 1000 cal

cal   = energy necessary to warm one gm of water 1°C (Centigrade)

kw-hr = kilowatt-hour

The kilogram-calorie is the energy unit used for expressing chemical energies in foods. A 4000-kilogram calorie diet furnishes enough energy to raise your (roughly) 100-kg bodyweight 40°C or 72°F. You use up most of this energy as heat. If all this chemical energy were converted to *PE*, it could lift the 200-kg bodyweight 17,100 m, or 57 times the height of the Eiffel Tower. This correctly suggests why it is so difficult to burn off fat by exercise.

As an illustration of power and work calculation, consider a 6-lb brick sliding down a board that is sloping just steeply enough so that the brick slides at a constant speed of 4 ft/sec. The board has the slope shown in Fig. 9-4(a). It is 20 ft long, with one end on the floor and the other raised 10 ft. During each second, the brick descends vertically 2 ft so that 2 ft × 6 lb = 12 ft-lb of *PE* "flows" into *HE*. A rate of energy flow is called **power.** This power of 12 ft-lb/sec = 16.3 watt is enough to light a 16.3-watt lamp bulb to full brightness.

If the power of the descending brick were used to run an electric generator (like one on a bicycle, for example), and 10 watts of electric power came out, the **efficiency** of the generator would be 10/16.3 = 0.613 or 61.3%.

The force exerted on the brick by the board can be understood by the vector diagram. This is drawn for the case shown in Fig. 9-4 in which the board is supposed to be frictionless (idealized limiting case of a brick supported by a piece of dry ice on a smooth metal plate). For this case the changes in *PE* of the two weights cancel because *B* moves down 10 ft (loss of 6 × 10 = 60 ft-lb) while *A* moves up 20 ft (gain of 3 × 20 = 60 ft-lb). Since *A* moves at constant speed, it is like a weight hanging from a spring balance in an unaccelerated elevator. This conceptual experiment leads to the correct conclusion that it produces a tension of 3 lb in the tension-gauge.

The resulting forces on *B* are shown in part (b): The down-force of gravity, 6 lb; the tension, 3 lb; and the push of the frictionless plane (this latter is perpendicular to *B*'s motion). *B* cannot tell whether the 3-lb force parallel to the plane is caused by tension or by friction. In both cases *B* exerts a force on whatever it is that resists its motion. By this force it imparts energy to whatever it exerts the force on.

Energy that is lost by an object when it pushes on another object or against any resisting force while it moves is called **work.** In moving down the slope, *B* does 3 lb × 20 ft = 60 ft-lb of work on the resisting force. It does the same amount of work in both cases: (1) tension and (2) fric-

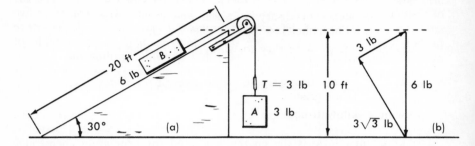

**Fig. 9-4.   Work equals force times distance. (a) This triangle is half an equi-
lateral triangle and is therefore a 30°-60° triangle with sides in ratio 2 : $\sqrt{3}$: 1
by Pythagoras' theorem. When the brick slides at constant speed, the ratio of
friction force resisting sliding to perpendicular force pushing the brick against
the board is $1/\sqrt{3} = 0.58$. This ratio is called the coefficient of friction. For
the brick to be just ready to slide on a 45° board, the coefficient of friction
would have to be 1.00. (When a road becomes wet the coefficient of friction
between a car's tires and the road is reduced, and the car skids easily.)
(b) Vector force diagram for unaccelerated motion.**

tion. In the tension case the energy transferred by the work goes into *PE*
for *A*; in the friction case it goes into *HE* in the board and the brick.

Rate of doing work is a form of power. Some well-known units of
power are the horsepower, the watt, and 1000 watts or the kilowatt, kw:

$$1 \text{ kw} = 1000 \text{ watt} = 1.3410 \text{ hp} = 737.56 \text{ ft-lb/sec}$$

The kilowatt is also the electrical unit of power, and the kilowatt-hour is
the corresponding unit of energy.

9-7   Applications of and Theorems Based on Conservation
of Energy

Conservation of energy is a theorem from the more basic laws of
quantum mechanics, but it can also be used as a postulate or key attribute
in developing acor patterns. To illustrate its power, we shall show how it
gives us insight into the law of moments.

Consider a system of weights mounted on a lever. Suppose the lever is
rocking. It will do work against the forces in its bearings and turn kinetic
energy into heat. It will rock back and forth until either friction or the
bearing holds it in place or until it has reached a position of minimum
potential energy. If it is at minimum potential energy, then its *CG* is as low
as it can get, directly below the axis. In this position it will produce zero
moment about the axis. Hence, zero moment is exactly what is to be expected from the conservation of energy principle including heat energy.
Reasoning based on energy explains the puzzle of the soda straw machine
of Fig. 1-8. The parallelogram geometry ensures that as one horizontal

arm goes down, the other arm goes up an exactly equal amount. The *PE* of the 10 paperclips remains constant: five lose exactly what the other five gain. There is no lost *PE* left over to go into *KE* to make the device move farther when it is disturbed. The soda straw machine is an example of **neutral equilibrium** contrasted to **stable** and **unstable equilibrium.**

Stable equilibrium is what occurs when any motion of the system raises its *PE*. Consequently such a system will move only when energy is introduced from outside.

Unstable equilibrium occurs when there are possible disturbances of the system which lower its *CG* or otherwise decrease its *PE*. If a pencil is standing on its point, perfectly balanced, then if a molecule of air moving with the *KE* of its heat energy budges the pencil off balance, the pencil will start to lose *PE*. This loss of *PE* will be converted to *KE* of the pencil and it will move off balance faster and faster.

Principles akin to that discussed for the parallelogram straw machine underly many other machines; for example, platform scales and also block-and-tackle arrangements and gear boxes or transmissions in cars. Consider how a scale to weigh a truck is made. The platform is mechanically contrived so that it **can move** only parallel to itself; hence, **no matter** where the load is located on the platform, a given motion always produces exactly the same change in *PE* for the load. Consequently, when the counter load, such as the weight on the balance arm of a scale, is so placed that the two changes in *PE* are equal and opposite, neutral equilibrium occurs. A small additional weight whose *CG* is lowest when the indicator stands at balance converts this neutral equilibrium to stable equilibrium. The **mechanical advantage** of the weight you move right or left to balance the scale is the ratio of its up and down motion to the platform motion.

The laws relating forces or loads transmitted through a machine are easily grasped by applying conservation of energy. Work done on one side, say, the platform, must equal work coming out the other side, say, lifting the balance weight.

This conservation law will not work if the machine contains elastic parts that can store elastic energy or sticky bearings that can turn energy to heat.

Block-and-tackle arrangements and automobile gear shifts can be understood in the same way. If pulling six feet of one rope lifts a weight that hangs on six ropes, the mechanical advantage is six, and 100 lb will hold 600 lb. [In Fig. 9-5(a), *A* has a 2 : 1 mechanical advantage over *B*.]

One very great advantage of these conservation of energy methods in mechanics is that they eliminate the need for examining the details, like the bye's in the tennis tournament problem of Chapter 2. *The emphasis of this importance of* **conservation laws** *is one of the chief aims of this book.*

Another form of stability in mechanics is **stability of frequency.** The simple pendulum as discussed in Fig. 9-2 is an example of a very general principle which is this: QLF 9-5 It is **always true** that a system with a potential energy that varies as the square of the disturbance from stable equilibrium and a kinetic energy that varies with the square of the speed will oscillate periodically at an invariant frequency **no matter** whether it undergoes large or small vibrations or whether the *PE* is gravitational or elastic or electrostatic **but not if** the vibrations exceed the limits of the square law relationships.

This principle underlies all clocks, musical instruments and radio and television broadcasting. It is the principle of tuned systems. It is what is involved when two systems are said to be in resonance. It is explained in terms of conservation of energy as follows: Consider the system vibrating with one total energy, call it TE_1. When it is at maximum displacement d_1, its *PE* is $PE_1 = TE_1$. When it goes through its minimum *PE* position, which we have defined as the zero of *PE*, its TE_1 is all in *KE* and $KE_1 = TE_1$. Now vibrate it again, this time with TE_2 which we take equal to 4 TE_1. This means that its displacement from minimum *PE* is just twice what it was before. But its KE_2 is also four times greater than it was before; consequently, its maximum speed is twice what it was for KE_1. Since it has to move twice as far and since it goes twice as fast, it will take exactly the same time as before. *The period and frequency are invariant.* The pitch of a musical tone is the number of vibrations per second. It is this frequency stability law of mechanics that makes the pitch stay the same while the *TE* gradually dies away as energy is lost in heat or radiated as energy in sound waves as the note from a piano string, for example, dies away while staying on key. These results depend on **linear laws.**

This type of motion has a name; it is called **simple harmonic** motion. It is closely related to circular motion for reasons described in connection with observation (4) of Fig. 9-2.

9-8   Newton's Second Law of Motion: $\vec{F} = m\vec{a}$

Probably the most basic law of mechanics in Newton's second law of motion which is expressed as

$$\vec{F} = m\vec{a} \quad \text{(in number of SU of force)}$$

Here are some conceptual experiments that establish it. Make a lightweight tension-gauge as discussed in Sec. 4-3 and Sec. 5-9. Imagine the idealized limiting case of a weightless, very small gauge that can be accurately read even though it stretches a negligible amount.

The standard units for this experiment are the **MKS** set of three: for length—the standard meter consisting of a platinum iridum alloy bar at the Bureau of Standards; for mass—the 1-kg object of Fig. 3-7; for time —the second as furnished by radio signals from the Bureau of Standards.

Hang a replica of the 1-kg standard, call it object *A*, on the gauge and mark it accurately at the 1-kg weight value. Next put the 1-kg object on a horizontal track on a frictionless, weightless cart. *A* sits at rest. The up-push of the table balances the down-force of gravity, QLF 5-6. Now attach one end of the tension-gauge to *A* and the other end to a string. The string passes over an ideal weightless, frictionless pulley to weight *B* which weighs 2 kg. When *B* is released, it moves down half as far as *A*. (The mechanical advantage *A* have over *B* in this simple block-and-tackle arrangement is

2:1.) It will be found that A moves in accordance with the $S_a = \frac{1}{2} gt^2$ law with $g = 9.8$ (in number of m/sec²), B falls with $S_b = \frac{1}{4} gt^2$, and *the tension-gauge T reads one kg wt*. In other words, 1 kg of force applied horizontally produces horizontal motion of the same acceleration that is produced by the 1-kg down-pull of the earth when A falls free.

This is an example of the vector conaddian aspects of Newton's law. The pull of gravity and the up-force of the table just cancel. The vector sum of all three forces is an $\vec{F}$ equal to 1-kg weight and directed horizontally along the string, and $\vec{a}$ is an acceleration of 1 g also horizontally directed. This is exactly what $\vec{F} = m\vec{a}$ predicts.

This experiment also confirms the conservation of energy law. Like Fig. 9-3 it involves three energies, but instead of 2 *PE* and 1 *KE*, Fig. 9-5 has 2 *KE* and 1 *PE*. The verification that Fig. 9-5 checks conservation of energy is given as a problem.

Next divide the scale of the tension-gauge, which we assume obeys Hooke's Law, into equal divisions in such a way that 1 kg of weight comes at 9.8 divisions. Each of these divisions measures force in a new standard unit called the **newt**on or **newt.** Both its name and its scientific importance as the unit of force in the MKS system make the newton the appropriate unit to use in this example of Newton's second law.

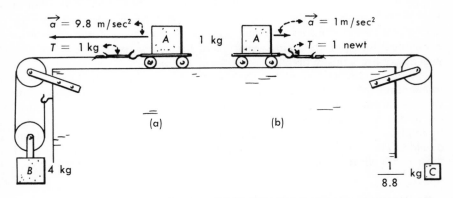

Fig. 9-5. Arrangements for producing string tensions of 1 kg and 1 newt. (The check of the accelerations by conservation of energy is a problem for the student).

To demonstrate the effect of 1 newt of force, hang weight C, which weighs $(1/8.8)$ kg (more generally the value should be $(g - 1)^{-1}$ for the value of g in the system of units used). When C is released, it is found that both A and C move according to $S_a = \frac{1}{2} t^2$ (in number of meters) so that both have one MKS unit of acceleration, 1 m/sec². The tension-gauge reads 1 newt so that A has a net force of 1 newt acting on it. This is the scientific definition of the MKS unit of force, the newton: *1 newt is the force that imparts an acceleration of 1 m/sec² to a mass of 1 kg.*

The MKS unit of energy is called the newt-m or the joule: 1 newt $\times$ 1 m = 1 joule. It is the work done by one newt of force acting over one meter. Does the formula for *KE*, i.e., $KE = \frac{1}{2} mv^2$ (in number of newt $\times$ meter, or joule), apply to energies in joules? Is the ku$\sim$ of Sec. 9-5 one joule? Consider what happens when *A* starts from rest and moves 1 m under a force of 1 newt. It should then have 1 joule of *KE*. We can check $\frac{1}{2} mv^2$ by seeing if it gives a value of 1. At $a\sim = 1$ m/sec^2 so that $S_a = \frac{1}{2} t^2$, it takes $t = \sqrt{2}$ to give $S_a = 1$. At $t = \sqrt{2}$, $v = at = \sqrt{2}$. Since $m = 1$, the formula $\frac{1}{2} mv^2$ does give $\frac{1}{2} \cdot 1 \cdot 2 = 1$. An equally good way of producing 1 newt $\times$ m or joule of energy is to let *A* be 2 kg = *m* kg of matter and the speed be *v* m/sec = 1 m/sec. Then $\frac{1}{2} mv^2 = \frac{1}{2} \cdot 2 \cdot 1^2 = 1$.

The newt $\times$ m unit of work or energy leads to a gravitational energy of $F \times h$ where $F = mg$, since a body of *m* kg of mass or matter has a down-force of *m* kg of weight, and this is *mg* newt. Applying conservation of energy to a falling body leads to

$$\frac{1}{2} mv^2 = mgh \quad \text{(in number of joules)}$$

and solving for *h* gives $h = v^2/2\,g$, the correct formula of Sec. 9-2.

The $\vec{F} = m\vec{a}$ law has many important applications. A body swinging in a circle like bob B_c of Fig. 9-2, has a constantly changing velocity vector. Analysis shows that the vector acceleration is directed inwards and has magnitude v^2/r, where *r* is the radius of the circle. The force that the string of Fig. 9-2(c) exerts on the bob is the **centripetal force.** The bob, by the action-reaction law, exerts an equal and opposite outward force, called the **centrifugal force,** on the string. Analysis of the vector force diagram of Fig. 9-2(c) confirms this in detail.

Action and reaction and Newton's second law lead to a conclusion about momentum that is like conservation of energy and is closely related to the *CG* law of moments, QLF 7-3 and 7-4. The *CG* (or center of mass according to Sec. 9-3) of a group of bodies has an acceleration that is not affected by internal forces between the bodies; it is determined by forces acting from outside. This leads to a conservation of momentum law for the center of mass of a collection of objects, for example, the solar system or a galaxy.*

9-9 Newton's Three Laws of Motion as QLF

The analysis of mechanics presented in this and the preceding chapters contains experimental facts that lead to Newton's three laws of motion. Conversely, these three laws may be taken as postulates from which the observed facts are deduced. From this second viewpoint it is evident that these laws together with their symbolic representation play a role in the interpretation of nature much as do the arrows on paper of Sec. 5-6 in acting as proxies for the invisible realities of nature, which can be detected only by their observable effects.

In Sec. 9-12, a history of Newton's discovery of his three laws of motion and his law of gravitational attraction is presented. For the desk-sized ex-

---

* See E. G. Ebbighausen, *Astronomy,* Merrill Physical Science Series.

periments of this book the law of gravitational attraction is not needed, and the other three laws can be expressed as follows:

QLF 9-6   Newton's Second Law: $\vec{F} = m\vec{a}$

WHAT ·	It is **always true** that the rate of change of momentum (this equals $m\vec{a}$ for a single mass) is equal to the total resultant vector force $\vec{F}_T$,
WHEN	**no matter** whether the mass is a baseball, a satellite, a planet, or an electron in a vacuum tube,
WHEN NOT	**but not if** $m\vec{a}$ is used when relativistic effects on m should be included, or if momentum in radiation or electromagnetic momentum density is overlooked.

Newton's first law, which states that a body continues in its straight line motion unless disturbed by some outside force, is a theorem from QLF 9-6.

QLF 9-7   Newton's Third Law: The Action-Reaction Law

WHAT	It is **always true** that if a first body exerts a force on a second body, then the second exerts an exactly equal and opposite force on the first along the same line,
WHEN	**no matter** whether the forces are electrostatic, magnetic, gravitational, or contact forces,
WHEN NOT	**but not if** the interactions are through electromagnetic fields in which the momentum densities change.

The law of conservation of momentum for a system of masses, discussed in Sec. 9-3, is a theorem from QLF's 9-6 and 9-7. Another conservation law, that for **angular momentum,** which is related to rotating levers, flywheels on machines, gyroscopes, and rotating molecules, can also be derived from these postulates.

Other very important conservation laws in science involve electric charge, magnetic charge (it is always zero), and aspects of nuclear phenomena. These belong to other phases of physical science.*

Before taking up the history of thought that led to Newton's laws, the linearity of the laws should be stressed. If two forces $\vec{F}_1$ and $\vec{F}_2$ act on a mass, and $\vec{F}_1$ leads to a velocity $\vec{v}_1(t)$ which depends on time, and $\vec{F}_2$ if alone would produce $v_2(t)$, then both together produce $\vec{v}(t) = \vec{v}_1(t) + \vec{v}_2(t)$. This is a conaddian aspect of the motion. This linearity was sensed by Galileo, see Sec. 9-10, and his work is perhaps the first example of the enormously important principle of linear systems that the effect of the sum of several causes is the sum of the effects on the causes acting individually. This principle is basic in the theory of electricity.†

---

* See Merrill Physical Science Series.
† See Francis Dart, *op. cit.*

9-10   Galileo's Creative Search in Terrestrial Mechanics

Six significant scientific attributes have been emphasized in this chapter: velocity, acceleration, force, mass, momentum, and energy. These concepts were largely formulated in the 16th and 17th centuries, as well illustrated by the works of Galileo (1564-1642), Kepler (1571-1630), and Newton (1642-1726). Since then, these attributes have been further extended into new relationships, and applied to different areas of scientific investigations.

One of the epochal stories in the history of science is an account by Galileo in his *Dialogue Concerning the Two Chief World Systems* about his investigations of the dynamics of free-falling bodies. At that time, the question of whether the earth was at rest or in motion was of great scientific and philosophical importance. Galileo was the first man to observe the moons of Jupiter through the then newly invented telescope. This fact, among an accumulation of other evidences, suggested that the earth was *not* at rest, nor was it a unique planet at the center of the universe. This new belief— that man lives on a rotating earth revolving about the sun—required new attributes and methods for understanding motion.

The speeds of the earth were calculated to be enormous. Yet, if the earth does move, why then do we not fly off the spinning earth, or great winds be set up, or objects fall behind us as they are thrown up and we are carried away by the moving earth?

There is a legend recorded by Vivani, one of Galileo's biographers, that Galileo observed the falling of a heavy and a light weight from the Leaning Tower of Pisa in Italy, and that he noted that the two weights reached the ground at nearly the same time. Whether the story is true or not, there is little doubt that he had the hunch that weight, one of the most important attributes for interpreting stationary balanced objects, is not an important attribute for understanding how objects fall on earth. In fact, the observations suggest that objects fall freely to earth in a straight line with exactly the same motion, **no matter** what the material, size, shape, or weight of the object, **but not if** there is air resistance.*

In 1604 Galileo proposed a wrong hunch to explain the idealized limiting case of free-fall motion with zero air resistance, which was that the velocity is proportional to the distance fallen. By 1609, however, Galileo had realized his mistake, and was arguing that the velocities are proportional to the time, or that the acceleration remains constant. Galileo used the logic of the postulate-proof-theorem reasoning, patterned after the style used by Archimedes in his treatise on the idealized limiting case of the balanced lever and center of gravity. Galileo's purpose was to derive from the non-observable attributes of instantaneous velocity and acceleration a testable theorem involving measurable distances and times. The new theorem he deduced, stated in its modern algebraic form as proved in Sec. 9-2, is $S = \frac{1}{2} gt^2$ (in number of ft). A consequence of this theorem, then, is this prediction: When any object is released from a rest position at any height, and freely falls through

---

* This is like "*CG* always exists on a straight line directly below the point of suspension".

zero air resistance, the distances fallen will increase in the ratio of $1^2 : 2^2 : 3^2$ etc., as time increases in the ratio of $1 : 2 : 3$ etc. Hence, the ratio of S/t^2 for any distance fallen is predicted to be always a constant number.

Since Galileo was unable to measure directly how objects freely fall through the air, he had to make another assumption, namely, that the motion along a frictionless inclined board is essentially the same kind of motion as that of a body freely falling vertically through space. To make this assumption more plausible, Galileo established a postulate about an oscillating pendulum (QLF 9-2). The velocity of a pendulum at the bottom of its swing depends only on the vertical height it falls, **no matter** the length of the pendulum or its weight.*

Galileo noted the *one-to-one correspondence* between the *chords of the arcs* and the *inclined planes*, and hence, the analogous assertion that the motion down an inclined plane also depends only upon the height that the object falls, **no matter** the length that the object falls down the inclined plane. In the limiting case, when the inclined plane is tipped towards the vertical position, he argued that the motion on the smooth inclined plane would approach the motion of a vertical, free-falling object.

Galileo then demonstrated experimentally his deduced relationship (that S/t^2 is a constant value) by comparing the measured values of the distances that the object fell down the inclined plane and the time elapsed, when the inclined board was rotated to different positions. He wrote:

> Next we tried other distances, comparing the time for the whole length with that for the half, or with that for two-thirds, or three-fourths, or indeed for any fractions; in such an experiment, repeated a full hundred times, we always found that the spaces traversed were to each other as the squares of the times, and this was true for all inclinations of the plane, i.e., of the channel, along which we rolled the ball.

Thus one of the main achievements of Galileo was that he experimentally observed and proved the constant acceleration motion law (QLF 9-8) that it is **always true** that all objects initially at rest fall with exactly the same motion, described as a constant acceleration motion, or that $v = gt$ and $S = \frac{1}{2} gt^2$, **no matter** the material, size, shape, or weight of the object, or the height that the object falls, **but not if** there are observably large, retarding friction forces on the object.

Galileo extended his results to the more general case of objects projected into a curved or projectile motion.† He imagined that when a ball is projected faster and faster, the projectile motion approaches the idealized limiting case of a straight-line, constant velocity motion. When the ball is projected at lower and lower velocities, the projectile path approaches that of a vertical straight-line, constant acceleration motion. *Hunch:* The curved projectile motion between these two idealized limiting cases consists of a combination of constant velocity and constant acceleration motion.

A new acor pattern for terrestrial motion was stated by Galileo in 1543,

---

* This is Galileo's famous argument for the idealized limiting case of an oscillating pendulum. Another more modern proof was given in Sec. 9-4.

† Projectile motion includes such phenomena as a ball thrown into the air, a stream of water from a hose, a bomb released from a moving plane, and a free-falling rocket in a suborbital flight.

when he noted that the resultant projectile motion is the vector sum of two separate, independent, and simultaneous components of motion. He wrote that one component is "uniform and horizontal", and that the other is "vertical and naturally accelerated". Consequently, as shown in Fig. 9-6, the resultant displacement* from P at the end of the first interval of time is $x = 1, y = 1$. At the end of the second equal interval of time, the resultant displacement is $x = 2, y = 4$, and so forth.

The geometrical curve that describes the path of the projectiles is called a **parabola,** which results when a cone is sliced parallel to one of its sides (Fig. 9-6). Cutting through the cone at other angles produces other conic curves (circle, ellipse, and hyperbola), all of which were studied by Apollonius of Perga about 200 B.C. Thus, Galileo's discovery was that the idealized limiting case of all projectile motion has a one-to-one correspondence with a geometric conic curve studied by the ancient Greeks.

Galileo's law of projectile motion (QLF 9-9) states that it is **always true** that the motion of a projectile is a parabolic path, which can be geometrically represented as the vector addition of the constant velocity and constant acceleration motions after successive equal intervals of time, **no matter** what the horizontal or vertical components of motion, or the shape, size, or weight of the projectile, **but not if** there are measureable retarding forces.

This acor pattern achieved by Galileo was capable of describing how a moving Jupiter or earth did not lose its satellites or atmosphere. The analogy he used was that of an object dropped from the mast of a ship moving with a constant velocity, where the ship represents the moving earth. An observer from the shore observes the free-falling object as a parabolic motion, but an observer on the deck of the ship from which the object is released sees only a vertical, downward component of motion. Galileo postulated that this is because both the object and the ship have the same horizontal component of motion, and the two things continue to move with each other in the same straight-line motion, thus appearing to have no horizontal motion with respect to each other. So all the free-falling objects on a terrestrial earth would also fall directly downward as if the earth were at rest.†

9-11 Kepler's Creative Search in Celestial Mechanics

Kepler, a friend of Galileo, believed that the natural motions of the planets could also be described by mathematical relationships. The measured celestial positions of Mars had for several years been accurately recorded by Brahe, Kepler's friend. Could these measurements of the orbit

---

* The distance of the projectile from any origin-point P after each equal interval of time can be represented in modern algebraic symbols. When the mathematical equation for the idealized horizontal motion ($x = vt$) is algebraically combined with the equation for the idealized vertical motion ($y = \frac{1}{2} gt^2$), the result is $y = kx^2$, where k is a constant quantity. This mathematical analysis of Galileo's problem is like the derivation of $\Sigma M_{x'} = (\Sigma W_i)(x_{CG} - x')$ in Sec. 7-14.

† The earth revolving about the sun does not move in a straight line like the idealized case of the ship's motion. However, for ordinary experiences dealing with projectiles, the departure of the earth from a straight-line motion is insignificant.

of Mars be described by a simple mathematical curve, such as Galileo had achieved when he described projectile motion by a parabola?

For almost two thousand years, the Ptolemaic theory had been accepted as a workable theory. It was based upon the fundamental postulate that planetary motions were basically circular orbits, qualified by such concepts as the epicycle, deferent, eccentric, and equant to explain those observations that a circular orbit alone could not explain. When Kepler compared Brahe's data to a circular orbit, he found a discrepancy greater than that due to the experimental error of the measurements.

Kepler's key hunch was that the data about Mars' orbit could be reduced to a single unique orbit, which was different from a circle, and which could be described by mathematics. He sought an answer by the "methods of areas", which compared the *area* of a circle representing the planet's orbit to the whole *time* of the planet's revolution. Thus, the area of any sector of the circle corresponded to the equivalent time necessary for the planet to move through the distance of the sector's particular arc. Using this hunch, Kepler found that the planet's orbit was more accurately represented by the figure of an oval (egg-shape) than by that of a circle.*

Kepler finally abandoned the simplest case of a one-center curve and tried to fit the data of Mar's orbit to that of a two-center curve called the **ellipse.** This proved to be the pay-off hunch. He stated the results of his study of planetary motion in 1609:

Law 1. The orbit of each planet is in the shape of an ellipse with the sun located at one focus.

Law 2. An imaginary line connecting the sun with the planet will sweep out equal areas of the elliptical orbit in equal intervals of time.

Now that Kepler had found a constant relationship to describe the motion of the planets, he devoted ten more years of effort to comparing the different attributes of the different orbits of the planets. In 1619, Kepler found an invariant relationship for all the planets:

Law 3. The squares of the periods of the different planets around the sun are proportional to the cubes of their mean distances from the sun, i.e., $\frac{R^3}{T^2} = k$.† This means that when T (in number of years) and R (in number of miles) are calculated in the ratio $\frac{R^3}{T^2}$ for each of the planets, the constant k is the same invariant number for each planet.

In sum, the motions of the planets were described accurately by Kepler's laws which state invariant numerical relationships between the measured observations of planetary motion. Galileo also described the motions of free-falling bodies on earth by invariant relationships of velocity and acceleration. What was lacking was a new acor pattern containing, as key attributes, a set of new scientific postulates from which these invariant attributes of nature

---

* For a more detailed historical account of Kepler's discovery of his famous three laws of planetary motion, see Norwood R. Hansen, *Patterns of Discovery* (New York: Cambridge University Press, 1958), Chapter 4.

† This law is like the $M = P - 1$ law in the tennis tournament puzzle.

could be systematically deduced. The man to do this was Newton, one of the greatest scientific thinkers of all times. What did Newton do to achieve such an immortal stature of greatness?

9-12   *Newton's Creative Search for the Universal Law of Gravitation*

"I offer this work as the mathematical principles of philosophy," Newton wrote in the preface to *Principia,* published in 1684, "for the whole burden of philosophy seems to consist in this—from the phenomena of motions to investigate the forces of nature, and then from these forces to demonstrate the other phenomena; and to this end the general propositions in the first and second Books are directed. In the third Book I give an example of this in the explication of the *System of the World*; for by the propositions mathematically demonstrated in the former Books, in the third I derive from celestial phenomena the forces of gravity with which bodies tend to the sun and the several planets. Then from these forces, by other propositions which are also mathematical, I deduce the motions of the planets, the comets, the moon, and the sea."*

Newton stated three axioms, or laws of motion:

Law 1. Every body continues in its state of rest, or of uniform motion in a right line, unless it is compelled to change that state by forces impressed upon it.

Law 2. The change of motion is proportional to the motive force impressed, and is made in the direction of the right line in which that force is impressed.

Law 3. To every action there is always opposed an equal reaction; or, the mutual actions of two bodies upon each other are always equal, and directed to contrary parts.

Newton then logically combined these three laws of motion with definitions and mathematical theorems to deduce mathematical propositions that described terrestrial and celestial motions. Thus *Principia* was cast in the logical postulate-proof-theorem structure of Euclidean geometry and Archimedean statics. The result was a master acor pattern that culminated centuries of man's striving to understand the System of the World. There follows a synopsis of some of the strands of Newton's search for the universal law of gravitation, based mainly on the contents of *Principia* and other historical documents.

What forces cause the planets to follow the elliptical motions described by Kepler? This was a significant scientific question of great interest in the 17th century. One prevalent hunch was that the motions were caused by the sun, which exerted a solar force in all directions, like sunlight, according to the inverse of the square of the distance. About 1684, Robert Hooke, Edmund Halley, and Sir Christopher Wren of the newly chartered Royal Society of London were involved in a dispute about how to *prove* that the solar force "decreased in the proportion of the squares of the distances reciprocally". When none could demonstrate such a proof, Halley consulted

---

* Sir Isaac Newton, *Principia,* Preface to First Edition (University of California Press, 1962).

Newton. The visit spurred Newton to continue his investigations of gravitational forces, which he began in his twenties, and after two years of intensive work, Newton published his results in *Principia*.

Newton proved that Kepler's second law (equal areas during equal intervals of time) was a theorem from the general laws of motion. He first made the proof for the simplest case of a body moving with an idealized straight-line inertial motion.* Then he extended the proof to the more general case of a body attracted by a continuous centripetal force towards an immovable center (center of force).

Newton also proved, for planets in elliptical motion, that "if the periodic times are as the 3/2th powers of the radii (Kepler's third law), the centripetal forces will be concisely as the square of the radii; and conversely" (Book One, Proposition IV). He first demonstrated the proof for the simplest case of an object in uniform motion attracted by a centripetal force towards the center of a circle. The proof then was generalized for the motions of a body in other conic paths (ellipse, hyperbola, and parabola), demonstrating that the "centripetal force tending to the focus of that conic section varies inversely as the square of the distance."

Thus planetary motions were mathematically described by Newton as idealized inertial motions curved into elliptical orbits by the continuous action of an attractive, inverse-square, centripetal force emanating from the sun. What about other similar systems of objects in planetary-type motion?

In the beginning of Book Three, Newton displayed observed facts about the satellites (moons) of Jupiter and Saturn. "Each of the moons describe areas proportional to the times of description;" he wrote, "and their periodic times, the fixed stars being at rest, are as the 3/2th power of their distances from its centre." In other words, the moons also moved according to Kepler's laws and hence were retained in their orbits by a centripetal, inverse-square force from the planets.

What about the centripetal force acting on the earth's moon? In the years 1665 and 1666†, according to Newton, when he was about 24 years old, he

---

* Regarding an idealized inertial motion along a straight line from A to B to C, Newton wrote in Book One, Proposition I: "For suppose the time to be divided into equal parts, and in the first part of that time let the body by its innate force describe the right (straight) line AB. In the second part of that time, the same would (by Law I), if not hindered, proceed directly to C, along the line BC equal to AB, so that by the radii AS, BS, CS, drawn to the centre, the equal areas ASB, BSC, would be described." (Area of a triangle equals one-half the product of its altitude and base. Since the two triangles have the same altitude and equal bases, their areas are equal.)

† The incident of the falling apple is believed to have occurred at this time. It gave Newton the key hunch that the gravitational force of the earth extended to the moon. There is another story, however, that as late as 1675 Hooke and Newton were involved in a debate about the path of an object free-falling from the top of a tall tower. Newton proposed that the path was a spiral, but Hooke pointed out his error. Hooke argued that the path of the free-falling object would be an ellipse (similar to the paths of planets falling perpetually around the sun), because of the inverse-square law of terrestrial gravity.

made the key hunch that the centripetal force of the moon was the same kind of force as terrestrial gravity. Newton wrote: "And the same year I began to think of gravity extending to the orb of the moon, . . . from Kepler's Rule [Third Law] . . . I deduced that the forces which keep the planets in their orbs must (be) reciprocally as the square of their distances from the centres about which they revolve, and thereby compared the force requisite to keep the moon in her orb with the force of gravity at the surface of the earth, and found them to answer pretty nearly." Over twenty years later, Newton wrote the experimental details of this earth-moon test of the law of gravitation in Book Three as Proposition IV.

Having related the inverse-square law to free-falling objects, Newton experimented with the force of terrestrial gravity. His experiments with pendulums conducted with an error of "less than the thousandth part of the whole" established what Galileo had observed earlier: that different quantities of matter descend to earth from equal heights in equal times. Newton combined this experimental result with the second law of motion: "Therefore if the times are equal, the quantities of matter in each of the bodies are as the weights." That is, different quantities of matter fall towards the earth with the same acceleration, because each quantity of weight (gravitational force) is proportional to the quantity of matter (mass), or $F_g \propto m$. For example, when the quantity of mass is doubled, the quantity of gravitational force also doubles, so the acceleration remains the same. Accordingly, the gravitational force depends upon a conservative, additive, invariant attribute of nature called *mass*, **no matter** whether the object is a stone or the moon free-falling towards the center of the earth! (This same conclusion is formulated as QLF 9-1.)

Does the gravitational force depend only upon the mass of the *attracted* body or does the force also depend on the *attracting* body? Newton reasoned from the third law of motion: "The attractive force is found in both. The sun attracts Jupiter and the other planets; Jupiter attracts its satellites; and, for the same reason, the satellites act as well one upon another as upon Jupiter, and all the planets mutually one upon another" (*System of the World*, Section 20). The attraction resides really in each body towards the other, stated Newton, and is therefore of the same kind in both. If the gravitational force is proportional to the quantity of matter in the attracted body, reason requires that the force should also be proportional to the quantity of matter in the body attracting. (This reasoning implicitly uses Newton's third law, which we have stated as the action-reaction law, QLF's 4-1 and 9-7.)

Newton's hunch was a bold one. The quantity of gravitational force attracting two objects is proportional to the product of the quantities of mass, or $F_g \propto m_1 m_2$. When this new relationship is combined with the inverse-square law that relates the gravitational force to the distance between the two objects, $F_g \propto \dfrac{1}{d^2}$, the modern algebraic form of Newton's **universal law of gravitation** results:

$$F_g = \frac{Gm_1m_2}{d^2} \quad \text{(in force)}$$

where G is a constant quantity determined by the physical quantities of the solar system and since found to apply to other mechanical systems. This algebraic statement of the law is not found in *Principia*, but in the *General Scholium* Newton stated for the sun and planets that gravity operates "according to the quantity of the solid matter they contain, and propagates its virtue on all sides to immense distances, decreasing always as the inverse square of the distances."

By combining the law of gravitation with the three general laws of motion, Newton deduced many new results concerning the bulging of the earth at the equator, the change of the force of gravity at different latitudes, the changes of the tides, the density of the moon, the motions and tails of the comets, the precession of the equinoxes, and others. Thus according to the experiments and deductions concerning the universal law of gravitation synthesized in *Principia* (QLF 9-10), it is **always true** that every quantity of matter attracts every other quantity with a mutually attractive gravitational force that operates according to the product of the masses and inversely as the square of the distances between the objects, so that for any two objects,

$F_g = \dfrac{Gm_1m_2}{d^2}$ (in force), **no matter** whether the terrestrial objects are free

falling or oscillating as pendulums or periodically changing as tides, or whether the celestial objects are wobbling about their axes or revolving as moons, planets, and comets in elliptical paths, **but not if** mass and length are not conserved.

CONCLUSIONS

This introduction to scientific thinking has been largely confined to the laws of **classical mechanics** investigated before and during the 17th century. In the 18th century the measurement of the invariance of mass in chemical reactions led to the law of conservation of mass and to the quantitative investigations of modern *chemistry*. In the 19th century the laws of Newtonian mechanics achieved initial successes at the molecular level, when the study of the motions of molecules resulted in the *kinetic theory* and the study of thermal equilibrium in the laws of *statistical mechanics*. At the beginning of the 20th century, the *special theory of relativity* generalized the laws of Newtonian mechanics for terrestrial and celestial objects that approached the speed of light. Also, during this century, the accumulation of detailed familiarity with atomic behavior resulted in new laws of *quantum mechanics* and the generalization of Newtonian mechanics for elementary atomic particles at non-relativistic speeds. The laws of *quantum field theory* apply to elementary atomic particles at relativistic speeds.

We chose to begin this study of mechanics with simplest cases of scientific thinking that emphasized invariance principles. You solved a select collection of games and puzzles (i.e., 2-coins, 2-kings, checkerboard puzzle, Take 1 or 4, and tennis tournament) to gain the experience of a creative search, the use of scientific thinking tools, the qualification of a law, and the mathematical analysis of a logical structure of laws. A classification of symbols used in physical science, the logical steps of measurement, and the qualified-equation were presented in the investigation of weight. When you investigated the vector force concept, you experienced the "messiness" of a scientific problem in a real situation. You were challenged to do some thinking on your own to discover the laws of statics. Finally, you studied the laws of dynamics outlined as survey and history.

It is our hope that you will continue to gain vivid, personal experiences in science as you attempt to make the chaotic diversity of reality correspond to unique and convincing, logical structures of thought.

Chapter 10

Problems

Introduction

The problems have classifying letters as discussed in the introduction: P, pencil and paper exercises; D, suitable for class discussions; E, experimental; L, laboratory apparatus preferred to home apparatus; N, new conceptual material not in the chapter.

Chapters 1, 2, and 6 have problems appropriate for application of the science-thinking diagram of Fig. 6-1, inside front cover. These may be selected out of order although the problems for Chapter 6 are more difficult than those for Chapters 1 and 2.

Chapter 1

1-1 P. Suppose that the two coins of Fig. 1-6 are both placed heads up, not on squares two and five of the five-square strip of Fig. 1-6, but on the second and fifth squares from the left end of bottom row No. 1 of the checkerboard of Fig. 1-2. The new rules permit coins to move either right or left or up or down, but never diagonally like checker pieces. As in Fig. 1-6, they must turn upside down when crossing either a horizontal or a vertical line. Can you ever place them both heads up on any square?

1-2 P. Suppose that the five-square strip of Fig. 1-6 is bent into a circle so that a coin can be moved all the way around until it comes back to its starting "square". Can you solve the two-coin turnover puzzle then?

1-3 P. Can you generalize Problems 1-1 and 1-2?

1-4 P. Evaluate the following statements, correct those that are wrong, and give proofs of all the true statements. (a) The sum of two odd numbers is an even number. (b) The difference between two odd numbers is an even number. (c) The product of two odd numbers is an even number. (d) No even number can ever be divided by an odd number to give a whole number quotient and no remainder. (e) The sum of n odd numbers has the same even-oddness as n. (f) There is no simple rule that predicts correctly when the sum or difference of two numbers will be even or odd.

1-5 P. Consider a garden path made of an alternating sequence of red and black cement squares like one row or one column of a checkerboard. (a) Can you divide the cement squares into two piles containing equal numbers of squares if both end squares of the path are red? (b) If both end squares are red and you step onto the first square of the path with your right foot, and take one step per square, with which foot do you step onto the driveway from the last square of the path? (c) What other end square situations can you consider for pathways made of red and black squares?

1-6 E. (a) Make the soda-straw parallelogram machine of Fig. 1-7 and verify the experiments described in Section 1-7. (b) Modify the machine by moving the pivot pins that support the parallelogram. Accomplish this modification by making the vertical straws from the book divide the long straws of the parallelogram into ⅓ and ⅔ instead of into ½ and 1½. (c) After you have balanced the ⅓ and ⅔ machine, by adding (if needed) fractional paperclip weights in the form of short pieces of soda straws, how many paperclips must you put on the short side to balance each additional paperclip on the long side?

1-7 E,D. (a) Find two parallel mirrors and verify the discussion that follows the one-mirror example of Fig. 1-4. (b) Can you describe what happens when the two mirrors are not quite parallel?

1-8 E,D. If you hold a newspaper up in front of a mirror, you observe that it changes right to left. (a) Why doesn't it change up to down? (b) Does it really change right to left? Cut from cardboard the letter L (or F or Z or S, if you prefer), stand facing a mirror and hold this letter at eye level directly in front of you so that it looks right-handed to you when you look straight at it. Next, look past it at its image in the mirror. (c) Is its image in the mirror left-handed? (d) Does it look like L backwards? (e) Color or shade the surface of the paper of the L nearest you. Does the mirror reverse near and far, or right and left, or what does it do?

1-9 E. Try the melting ice-cube problem of Fig. 1-9. The technique can be improved by filling the glass less full than shown and marking the water level with a rubber band around the glass. The glass can then be covered with a saucer or a plastic food wrapper to prevent moisture in the air from condensing into the glass. (a) After the ice melts, has the water level moved upward enough to account for the volume of ice above water level? (b) Has the water level moved up at all?

Similar pencil-and-paper problems are given in later chapters, particularly 2, 3, and 6.

Chapter 2

2-1 P,D. Consider either square or rectangular checkerboard puzzles, with two E squares in the diagonal corners; the figures have an extra number of rows and an even number of columns (e.g., 2×2, 2×4, 8×8, 100×122). (a) Prove that the two E's will always be the same kind of square (e.g., both E's are "shaded", or both E's are odd). (b) Draw a logical structure (PPT) diagram that outlines why you can't solve such checkerboard puzzles that have an even number of rows and even number of columns.

2-2 P. Invent and draw a checkerboard pattern with five shaded and five plain squares, each square touching at least one other square on its side, on which no more than three paperclips may be placed.

2-3 P,D. Draw a logical structure (PPT) diagram that outlines why it is always true that the second player wins in the Take 1 or 4 game of 20 objects.

2-4 P,D. How many matches are required to produce one final winner in a 137-player double-elimination tournament? Can you prove your answer? (In a "double-elimination" tennis tournament, a player is eliminated when he loses two matches.)

2-5 E,N. In the Take 1 to 5 game, two players take turns picking up 1 to 5 toothpicks from a pile of 20 toothpicks. The player who picks up the last toothpick wins the game. Play the game with an opponent until one player can consistently defeat the other. (a) Use simplest cases to find the QLF that allows you to win the game. (b) What quantity is conserved in this game?

Chapter 3

3-1 P. A box B has four square surfaces S each having four edges E. A yardstick fits an edge perfectly. Since B has six square surfaces, we can say $B = 6S$, and since each S has four edges, we can say $S = 4E$; however, each edge is shared between two surfaces so that, really, $S = 2E$. Substituting equals for equals gives $B = 6S = 6(2E) = 12E$, and since $E = 3$ ft, evidently $B = 36$; and since B is a box, it contains 36 cu ft. One way of checking this reasoning is to count the edges of a cube; this results in $12E$. (a) What is the volume of a cube 3 ft long on each edge? (b) What is the matter with the reasoning above? (c) Discuss the symbols used above and make up a set of your own for the same purpose; define them in a table, and rewrite the discussion.

3-2 D. What aspects of **con** (conservative), **add** (additive), and **ian** (invariant attribute of nature) are possessed by the following items: (1) the blue of the sky; (2) the amount of light falling on a piece of paper; (3) an interval of time—for example, from the start to finish of a one-mile race; (4) temperature in degrees Fahrenheit, °F, or degrees centigrade, °C; (5) the heat you feel when you take a plate or a piece of aluminum foil from an oven; (6) area—for example, a ½-acre lot; (7) the amount of effort required to wash a collection of dirty dishes.

3-3 E,D. This experiment involves making a direct-reading, distance-measuring instrument by the binary method. Start by making your own personal standard-length object, name-symbol *SLO*, which is defined to be 1 lup~ long as follows: Fold a sheet of paper to get a good straight edge; use a ruler and put two pencil marks 4 in. apart on *SLO*. Now by marking 1 lup~ from *SLO* onto other sheets of paper and by folding them in half, make a binary fractional set of lengths down to $\frac{1}{32}$ lup~ or $\frac{1}{8}$ in. Make a "yard-strip" by joining (with scotch tape, glue, etc.) folded strips that are about 1 in. wide after folding into a strip more than 9 lup~ long. Mark this off in $\frac{1}{4}$ lup~ (about 1 in.) intervals, marking the last first 1 lup~ into four strips of 1 in. each divided into $\frac{1}{8}$ in. Compare your 36 in. direct-reading instrument based on your *SLO* with one, or better, with two yardsticks. (a) How much error is there in 36 in.? (b) What per cent error (see Section 5-4 to review per cent) is there? (c) Discuss the relationship of your "yard-strip" to the content of the paragraph of which QLF 3-1 is a part.

3-4 P. (a) Prove that there are $n + 2$ weight objects in the set containing 1, 1, 2, 4, 8, . . . , 2^n individual weight-objects and that the total weight of all weight-objects combined is $2 \times 2^n = 2^{n+1}$. (b) Prove that every total weight except the largest can be obtained by two combinations of the $n + 2$ objects.

3-5 P. (a) Prove that there are a total of $n + 1$ weight-objects in the binary set of individual objects weighing 1, 2, 4($= 2^2$), 8($= 2^3$), ..., 2^n times a standard unit. (b) Prove that the whole collection weighs $2^{n+1} - 1$. (c) Prove that any weight value from 1 to $2^{n+1} - 1$ standard units can be produced in exactly one way.

3-6 P. (a) What systematic scheme for selecting weight values would you use to make it simplest for you to add up weights to match decimal numbers like 143, 798, 1005, 12,345? (b) How many weight-objects would you need to reach 1023 which can be done with nine weight-objects in the binary set described in Problem 3-5.

3-7 E. Check QLF's 3-3 and 3-4 on your own. Buy at least four lightweight springs at your hardware store—preferably of several weights or lengths. Each should be strong enough to support about 3 lb without permanent distortion. (Springs are often made with *initial tension:* this means that their wire is so bent that they try to pull themselves shorter than they actually can because they are stopped when their turns hit together. This initial tension can be removed from the springs that you use for the most sensitive devices by overstretching each spring until it is permanently deformed a little. To do this, mark the length of the spring on a piece of paper and stretch the spring several times, pulling a little farther each time until it does not quite pull back to its original length.) Make two weight-sensing devices like those of Fig. 3-3(a), but make one more sensitive than the other. Then verify QLF's 3-3 and 3-4 and write a report of your observations describing your two weights, how you put them on the platform in different places, and how sure you are that they were equal.

3-8 D. (a) How would you set up a series of experiments, like those discussed in Chapter 3 for weight, to show that volume is a conaddian property of solid bodies and liquids? (b) If you mix 1 cup of water with 1 cup of pure methyl alcohol, you do not obtain exactly 2 cups (or 1 pint) of mixture, but instead about 3.5% less than 1 pint. What does this mean? How do you include it in a QLF?

3-9 E. Obtain some methyl alcohol and carry out Problem 3-8(b).

Chapter 4

4-1 P. Consider the problem of weighing coal that is to be delivered. One way to do this is to weigh the coal shovel by shovel as it is being loaded into a truck, but this method is impractical. Suppose that the fuel supply company has a big scale which can weigh a whole loaded coal truck. (a) How can this be used to weigh the coal? (b) What QLF have you used to justify your answer to (a)? (c) Suppose that the company has a scale that is mounted flush with the roadway surface and is only large enough to support one wheel of the truck. Can the load of coal be weighed?

4-2. P,D,N. Consider a large bucket partly filled with water sitting on a scale. Imagine that you raise the water level in the bucket from its partly filled level L_1 to a new higher level L_2 in three different ways: (1) Raise the level from L_1 to L_2 by adding one gallon of water weighing 8.3 lb. (2) Again starting at level L_1, lower a 1-gal glass bottle of water into the bucket until the water rises from level L_1 to level L_2. (3) Take an empty 1-gal glass bottle and lower it into the bucket until the water level rises from L_1 to L_2. Provided that the bottle touches only the water and no part of the bucket itself, the increase in the scale reading will be the same, namely, 8.3 lb for each of the three cases. (a) State this result in a QLF. (b) Given the fact that 1 gal of water weighs 8.3 lb, can you predict the increase in weight for experiment (1)? What QLF's do you use in your reasoning? (c) Suppose that you have a large scale S_L on which you put two identical bathroom scales: S_B has the bucket on it, and you stand on the other, call it S_Y, holding the full 1-gal bottle in your hand. Suppose that the readings of the scales are 160 lb on S_Y, 30 lb on S_B, and 200 lb on S_L. What does each bathroom scale weigh? (d) If you lower the bottle into the bucket so that the water level rises from L_1 to L_2, what do the three scales read? What QLF's do you use in your reasoning? (e) From the result of (d), can you predict Archimedes' principle that the loss of weight of a submerged body is equal to the weight of the water it displaces? (Section 8-7 presents a more basic derivation of Archimedes' principle.)

4-3 P,N. (a) Can you use the facts of Problem 4-2 to predict that the water level of Fig. 1-8 stays constant as the ice melts? (b) Write a description of your reasoning. (c) Represent (b) as a logical structure diagram.

4-4 E,L. Do an experiment of your own designed to verify the experimental facts listed in (1), (2), and (3) of Problem 4-2. You can replace the bathroom scale with a postal scale and the bucket with a paper cup or use laboratory apparatus.

Chapter 5

5-1 P,N. Suppose that you make three measurements and obtain three different values for a quantity such as L_B^4 of Sec. 5-3, and that you next make a fourth reading which does not equal any of the first three. Assume that all four readings have been taken with equal skill. (a) Analyze this situation so that you conclude that the chance that your fourth reading lies outside the first set is exactly 50%. (b) Check this result by selecting ten columns from a telephone directory and reading the last four digits of each of the first four numbers. Find the number of times the fourth number down the column lies outside the range determined by the first three. (c) What is the chance that if you read n values, the $n + 1$st value will fall outside the first n?

5-2 P. A steel tightrope is suspended between two rigid supports 20 ft apart. A 170-lb tightrope walker standing on the center of the tightrope pushes the center down 4 in. with respect to the two ends. What is the tension in the tightrope?

5-3 P. Analyze the following statement: "There is no force, however great, can stretch a string, however fine, into a horizontal line that shall be absolutely straight."

5-4 E. Find three points of support all lying about 4 to 7 ft above the floor, and make a Y of string. Attach plumb lines near the midpoint of each Y and hang equal weights on each line. By using paper and pencil dashes as discussed for Fig. 5-10, determine the tensions in the three string segments that meet at the center knot of the Y. Evaluate the resultant force at this knot, again using a sheet of paper to establish directions. Compare your result with prediction and estimate the per cent accuracy with which you check the prediction.

5-5 E,N. Repeat Problem 5-5 with a fourth weight hanging directly from the center knot of the Y. Devise a scheme for determining whether the resultant of the four forces on the knot is equal to zero within experimental accuracy.

5-6 P. Consider an idealized case of an H-like string having not two, but many, weights hanging from plumb lines. Suppose that the plumb lines are exactly 1 ft apart and all the weights are exactly equal. Call the knot for the lowest weight K_0, the next knot to the right K_1, second to the right K_2, etc. Knots to the left are called K_{-1}, K_{-2}, etc. Suppose that K_1 is $1\frac{1}{2}$ in. higher than K_0, and K_{-1} is $\frac{1}{2}$ in. higher than K_0. (a) Prove that K_2 is $3\frac{1}{2}$ in. and K_{-2} is $2\frac{1}{2}$ in. higher than K_0. (b) Draw a picture on graph paper of the shape of the string out to knots K_{-6} and K_{+6}. (c) Discuss the relationship of this to a suspension bridge.

5-7 P,N. Consider per cent changes of products and powers as follows: (a) Prove that if a rectangle 50 in. by 200 in. is increased by 2% on the short side and 1% on the long side, the area is increased by 3%. (b) Prove that you still get 3% from 2% and 1% if the sides are 200 in. and 50 in. instead of 50 in. and 200 in. (c) Prove that you still get 3% for two sides of your own choosing. (d) Prove that you get 3% if the sides have NSU values a and b. (e) Prove that if you increase all the edges of a cube by 1%, the volume increases by 3%.

5-8 P,N,D. Generalize Problem 5-7.

Chapter 6

6-1. Use the science-thinking diagram of Fig. 6-1 (inside front cover) to analyze the following game: Two Pile–Last Match Wins. There are two piles, each of ten matches, on the table between players A and B. On his play, each player has three choices: (1) he can take a match from one pile, or (2) he can take a match from both piles, or (3) he can take one match from each of the two piles. If one player reduces one pile to zero, the next player must take one match from the remaining pile. The winner is the one who takes the last match from the table leaving his opponent no possible play.

6-2 P. (As for Problem 6-1) One bowl contains 100 red marbles and another 100 white marbles of the same size. Take ten red marbles from their bowl and mix them with the white marbles. Without looking, take ten marbles from the mixed bowl so that chance determines whether each is red or white, and put them in the red bowl. (a) What will be the result on the average? (b) Which bowl will be more impure, i.e., which will contain more wrong-colored marbles? (c) How can you generalize your results?

6-3 P. Consider the hunch that if a number like 738 (or, more generally, *abc*) has digits that add up to a multiple of 9, i.e., $7 + 3 + 8 = 18 = 2 \times 9$ (or, more generally, $a + b + c = n \times 9$), then the number is divisible by 9.

6-4 P. A "dot-link" diagram* is made as follows: On a sheet of paper mark several dots, (like large periods) no closer to each other than $\frac{1}{2}$ in. Then draw "links" in the form of pencil lines from dot to dot. The simplest dot-link diagram has only one dot and one link that goes out from the dot and curves around and returns to the dot. Links are permitted to cross each other; a diagram that has no crossing links is called "planar". A dot that has an even number of ends of links touching it is called an "even dot"; if the number of ends is odd, it is an "odd dot". For example, a diagram with two dots connected by one link has two odd dots. (a) Prove that it is **always true** that any dot-link diagram has an even number of odd dots (a dot all by itself with zero link ends attached is classified as an even dot), **no matter** how many dots or links there are, **but not if** a mistake is made such as a link ending without reaching a dot, or a link branching so that it has three or more ends.

6-5 P. The "*n*-acquaintance problem" (thanks to George Polya) can be put in dot-link terms like Problem 6-4. Suppose that *n* people (where *n* may be any whole number, such as 2, 3, . . . 9, . . .) are acquainted with each other. Represent each person by a dot and each acquaintanceship between two persons by a link connecting the two dots that represent the persons. Then there can be no link from a dot back to itself. (a) Prove that at least two of the people have the same number of acquaintances; i.e., in the dot-link diagram at least two dots have the same number of link ends attached to them. (For example, two dots connected by one link each have one link end attached so that two dots do have the same number of links attached.) *Hint:* This problem is easily solved by the *reductio ad absurdum* method discussed in Fig. 1-3.

Chapter 7

7-1 P. Suppose that the *CG* of the plank in Fig. 4-4 is *a* ft to the right of the ball and *b* ft to the left of the board on the scale to the right, and that the corresponding distances for the *CG* of the cement block are *c* and *d*. Suppose the weights in lb are W_p and W_c. Then show that the scales on the left and right will read respectively

$$\frac{b}{a + b} W_p + \frac{d}{c + d} W_c \text{ and } \frac{a}{a + b} W_p + \frac{c}{d + c} W_c$$

so that the sum of the two readings is $W_p + W_c$. Why does this call for the precaution discussed in connection with Fig. 4-4 when only one scale and the stack of books are used?

7-2 E. Place three pennies one at a time anywhere on the initially balanced square "tipboard" (Fig. 7-5), so that the tipboard is unbalanced. (a) Rebalance the tipboard by placing on it an additional stack of three

---

* Such diagrams are discussed in mathematics texts. See, for example, Oystein Ore, *Graphs and Their Uses*, (New York: Random House, 1963). Dots are called "vertices" and links are called "edges" in such texts.

pennies. (b) Now combine any two stacks of pennies into one stack by the method of successive balance points until there is only one stack of 6 pennies. Where must this single stack of six pennies be located?

7-3 E. Attach with a rubber band another straight wire across the tipboard, so that there are two wires at right angles to each other on the square tipboard (Fig. 7-5). The tipboard can now be made to balance on two axes by rotating it 90 degrees. Place three stacks of pennies of 1, 2, and 3 pennies each anywhere on the tipboard. Can you place a single stack of 5 pennies on the tipboard so that it balances on both axes? Experiment with this problem until you can predict with certainty where to place the single stack of pennies.

7-4 E. Obtain six square cards (such as by cutting up some filing cards). First predict and then experimentally check the exact location of the combined *CG*-weight point for each of the following cases: (a) six cards placed in one stack; (b) three cards placed to form a *T*-shape; (c) three cards placed to form an *L*-shape; (d) five cards made into a box with no lid; and (e) six cards made into a box.

7-5 E. Place a nickel and a dime anywhere on the tipboard. (a) Measure the number of penny-inches of moment exerted on the tipboard. (b) Measure the number of quarter-centimeters of moment.

7-6 E. Place a nickel on the tipboard and balance it with a penny. (a) What is equal? (b) What is the NSU value of the each moment in number of penny-inches?

7-7 P,D. Leonardo da Vinci (1452-1519), the famous painter, recognized the conceptual nature of the "moment arm". He solved this problem. A weightless bar *AB* is free to rotate about *A*. A weight *Q* is suspended from end *B* of the bar, and a second weight *R* is suspended from a string that passes over a pulley *P*. What must be the ratio of the weights of *Q* and *R* in order for the objects to be in equilibrium?

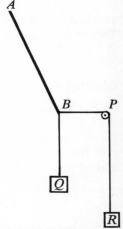

7-8 P,D. Determine the relative weights of the cardboard square, fish, and circle shown in Fig. 7-4.

7-9 P. Consider any three objects *A*, *B*, and *C* whose *CG*'s are on a plane. Write a mathematical equation for the sum of the moments about (a) an *x* axis and (b) a *y* axis on the plane.

Chapter 8

8-1 P. Apply Archimedes' buoyancy principle to the ice-cube problem of Fig. 1-8.

8-2 P. What is the shortest length of the giant lever machine that can be designed for moving the two weights in trial 1 of Fig. 8-6?

8-3 E,P. Display 1 pufl~. Use it as 1 standard potential energy unit to measure (a) a positive quantity of *PE*, and (b) a negative quantity of *PE*.

8-4 P. How would you move, with one rotation of the lever, the seven weights of Fig. 8-5 to the desired final positions? Show by a diagram the length of the lever, where each weight is attached to the lever, and the angle of rotation.

8-5 P,D. From Archimedes' principle, derive a theorem for calculating the weight of a floating object. What additional information would you need to calculate the weight of a battleship?

8-6 E. Pour two tablespoons of crushed dry-ice into a deflated rubber balloon. Suspend the rubber balloon from a lever and balance it. Now knot the opening of the balloon, so none of the carbon dioxide gas in the balloon (given off by the evaporating dry-ice) can escape. As as the gas expands the balloon, what happens to the initially balanced lever? Explain.

8-7 P. The famous problem of whether or not the king's crown was pure gold was solved by Archimedes. Describe at least two procedures for solving this problem.

Chapter 9

9-1 E. (a) Obtain a satisfactory bob for a pendulum and adjust a piece of string so that if you hang the pendulum from a screw eye it will make 30 complete, back-and-forth swings within 1 second of exactly 1 minute, i.e., a swing from right to left takes almost exactly 1 sec. (b) Bring this to class to demonstrate. (You may find Problem 9-2 of help in doing this.)

9-2 E,N. From Problem 5-7 conclude that if the period of a pendulum varies as the square root of the length, then a 10% increase in length will produce a 5% increase in period. Make two identical pendulums (3 ft is a good length and a 6-oz sinker is a good weight). Adjust them until the periods differ by less than 0.5 per cent (i.e. in 100 swings they get half a swing out of step and are going opposite to each other if they were started together). Next increase the length of one by 10 per cent. Start the two together and count to 60 or 80 swings of the long one noting on what counts the two are again in step. (a) The prediction is that they will be in step on counts 20, 40, and 60. Show the reasoning for this prediction. (b) Suppose they are in step on counts 22, 44, and 66. How much has the period of the long one been increased? (c) By what percentage has the prediction failed? (d) Carry out some experiments of your own invention involving varying the length of pendulums and checking predictions.

9-3 E. Carry out and check the experiment of Fig. 9-3.

9-4 E,D. (a) Observe the workings of a manufactured weight scale and verify that it satisfies the geometrical conditions for Fig. 1-8 as discussed in Sec. 9-7. (b) Write a description, including diagrams.

9-5 P. Prove that the sum of the first n odd integers is n^2. (See Sec. 9-2.)

9-6 P. Verify that conservation of energy holds for the two cases of Fig. 9-5 if the accelerations are as shown. Do this by calculating the changes in all necessary energies after the weights have either fallen for a time t, or have moved through a specified distance D. (See text in Sec. 9-8.)

9-7 P,N. Analyze the circular motion of Fig. 9-2(c) and show that it leads to a component of force acting inwards on the bob equal to mv^2/v as discussed in Sec. 9-8.

Index

A page number in boldface type indicates that the item appears in boldface on that page. A section number usually means extended discussion of the item. When an item is most easily located from a figure caption, the figure number is listed.

211